CONTENTS / SOMMAIRE /

Cover Picture / En couverture / Titelbild: Monte-Carlo Beach Hotel, Monaco (

Hotel Claris, Winner of the Johansens
2000 European City Hotel of the Year Award / Prix Johansens du Meilleur "City" Hôtel Européen 2000 / Gewinner der Johansens-Auszeichnung Europäisches Stadthotel des Jahres 2000 (see page 285 / voir page 285 / siehe Seite 285) 10

Hotel Relais la Suvera, Winner of the Johansens
2000 European Country Hotel of the Year Award / Prix Johansens du Meilleur Hôtel "Countryside" Européen 2000 / Gewinner der Johansens-Auszeichnung Europäisches Landhotel des Jahres 2000 (see page 219 / voir page 219 / siehe Seite 219) 12

Hôtel du Palais, Winner of the Johansens
2000 European Waterside Resort of the Year Award / Prix Johansens du Meilleur Hôtel "Waterside" Européen 2000 / Gewinner der Johansens-Auszeichnung Europäisches "Waterside" Resort-Hotel des Jahres 2000 (see page 131 / voir page 131 / siehe Seite 131) 14

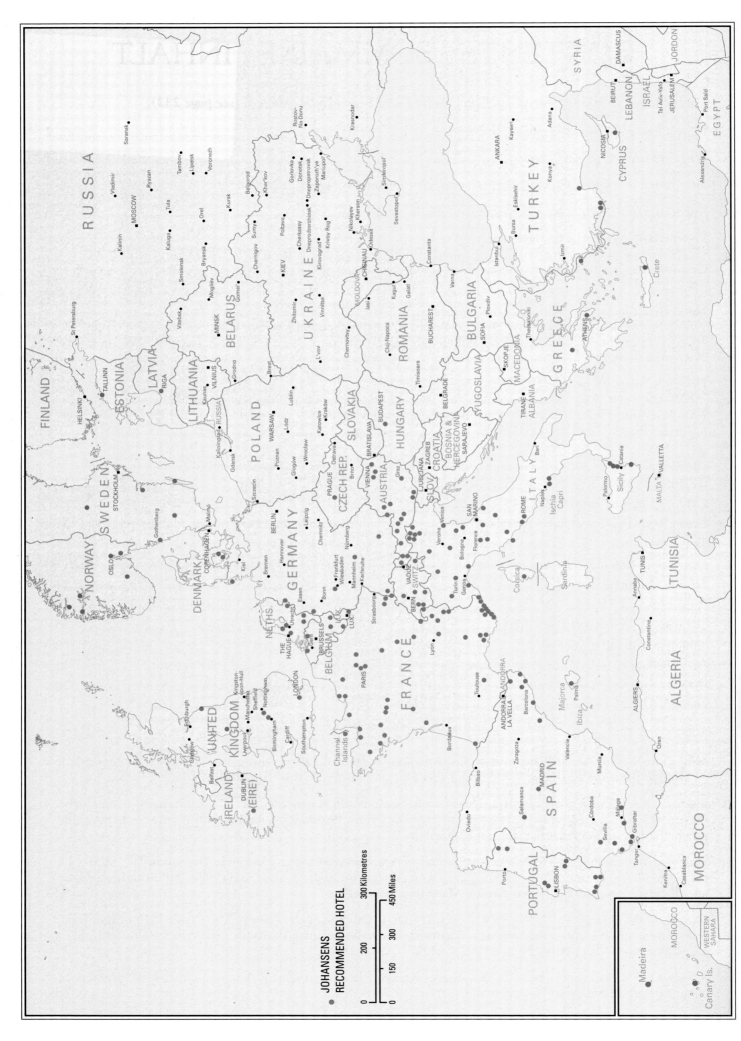

JOHANSENS
RECOMMENDED HOTEL

2

FOREWORD

Welcome to the 6th edition of "Johansens Recommended Hotels – Europe & The Mediterranean".

We are pleased to announce several new developments in this year's guide. For further ease of reference, properties in Austria, France, Italy and Spain are now classified by region. In addition, some of the French establishments now feature a new logo, "Hôtel de Charme", which indicates that they provide a more homely and charming atmosphere.

Our first Guide to 'Recommended Hotels & Lodges – Australia, New Zealand, The Pacific' is also published this year, which means that Johansens now recommend over 1400 annually inspected Hotels, Country Houses, Traditional Inns, Game Lodges and Business Meeting Venues throughout four continents.

Order forms to purchase all Johansens titles are provided at the back of this guide together with a list of all our recommendations. These can also be found on our website: www.johansens.com; many display a "Call Free Now" facility enabling you to speak directly to the hotel, free of charge.

Finally, you will discover that to mention Johansens when you make your booking and again when you arrive will make you a most welcome guest.

Bienvenue dans la 6ème édition du guide "Johansens Hôtels Recommandés – Europe & Méditerranée".

Nous avons amélioré le guide cette année en introduisant quelques changements. Tout d'abord, pour une plus grande facilité d'utilisation, les hôtels en Autriche, France, Italie et Espagne sont maintenant classés par région. De plus, un nouveau logo "Hôtel de Charme" figure sur la page de certains établissements français et permet de distinguer les établissements n'offrant pas toutes les prestations d'un hôtel de grand luxe. Ce sont de belles maisons confortables et accueillantes situées dans des villages ou à la campagne.

Notre premier guide couvrant l'Australie, la Nouvelle-Zélande et les Iles du Pacifique est publié cette année, portant ainsi les recommandations annuellement inspectées de Johansens à plus de 1400, réparties sur 4 continents.

Des bons de commande pour l'acquisition de tous les titres publiés par Johansens sont à disposition au dos de ce guide, accompagnés de la liste de toutes nos recommandations. Celles-ci peuvent également être consultées sur notre site Internet www.johansens.com; la plupart possèdent une îcone "Call Free Now" vous permettant de contacter directement l'hôtel sans frais.

Enfin, vous découvrirez également que le fait de mentionner Johansens lors de votre réservation et lors de votre arrivée fera de vous un hôte de marque.

Ich begrüsse Sie herzlich zur 6. Ausgabe unseres Guides "Johansens Empfohlene Hotels – Europa & Mittelmeerraum".

Mit Freude können wir einige Neuerungen bekanntgeben: Hotels in Österreich, Frankreich, Italien und Spanien sind dieses Jahr zur Vereinfachung nach Region geordnet, und einige unserer ländlichen Hotels in Frankreich wurden mit einem neuen Logo, "Hôtel de Charme", versehen. Dieses Logo bedeutet, dass das Hotel zwar weniger Annehmlichkeiten als ein Luxushotel, aber dafür eine heimelige und "charmante" Atmosphäre bietet.

Ausserdem erscheint dieses Jahr die erste Ausgabe unseres Guides "Johansens Empfohlene Hotels und Lodges – Australien, Neuseeland, Pazifik". Johansens empfiehlt nun über 1400 jährlich inspizierte Hotels, Landhäuser, traditionelle Inns, Game Lodges und Tagungsorte in vier Kontinenten.

Bestellformulare für alle Johansens-Titel, sowie eine Auflistung aller unserer Empfehlungen finden Sie am Ende dieses Führers. Ausserdem erscheinen alle Empfehlungen auch auf unserer Website: www.johansens.com. Zahlreiche Hotels bieten hier eine "Call Free Now" Option, mit der Sie kostenfrei direkt mit dem jeweiligen Hotel telefonischen Kontakt aufnehmen können.

Sie werden feststellen, dass sich das Erwähnen von Johansens bei der Buchung und bei der Ankunft im Hotel sehr positiv auf Ihren Aufenthalt auswirkt.

Andrew Warren
Managing Director / Directeur Général / Geschäftsführer

Published by
Johansens Limited, Therese House, Glasshouse Yard, London EC1A 4JN
Tel: +44 20 7566 9700 Fax: +44 20 7490 2538
Find Johansens on the Internet at: **www.johansens.com**
E-Mail: info@johansens.com

European Manager:	Stéphanie Court
Regional Inspectors:	Gianna Illari
	Tunde Longmore
	Renzo Miracco
	Murat Özgüç
	Henrik Sejr
	Hilary Soul
	Agnes Szent-Ivanyi Exton
	Christopher Terleski
	Chara Tsitoura
Production Director:	Daniel Barnett
Production Controller:	Kevin Bradbrook
Production Assistant:	Rachael Gasiorowski
Sub-editor:	Stephanie von Selzam
Senior Designer:	Michael Tompsett
Designers:	Sue Dixon
	Kerri Bennett
Copywriters:	Simon Duke
	Norman Flack
	Debra Giles
	Rozanne Paragon
	Leonora Sandwell
	Elizabeth Willens
Map Ilustrations:	Linda Clark
Sales and Marketing Manager:	Laurent Martinez
Marketing Executive:	Adam Crabtree
Sales Administrator:	Susan Butterworth
P.A. to Managing Director :	Joanne Jones
Managing Director:	Andrew Warren

Copyright © 2000 Johansens Limited

Johansens is a subsidiary of the Daily Mail & General Trust plc

ISBN 1 86017 7204

Printed in England by St Ives plc
Colour origination by Graphic Facilities

Distributed in the UK and Europe by Johnsons International Media Services Ltd, London (direct sales) & Portfolio, Greenford (bookstores). In North America by Hobsons DMI, Cincinnati (direct sales) and Hunter Publishing, New Jersey (bookstores). In Australia and New Zealand by Bookwise International, Findon, South Australia. In Southern Africa by Liquid Amber Distributions, Gillitts, South Africa.

HOW TO USE THIS GUIDE

If you want to identify a Hotel whose name you already know, look for it in the Indexes from page 314.

These indexes are arranged by country.

If you want to find a Hotel in a particular area,

- Turn to the Map of Europe on page 2 which will show you the countries in which there are Johansens Recommended Hotels

- Turn to the title page of the country that you want, where you will find a map. The location of each hotel appears in red on the map with a number corresponding to the page on which the Hotel entry is published.

The countries and place names appear in alphabetical order throughout the guide.

Mini Listings on pages 319–323: You will find the names, locations and telephone numbers of all Johansens Recommendations in the British Isles.

Illustrated Mini Listings on pages 324–338: You will find the names, locations, telephone numbers and pictures of all Johansens Recommendations from the guide to North America, Bermuda & The Caribbean, the guide to Southern Africa, Mauritius & The Seychelles and the guide to Australia, New Zealand & The Pacific.

Rates are correct at the time of going to press but should always be checked with the hotel before you make your reservation.

We occasionally receive letters from guests who have been charged for accommodation booked in advance but later cancelled. Readers should be aware that by making a reservation with a hotel, either by telephone, e-mail or in writing, they are entering into a legal contract. A hotelier under certain circumstances is entitled to make a charge for accommodation when guests fail to arrive, even if notice of the cancellation is given.

All guides are obtainable from bookshops or by calling Johansens direct on +44 20 7538 3597. Alternatively, use the order coupons from page 339.

WE CHANGED FOR THE BETTER!
HILDON SPORT
STILL NATURAL MINERAL WATER
HILDON SPORT
The ultimate refreshment for leisure & sport.
HILDON SPORT
The ultimate refreshment for leisure & sport.
A HELPING HAND FOR YOUNG PEOPLE: THE HILDON FOUNDATION
The Hildon Foundation has been created to help young people realise their potential – wherever their ambitions lie. **For each bottle of Hildon Sport sold, a donation of 1 p will be made to the Foundation.** The intention is to raise at least £100,000 in the first year for budding musicians, sports students, disabled causes, science and technology schemes, and other deserving projects.
"Helping young people is the best possible foundation for the future."
David Gower OBE, patron.
To find out more about the Hildon Foundation, please write to
THE HILDON FOUNDATION, PO BOX 1, BROUGHTON SO20 8WP

BENUTZER-HINWEISE

Wenn Sie ein Hotel suchen, dessen Namen Sie schon kennen, hilft Ihnen das Verzeichnis ab Seite 314.

Dieses Verzeichnis ist nach Ländern geordnet.

Wenn Sie ein Hotel in einer bestimmten Region finden wollen,

- Blättern Sie auf Seite 2, wo die Europakarte die Länder zeigt, in denen sich Johansens-Hotels befinden.

- Blättern Sie auf die Titelseite des Landes, das Sie suchen, hier finden Sie eine Karte. Die Lage eines jeden Hotels ist mit einem roten Punkt auf der Karte markiert sowie mit einer Zahl versehen, die der Seite gleicht, auf der das Hotel zufinden ist.

Die Länder und Ortsnamen in diesem Guide erscheinen in alphabetischer Reihenfolge.

Auflistungen auf den Seiten 319 – 323: Hier finden Sie die Namen, Lage und Telefonnummern sämtlicher Johansens Empfehlungen in Grossbritannien.

Illustrierte Auflistungen auf den Seiten 324 – 338: Hier finden Sie die Namen, Lage, Telefonnummern und Bilder sämtlicher Johansens Empfehlungen in Nord Amerika, Bermuda & der Karibik, im Südlichen Afrika, Mauritius & den Seychellen, und in Australien, Neuseeland & im Pazifik.

Die Preise hatten zur Zeit der Drucklegung ihre Gültigkeit. Vor einer Reservierung sollte man sich diesbezüglich beim Hotel informieren.

Manchmal erhalten wir Briefe von Gästen, die für stornierte Zimmer eine Rechnung erhalten. Die Leser sollten sich darüber im klaren sein, dass sie bei einer Reservierung per Telefon, E-Mail oder auch schriftlich, einen rechtsgültigen Vertrag mit dem Hotel eingehen. Ein Hotelier kann unter bestimmten Umständen, auch bei rechtzeitiger Stornierung, eine Gebühr verlangen.

Alle Guides sind im Buchhandel erhältlich oder direkt von Johansens unter Tel. +44 20 7538 3597. Alternativ können die Bestellformulare ab Seite 339 verwendet werden.

COMMENT UTILISER CE GUIDE

Si vous souhaitez trouver un hôtel dont vous connaissez le nom, cherchez-le dans les index à partir de la page 314.

Dans ces index, les hôtels sont classés par pays.

Si vous souhaitez trouver un hôtel dans une région donnée,

- référez-vous à la carte d'Europe de la page 2 : elle vous permettra de voir quels sont les pays qui comptent des hôtels recommandés par Johansens ;

- passez à la page de titre du pays choisi : vous y trouverez une carte du pays. L'emplacement de chaque hôtel est indiqué en rouge avec un chiffre correspondant à la page à laquelle l'hôtel est présenté.

Les noms de pays et de lieux apparaissent par ordre alphabétique tout au long de ce guide.

Mini-catalogue des pages 319 à 323: vous y trouverez les noms, les emplacements et les numéros de téléphone de toutes les recommandations de Johansens relatives aux Îles britanniques.

Mini-catalogue illustré des pages 324 à 338: vous y trouverez les noms, les emplacements, les numéros de téléphones et des photos de toutes les recommandations de Johansens du guide sur l'Amérique du Nord, les Bermudes et les Caraïbes, du guide sur l'Afrique du Sud, Maurice et les Seychelles et du guide d'Australie, Nouvelle-Zélande & le Pacifique.

Les tarifs sont exacts au moment de l'impression, mais il vous est recommandé de les vérifier auprès de l'hôtel concerné avant de réserver.

Il nous arrive parfois de recevoir des lettres de clients qui ont dû payer des chambres réservées à l'avance puis annulées. Les lecteurs doivent savoir qu'en effectuant une réservation auprès d'un hôtel, que ce soit par téléphone, courrier électronique ou lettre, ils passent un contrat légal avec cet hôtel. Dans certaines circonstances, un hôtelier est en droit de facturer une chambre lorsque le client ne se présente pas à l'hôtel même s'il a été avisé de l'annulation.

Tous les guides peuvent être obtenus dans les librairies ou en appelant directement Johansens au +44 20 7538 3597. Vous pouvez aussi utiliser les coupons de commande fournis dans ce guide à partir de la page 339.

As recommended

AWARD WINNER 2000

Hôtel du Palais, Biarritz, France
Winner of the 2000 Johansens Most Excellent European Waterside Hotel Award

The Hôtel du Palais and its staff were honoured to receive the Most Excellent European Waterside Resort Hotel Award 2000.

Hôtel du Palais, the former mansion of Napoleon III and Empress Eugeniea, was built in 1855 and is now one of the last of the great palaces of Europe. With an atmosphere redolent of the harmony and sophistication of its golden days, our hotel combines luxury and elegance and offers top quality service to its guests in a unique oceanfront setting.

We are very proud of this award and are looking forward to welcoming Johansens readers.

L'Hôtel du Palais et son équipe sont très honorés de recevoir le Prix d'Excellence du Meilleur Hôtel "Waterside" Européen pour l'année 2000.

L'Hôtel du Palais, ancienne résidence de Napoléon III et de l'Impératrice Eugénie, fut construit en 1855 et est aujourd'hui l'un des derniers grands palais en Europe.

Entre l'harmonie et la sophistication héritées du début du siècle et son unique emplacement au bord de l'Océan, notre hôtel offre à ses hôtes luxe, élégance et un service de très grande qualité.

Nous sommes très fiers de ce prix d'excellence et sommes heureux d'accueillir chaque année les lecteurs du guide Johansens.

Das Hôtel du Palais und seine Belegschaft fühlen sich geehrt, mit dem Johansens-Titel Bestes Europäisches "Waterside" Hotel 2000 ausgezeichnet worden zu sein.

Das Hôtel du Palais, der einstige Wohnsitz Napoleons III und der Kaiserin Eugénie, wurde 1855 erbaut und ist heute einer der letzten grossen Paläste in Europa. Mit einer Atmosphäre, die an die Harmonie und Raffinesse seiner 'goldenen Tage' erinnert, und einer Mischung von Luxus und Eleganz, bietet das Hotel seinen Gästen besten Service in einer einmaligen Lage am Meer.

Wir freuen uns darauf, Johansens-Leser willkommen heissen zu dürfen.

Jean-Louis Leimbacher
Managing Director

Austria

HOTEL PALAIS PORCIA

NEUER PLATZ 13, 9020 KLAGENFURT, AUSTRIA
TEL: +43 463 51 15 90 FAX: +43 463 51 15 90 30 E-MAIL: schlosshotel@mail.palais-porcia.co.at

Originally built in the 17th century, this elegant townhouse is now a hotel of distinction in the heart of the capital of Carinthia. The décor is the quintessence of opulence, with a marble-floored reception room and a glamorous bar, housing inviting period chairs and rich Persian rugs. Each bedroom and suite is a colourful work of art, none more so than the deep red four-poster suite. The breakfast room is simply magnificent, and numerous restaurants are within easy reach.

Construit originellement au XVIIème siècle, cet élégant hôtel particulier est à présent un hôtel sélectif en plein coeur de la capitale de Carinthe. Le décor est une incarnation d'opulence, avec sa réception en sol marbré et son bar accueillant. La maison a des meubles d'époque et de riches tapis persans. Les chambres et suites sont de véritables oeuvres d'art de couleurs à l'exemple de la suite rouge avec so lit à baldaquin. La salle des petits déjeuners est simplement superbe, et de nombreux restaurants sont à proximité.

Dieses elegante Stadthaus aus dem 17. Jahrhundert ist nun ein stilvolles Hotel im Herzen von Kärntens Hauptstadt Klagenfurt. Die Einrichtung ist opulent, mit Marmorboden in der Eingangs-halle und einladenden Stilmöbeln und kostbaren Perserteppichen im prächtigen Salon. Alle Zimmer, insbesondere die Suiten, bestechen durch ihr farbenprächtiges Ambiente, wie z.B. das kardinalsrote Himmelbettzimmer. Der Frühstücks-raum ist einfach prachtvoll, und zahlreiche Restaurants liegen in nächster Nähe.

Directions: Follow signs towards the Neuer Platz in Klagenfurt. **Price guide:** *Single AT1050; double/twin AT1550–4800; suites ATS2800–4800.*

ALMDORF "SEINERZEIT"

FELLACHERALM, 9564 PATERGASSEN, AUSTRIA
TEL: +43 4275 7201 FAX: +43 4275 7380 E-MAIL: office@almdorf.com

This exclusive chalet resort is situated in beautiful countryside close to the up-market spa town of Bad Kleinkircheim between Salzburg and Slovenia. Opened in 1995 and constructed using 18th century building methods, the wood-heated chalets offer guests unparalleled comfort and luxury. After a hard day on the piste, visitors can enjoy hearty meals in the intimate restaurant, whose local wines, beers and schnapps should not be missed.

Ce complexe de chalets exclusif est situé au milieu d'un beau paysage proche de la célèbre ville thermale Bad Kleinkircheim entre Salzburg et la Slovénie. Ouvert en 1995 et bâti selon les méthodes de construction du XVIIIème siècle, les chalets chauffés au feu de bois offrent aux clients un degré de confort et de luxe inégalé. Après une journée fatigante de ski, les visiteurs pourront se régaler d'un repas savoureux dans le restaurant intime, arrosé d'un excellent choix de vins locaux, de bières et de schnaps.

Dieses exklusive Chalet-Resort befindet sich in der herrlichen Landschaft um Bad Kleinkirchheim zwischen Salzburg und Slowenien. 1995 eröffnet und nach Baumethoden aus dem 18. Jahrhundert erbaut, bieten die mit Holz beheizten Chalets unvergleichlichen Komfort und Luxus. Nach einem anstrengenden Tag auf der Piste können sich die Gäste an der herzhaften Küche im gemütlichen Restaurant erfreuen und ein Glas erlesenen österreichischen Wein, Bier oder Schnaps geniessen.

Directions: 1 km after Turracher Höhe, turn left to Falkert. Almdorf is 4 km on right. **Price guide:** *Single/double/twin ATS2270–2850.*

SEESCHLÖSSL VELDEN

KLAGENFURTER STRASSE 34, 9220 VELDEN, AUSTRIA
TEL: +43 4274 2824 FAX: +43 4274 2824 44

With its own private water front and pier, and shielded by a thick wall of imposing trees, this friendly secluded hotel is a mere five minutes from Velden's bustling town centre. The public rooms are luxuriously appointed with their panelled walls, polished wooden floors and delightful rustic furnishings. This high level of comfort extends to the bedrooms – all individually designed – some of which have scenic views over the waterfront.

Bénéficiant de son propre quai d'amarrage et entouré d'un mur épais de superbes arbres, cet hôtel sympathique est très calme, tout en étant à 5 minutes du centre bruyant de Velden. Les pièces communes sont luxueusement décorées avec des murs en lambris, des parquets polis et un ameublement délicieusement rustique. Le haut niveau de confort s'étend aux chambres – toutes individuellement décorées – dont certaines ont une vue scénique sur le bord de l'eau.

Dieses freundliche Hotel, durch hohe Bäume von der Aussenwelt abgeschirmt und mit eigenem Steg und Anlegestelle, ist nur fünf Minuten vom geschäftigen Stadtzentrum von Velden entfernt. Die Aufenthaltsräume sind luxuriös mit holzverkleideten Wänden, polierten Holzböden und bezaubernden rustikalen Möbeln ausgestattet. Auch die individuell gestalteten Schlafzimmer sind luxuriös und komfortabel, und einige bieten herrliche Blicke auf den See.

Directions: *Near Velden town centre.* **Price guide:** *Single/double ATS750–ATS1,620 (per person).*

HOTEL SCHLOSS DÜRNSTEIN

3601 DÜRNSTEIN, AUSTRIA
TEL: +43 2711 212 FAX: +43 2711 21230 E-MAIL: hotel@schloss.at

Standing on the banks of the Danube, this exclusive fairytale hotel, originally built in the 17th century boasts impressive views of the verdant Wachau Valley. As befits a former royal summer retreat, the antique-laden guest rooms are magnificent, with elaborate drapes and beautifully appointed bathrooms. Sumptuous meals are served in the traditional dining room, with its lofty arches, or on the romantic Danube Terrace.

Situé sur la rive du Danube, cet hôtel huppé a été aménagé dans un château féerique construit au XVIIème siècle. L'établissement jouit de vues superbes sur la vallée Wachau. Autrefois une retraite royale estivale, les anciennes chambres sont somptueuses, avec des tentures ouvragées et de merveilleuses salles de bain. Des repas irrésistibles sont servis dans le restaurant traditionnel avec ses voûtes élevées sur la ravissante terrace surplombant le Danube.

Hoch über der Donau gelegen bietet dieses exclusive, märchenhafte Hotel aus dem 17. Jahrhundert traumhafte Aussichten über die Wachau. Wie es sich für eine ehemalige königliche Sommerresidenz gehört, sind die Zimmer mit Antiquitäten, kostbaren Stoffen und opulenten Bädern prachtvoll eingerichtet. Köstliche Speisen werden im traditionellen Speisesaal mit seinem hohen Gewölbe oder auf der romantischen Donauterrasse serviert.

Directions: *In the centre of Dürnstein.* **Price guide:** *Single ATS2150–2250; double/twin ATS1450–2400; suites ATS2100–2400.*

HOTEL & SPA HAUS HIRT

KAISERHOFSTRASSE 14, 5640 BAD GASTEIN, AUSTRIA
TEL: +43 64 34 27 97 FAX: +43 64 34 27 97 48 E-MAIL: info@haus-hirt.com

With awe-inspiring views over the Gastein valley and the mountains beyond, and set in a glorious parkland garden, the Haus Hirt is one of Austria's finest rural hideaways. The Haus, built in the 1930s as a private villa, has hosted famous persons such as the writers Thomas Mann and Stefan Zweig. Relaxation is guaranteed – the hotel offers a thermal spa with hot spring, health and beauty centre, panorama pool, a good restaurant and cosy bar, clean air, great mountain sports and superb skiing. Guided ski and mountain tours are offered.

Avec ses vues impressionnantes sur la Vallée Gastein et les montagnes, le Haus Hirt, au coeur d'un parc magnifique, est l'un des refuges le plus raffinés d'Autriche. Le Haus, construit dans les années 1930 en tant que villa privée, a accueilli de nombreuses personnalités tels que les écrivains Thomas Mann et Stefan Zweig. Une totale relaxation est garantie – l'hotel propose spa thermal, centre de beauté, piscine avec vue panoramique, un bon restaurant, un bar agréable, de l'air pur, tous sports de montagne et un ski de rêve. Ski et excursions guidés sont possibles.

Das Haus Hirt, in den 30er Jahren als Privatvilla erbaut und inmitten eines Parks gelegen, zählt mit seiner atemberaubenden Aussicht auf das Gasteiner Tal und die Berge zu den besten Landhotels in Österreich und beherbergte bereits Persönlichkeiten wie Thomas Mann und Stefan Zweig. Erholung wird garantiert – angeboten werden Thermalspa mit heisser Quelle, Beauty-farm, Panoramapool, Restaurant und gemütliche Bar, klare Bergluft, hervorragende Bergsport-möglichkeiten und ein Traumskigebiet. Geführte Ski- und Bergtouren werden angeboten.

*Directions: Signposted from town centre. **Price guide:** Single ATS790–1350; double/twin ATS890–2780.*

DAS MOSER

KAISER–FRANZ–PLATZ 2, 5630 BAD HOFGASTEIN, AUSTRIA
TEL: + 43 6432 6209 FAX: +43 6432 6209 88 E-MAIL: info@gourmethotel–moser.com

This family-owned hotel, once the home of a 13th century Patrician family, is now a 50-room hotel offering all the creature comforts of a well-groomed home. A veritable gastronomic oasis, its two restaurants provide the full spectrum of dining experience, from the informality of the café to the set-piece dining room. Visitors may take advantage of the swimming pool, sauna, thermal baths and other relaxation facilities that the hotel offers.

Cet hôtel familial, autrefois demeure d'une famille patricienne au XIIIème siècle, est à présent un hôtel de 50 chambres offrant tout le confort d'une maison fort bien entretenue. Un superbe choix gastronomique est proposé grâce à ses 2 restaurants qui couvrent une palette étonnante d'expériences culinaires: de l'atmosphère détendue de son bar à sa salle à manger fastueuse. Les clients peuvent profiter de la piscine, du sauna, du bain thermal et d'installations destinées à la relaxation.

Dieses im Familienbesitz befindliche Hotel war im 13. Jahrhundert das Zuhause einer Patrizierfamilie. Nun steht es als Hotel mit 50 Zimmern zur Verfügung und bietet höchsten Komfort. Die zwei Restaurants sind eine wahrhaft gastronomische Oase und bieten eine grosse Auswahl vom zwanglosen Cafe bis hin zu genussvollem Dinieren im elegant gedeckten Speisesaal. Die Gäste sollten unbedingt die zahlreichen Entspannungseinrichtungen des Hauses wie Hallenbad, Sauna und Thermalbad nutzen.

Directions: *Situated at the heart of Bad Hofgastein.* **Price guide:** *Single supplement ATS50; double/twin ATS800–ATS1,250.*

HOTEL AUERSPERG

AUERSPERGSTRASSE 61, 5020 SALZBURG, AUSTRIA
TEL: +43 662 88 9440 FAX: +43 662 88 944 55 E-MAIL: info@auersperg.at

Situated just a stone's throw away from the historic old town of Salzburg, the Auersperg is an intimate, family-run hotel. The 19th century reception room, with its marble floor and moulded ceiling, leads into a splendid drawing room overflowing with antiques and period furniture. The individually-decorated bedrooms, with big windows and chintz covers, are a sight to behold.

Situé à deux pas à peine de la vieille ville historique de Salzburg, le Auersperg est un hôtel familial et intime. Le hall de réception XIXème, avec son sol marbré et ses moulures aux plafonds, mène à un splendide atelier de dessin qui regorge d'antiquités et de meubles d'époque. Les chambres décorées de manière individuelle, avec de grandes fenêtres et des tentures de chintz, sont un plaisir des yeux dont on se souvient.

Nur einen Katzensprung von der historischen Altstadt Salzburgs entfernt liegt das persönliche, familiengeführte Hotel Auersperg. Die Empfangshalle aus dem 19. Jahrhundert ist mit Marmorboden und einer stuckverzierten Decke geschmückt und führt zu einem herrlichen Salon, der mit Antiquitäten und Stilmöbeln aufwartet. Die individuell eingerichteten Zimmer sind mit ihren grossen Fenstern und Chintzbezügen einfach eine Augenweide.

Directions: *Take the Salzburg North exit from the Autobahn – the hotel is near Kongress-Haus.* **Price guide:** *Single ATS1290–1590; double/twin ATS1460–2280; suites ATS1960–2980.*

HOTEL SCHLOSS MÖNCHSTEIN

MÖNCHSBERG PARK 26, 5020 SALZBURG–CITY CENTER, AUSTRIA
TEL: +43 662 84 85 55 0 FAX: +43 662 84 85 59 E-MAIL: salzburg@monchstein.at

Dating from the 14th century, and standing on Mönchsberg, a hill at the very heart of Salzburg, this enchanting castle-hotel offers bewitching views over the city. The hotel prides itself on the richness of its cuisine, which is reputed to be the best in the city. With music such an important part of Salzburg, the birthplace of Mozart, the castle also holds harp concerts every Saturday and Sunday.

Dâtant du XIVème siècle et perché sur le Mönchsberg, une montagne en plein coeur de Salzburg, cet hôtel enchanteur sous forme de château a des vues imprenables sur la ville. L'hôtel prend grand soin de la richesse de sa table, qui est réputée pour être une des meilleures de la ville. La musique étant si importante à Salzburg, la ville de naissance de Mozart, le château donne également des concerts de harpe chaque samedi et dimanche.

Dieses bezaubernde, aus dem 14. Jahrhundert stammende Schlosshotel liegt auf dem Mönchsberg, einem Hügel im Herzen von Salzburg, und bietet herrliche Ausblicke auf die Stadt. Das Hotel ist stolz auf seine phantastische Küche, die als eine der besten der Stadt angesehen wird. Natürlich spielt die Musik in Salzburg, der Geburtsstadt Mozarts, eine grosse Rolle, und Musikfreunde werden sich über die Harfen-konzerte freuen, die jeden Samstag und Sonntag auf Schloss Mönchstein für Unterhaltung sorgen.

Directions: Salzburg city centre. *Price guide:* Single ATS2900–3900; double/twin ATS2900–6500; suites ATS5400–30,000.

SCHLOSSBERG HOTEL

KAISER-FRANZ-JOSEF-KAI 30, 8010 GRAZ, AUSTRIA
TEL: +43 316 80700 FAX: +43 316 807070 E-MAIL: office@schlossberg–hotel.at

Nestled at the foot of the Schlossberg, only three minutes from the heart of the historic old town, the charming and hospitable Schlossberg Hotel offers a truly warm and homely welcome to its guests. Three 16th century town houses overlooking peaceful courtyards provide the perfect setting for 54 bedrooms, all individually decorated and furnished with antiques. A Sauna, solarium, steam bath and rooftop swimming pool make this the perfect place to unwind.

Niché au pied du Schlossberg, à trois minutes seulement du centre de la vieille ville, cet établissement séduisant s'ouvre sur un univers très accueillant. Formé de trois hôtels particuliers du XVIe siècle donnant sur des cours paisibles, le Schlossberg compte 54 belles chambres toutes décorées différemment et agrémentées de meubles anciens. Un sauna, un solarium, un bain de vapeur et une piscine aménagée sur le toit se chargent de parfaire le bien-être des visiteurs.

Direkt am Fusse des Schlossberges, nur drei Minuten vom Herzen der historischen Altstadt entfernt, präsentiert sich das Schlossberg Hotel mit seinem reizvollen Ambiente und familiärer Gastlichkeit. In drei miteinander verbundenen Bürgerhäusern, deren Grundmauern aus dem 16. Jahrhundert stammen, warten 54 individuelle, mit Antiquitäten ausgestattete Zimmer, die sich fast alle um die ruhigen, lauschigen Innenhöfe gruppieren. Sauna, Solarium, Dampfbad und ein Swimmingpool auf der Dachterrasse sorgen für Wohlbefinden.

Directions: *Near train station in Graz.* **Price guide:** *Single ATS1700–2250; double/twin ATS2450–3050; suites ATS4000–5000.*

ROMANTIK HOTEL BÖGLERHOF

6236 ALPBACH, AUSTRIA

TEL: +43 5336 5227 FAX: +43 5336 52274 02 E-MAIL: boeglerhof@telecom.at

Dating from the 16th century, this magnificently restored former bowmaker's workshop is situated at the centre of an idyllic Alpine valley. One is immediately struck by the warm and welcoming ambience, with a blazing log fire and luxurious, inviting leather couches. Breathtaking views can be enjoyed from the bedroom balconies. The hotel's two saunas and indoor pool are the perfect antidote to a hard day on the slopes.

Dâtant du XVIème siècle, cet ancien atelier d'un archer restauré est situé au centre d'une splendide vallée alpine. Chacun sera immédiatement frappé par l'ambiance chaleureuse et accueillante, avec ses feux de cheminée crépitants et ses canapés luxueux en cuir. Des vues époustouflantes sont appréciables des chambres avec balcons. Les 2 saunas de l'hôtel et la piscine couverte sont un parfait palliatif à une journée fatigante sur les pistes.

Dieses hervorragend restaurierte Hotel, die ehemalige Werkstatt eines Bogenmachers aus dem 16. Jahrhundert, liegt mitten in einem idyllischen Alpendorf. Gemütliche Kaminfeuer und luxuriöse, einladende Ledersofas schaffen eine warme und herzliche Atmosphäre, und von den Balkonen der Zimmer hat man eine spektakuläre Sicht auf die Berge. Zwei Saunen und ein Hallenbad sind der perfekte Ausgleich zu einem harten Tag auf der Piste.

Directions: *From Innsbruck, follow the signs to Alpbach.* **Price guide:** *Single ATS650–2040; double/twin ATS720–1700; suites ATS1050–1205.*

SCHLOSSHOTEL IGLS

VILLER STEIG 2, 6080 IGLS, TIROL, AUSTRIA
TEL: +43 512 37 72 17 FAX: +43 512 37 86 79 E-MAIL: schlosshotel–igls@netway.at

Set in Igls, on a sunny terrace above Innsbruck, the Schlosshotel is an enchanting Tyrolean castle with turrets and spires and surrounded by a beautiful tree-lined site. The interior is exquisite. The bedrooms and suites are charming, with views across the countryside to the Patscherkofel Mountains. The spacious reception area is welcoming, guests relax in the elegant dining room or in the convivial bar with its baroque fireplace. An indoor and outdoor swimming pool, steam room, sauna and solarium are also available.

Situé à Igls, sur un plateau ensoleillé au dessus d'Innsbruck, le Schlosshotel est un merveilleux château tyrolien orné de tourrelles et de pics et entouré d'un parc boisé. L'intérieur est très raffiné. Les ravissantes chambres et suites offrent des vues sur le paysage jusqu'aux montagnes Patscherkofel. La grande réception est accueillante et les visiteurs peuvent s'attarder dans l'élégante salle à manger ou au bar convivial, avec sa cheminée baroque. Deux piscines, une couverte et une en plein air, sauna, hammam et solarium sont également disponibles.

In Igls, auf einem sonnigen Plateau oberhalb von Innsbruck liegt dieses zauberhafte Tiroler Schloss mit seinen spitzen Türmchen, umgeben von bewaldetem Grund. Das Interieur ist einfach prachtvoll, und die bezaubernden Zimmer und Suiten bieten atemberaubende Blicke auf die Umgebung und den Patscherkofel. Der geräumige Empfangsraum ist gemütlich, und die Gäste entspannen sich im eleganten Speisesaal oder in der einladenden Bar mit ihrem barocken Kamin. Hallen- und Freibad, Dampfbad, Sauna und Solarium sind ebenfalls vorhanden.

Directions: Leaving Innsbruck on Inntal highway, follow signs to Igls. **Price guide:** *Single ATS2,120-2,670; double/twin ATS3,840-4,940; suites ATS4,440-5,540.*

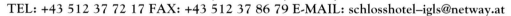

SPORTHOTEL IGLS

HILBERSTRASSE 17, 6080 IGLS, TIROL, AUSTRIA
TEL: +43 512 37 72 41 FAX: +43 512 37 86 79 E-MAIL: sporthotel–igls@netway.at

In Igls, on a sunny terrace above Innsbruck, stands this elite chalet-style hotel, offering traditional Austrian hospitality all year round. During winter, Igls is a premier ski resort, and in summer, visitors enjoy the many sporting activities and walking through the scenic countryside. It is also an exceptional venue for conferences. The leisure centre is magnificent: indoor/outdoor pool, sauna, solarium, gymnasium with modern equipment, whirlpools and Polly Vital & Beauty Centre.

A Igls, sur un plateau ensoleillé au dessus d'Innsbruck se dresse ce chalet-hôtel élitiste réputé pour son hospitalité autrichienne tout au long de l'année. En hiver, Igls est une station de ski de premier ordre, et en été, les visiteurs s'adonnent aux nombreuses activités sportives ou se promènent dans la campagne pittoresque. L'hôtel est également un lieu idéal de conférences. Le superbe centre de loisirs comprend piscine intérieure/extérieure, sauna, solarium, gymnase moderne, bains bouillonnants et centre de beauté Polly Vital.

Dieses feine Hotel im Chaletstil liegt in Igls, auf einem sonnigen Plateau über Innsbruck und bietet das ganze Jahr über traditionelle österreichische Gastfreundschaft. Im Winter ist Igls ein hervorragendes Skiresort und im Sommer stehen zahlreiche andere Sportarten oder Wanderungen durch die herrliche Umgebung auf dem Programm. Das Hotel ist auch ideal für Konferenzen. Das Freizeitzentrum umfasst Frei- und Hallenbad, Sauna, Solarium, einen gutausgestatteten Fitnessraum, Whirlpools und das Polly Vital & Beauty Centre.

Directions: Leaving Innsbruck on Inntal highway, follow signs to Igls. **Price guide:** *Single ATS1,140–1,530; double/twin ATS1,880–2,660; suites ATS2,600–3,740.*

ROMANTIK HOTEL SCHWARZER ADLER

KAISERJÄGERSTR. 2, 6020 INNSBRUCK, AUSTRIA
TEL: +43 512 587109 FAX: +43 512 561697 E-MAIL: schwarzer–adler@romantik.de

Just a few yards from the old town of Innsbruck, the Romantik Hotel Schwarzer Adler, with its stunning interior design, extends a warm and friendly welcome to its guests. The hotel boasts crystal bathrooms designed by Swarvski and each room is decorated with imagination and style. The top floor offers an open terrace with stunning views over the roofs of Innsbruck and the Tyrolean Mountains. The restaurant offers very tasty traditional dishes. Two rooms are designed to provide meeting facilities in a historic ambience.

A deux pas de la vieille ville d'Innsbruck, cet hôtel réserve un accueil chaleureux à ses visiteurs. Il s'ouvre sur un intérieur décoré de façon éblouissante. Des salles de bains parées de cristal Swarovski accompagnent les chambres aménagées avec imagination et élégance. Au dernier étage, une terrasse offre une vue splendide sur les toits d'Innsbruck et les montagnes tyroliennes. Le restaurant propose des plats traditionnels savoureux. Deux salles sont disponibles pour organiser des réunions dans un cadre historique.

Nur wenige Meter von der Innsbrucker Altstadt entfernt bietet dieses Hotel mit seiner phantastischen Inneneinrichtung seinen Gästen einen herzlichen Empfang. Es verfügt über kristallene, von Swarvski entworfene Badezimmer, und jedes Zimmer ist individuell und stilvoll eingerichtet. Im Obergeschoss befindet sich ein offener Balkon mit atemberaubendem Blick über Innsbruck und die Tiroler Berge. Im Restaurant werden köstliche, traditionelle Gerichte serviert, und zwei Räume bieten Konferenzeinrichtungen inmitten eines historischen Ambientes.

Directions: East of the old town of Innsbruck. **Price guide:** *Single ATS1200–1700; double/twin ATS1800–2500; suites ATS3400–4900.*

ROMANTIK HOTEL TENNERHOF

GRIESENAUWEG 26, 6370 KITZBÜHEL, AUSTRIA
TEL: +43 5356 6 3181 FAX: +43 5356 6 318170 E-MAIL: tennerhof@netway.at

Set in its own beautifully designed gardens, the Tennerhof – the only 5 star hotel in the area – is a superb chalet-style hotel that offers a homely and welcoming ambience. The reception rooms are elegantly furnished, and the traditional stone-floored sitting room boasts an open fireplace. The award-winning cuisine imaginatively blends local and international dishes, complemented by an impressive wine list. The leisure complex has a magnificent pool, sauna and steamroom.

Au coeur de magnifiques jardins, le Tennerhof – le seul hôtel 5 étoiles dans la région – est un chalet hôtel offrant une ambiance chaleureuse et accueillante. La réception est élégamment meublée, et le salon se distingue par un sol en pierre et une superbe cheminée. La cuisine, hautement récompensée, marie de façon imaginative les plats locaux avec des spécialités internationales, et est complétée par une carte de vins impressionnante. Le centre de loisirs comprend une magnifique piscine, un sauna et des bains turcs.

Der Tennerhof, ein exzellentes Hotel im Chalet-Stil und das einzige 5-Sterne-Hotel der Region liegt inmitten von herrlich gestalteten Gärten und bietet ein herzliches Ambiente. Die Empfangsräume sind elegant und der Aufenthaltsraum mit seinem traditionellen Steinfussboden wird von einem offenen Kaminfeuer gewärmt. Die mehrfach ausgezeichnete Küche ist eine interessante Mischung aus regionalen und internationalen Gerichten, ergänzt von erlesenen Weinen. Das Freizeitzentrum bietet Pool, Sauna und Dampfbad.

Directions: *In the centre of Kitzbühel.* **Price guide:** *Single ATS1520–2600; double/twin ATS2220–5200; suites ATS3540–8200.*

ARLBERG HOSPIZ HOTEL

6580 ST CHRISTOPH, AUSTRIA
TEL: +43 5446 2611 FAX: +43 5446 3545 E-MAIL: info@hospiz.com

Situated at the heart of the picturesque hamlet of St Christoph high in the Austrian Tyrol, the Arlberg Hospiz is a stylish and friendly hotel ideally suited to the winter sports fanatic. The interior is the epitome of opulence, with the foyer boasting some wonderful metalwork chandeliers and antique Persian rugs. Gourmet meals are complemented by one of the most extensive collections of Bordeaux vintages in the world. Free childcare available from 9am to 9pm.

Situé en plein coeur du hameau pittoresque de St Christoph, haut perché dans le Tyrol autrichien, l'Arlberg Hospiz est un hôtel de style et chaleureux idéalement localisé pour les fanatiques de sport d'hiver. L'intérieur est l'incarnation même de l'opulence, avec feu de cheminée mettant en avant des chandeliers en métal fantastiques et des tapis persans anciens. Des repas gourmands sont agrémentés d'une des caves de bordeaux les plus riches du monde. Crèche gratuite de 9h à 21h.

Im Herzen des pittoresken Dorfes St. Christoph, hoch oben im österreichischen Tirol, liegt das Arlberg Hospiz, ein stilvolles und freundliches Hotel, das ganz auf Wintersport eingestellt ist. Herrliche schmiedeeiserne Rokoko-Lüster und kostbare Perserteppiche im Foyer deuten auf die Opulenz der Inneneinrichtung im ganzen Hause hin. Die hervorragende Gourmet-Küche wird durch eine der weltgrössten Sammlungen von Bordeaux-Spitzenweinen ergänzt. Freie Kinderbetreuung von 9 bis 21 Uhr.

Directions: *Before Arlberg Tunnel > signs to Lech, Zürs and St. Christoph.* **Price guide:** *Single ATS2100–4500; double/twin ATS2160–5650; suites ATS3450–8560.*

HOTEL KLOSTERBRÄU

6100 SEEFELD, TIROL, AUSTRIA
TEL: +43 5212 26210 FAX: +43 5212 3885 E-MAIL: info@klosterbrau.com

Set against a stunning mountainous backdrop, the Klosterbräu is an enchanting 5-star chalet-style hotel with fairy tale architecture. The vibrant, yet traditional atmosphere is augmented by the stone-walled historic rooms, wooden ceilings and panelled walls. With four restaurants, the Klosterbräu is ideal for the bon vivant, who would not want to miss out on inspecting the incredible wine cellar in the vaults below the hotel.

Situé sur le flanc d'une superbe montagne, le Klosterbräu est un chalet enchanteur 5 étoiles à l'architecture féerique. L'atmosphère remarquable, tout en étant traditionnelle, est soulignée par les pièces historiques aux murs de pierre, les plafonds boisés et les murs lambrisés. Avec ses 4 restaurants, le Klosterbräu est idéal pour le bon vivant, et une visite des caves à vins sous l'hôtel s'impose absolument.

Das Klosterbräu ist ein bezauberndes 5-Sterne-Hotel im Chalet-Stil, mit märchenhafter Architektur und von Bergen umrahmt. Die lebendige und doch traditionelle Atmosphäre kommt durch die historischen Räume mit Steinmauern, Holzdecken und getäfelten Wänden bestens zur Geltung. Mit vier Restaurants ist das Klosterbräu ein Paradies für Feinschmecker, und auch der beachtliche Weinbestand im Kellergewölbe sollte nicht ausser Acht gelassen werden!

Directions: *Centre of Seefeld.* **Price guide:** *Single ATS1380–1840; double/twin ATS1380–1840; suites ATS1950–3500.*

ROMANTIK HOTEL ALMTALHOF

4645 GRÜNAU IM ALMTAL, AUSTRIA
TEL: +43 7616 82040 FAX: +43 7616 820466 E-MAIL: almtalhof@magnet.at

This idyllic rural hideaway lies in a romantic valley of pines and mountains, gloriously illuminated by bright sunshine in summer, and crisp white snow in winter. Beautifully appointed throughout, with wooden floors and ceilings, the hotel is full of antiques, paintings and local knick-knacks. Many of the cosy bedrooms have four-poster beds and offer breathtaking views. The award-winning fare, using finest local produce, is not to be missed.

Ce refuge campagnard idyllique est situé dans une vallée romantique de pins et de montagnes, illuminé par un soleil radieux en été et une neige étincelante en hiver. Superbement arrangé à l'intérieur, avec ses beaux parquets et plafonds, l'hôtel foisonne d'antiquités, de peintures et de bric-à-brac local. La plupart des confortables chambres ont des lits à baldaquins et des vues époustouflantes. La table qui a gagné plusieurs prix, utilise des produits locaux merveilleux, et se doit d'être visitée.

Dieses idyllische ländliche Versteck befindet sich in einem romantischen Tal. Im Sommer scheint die klare Alpensonne auf die Kiefernwälder, und im Winter strahlen die Berge in blendendem Weiss. Das Hotel hat Holzboden und -decken und ist mit herrlichen Antiquitäten, Gemälden und Kleinigkeiten aus der Umgebung gefüllt. Viele der gemütlichen Zimmer haben ein Himmelbett, und bieten herrliche Aussichten. Die preisgekrönten Speisen werden mit einheimischen Zutaten bereitet und sind wahre Gaumenfreuden.

Directions: *On the outskirts of Grünau on the road to Aimsee.* **Price guide:** *Single ATS750–1050; double/twin ATS1500–2600.*

ROMANTIK HOTEL IM WEISSEN RÖSSL

5360 ST WOLFGANG AM SEE, SALZKAMMERGUT, AUSTRIA
TEL: +43 6138 23060 FAX: +43 6138 2306 41 E-MAIL: hpeter@weissesroessl.co.at

Perched on the shores of Lake St Wolfgang, one of the most famous lakes in the Austrian Salzkammergut, this magnificent hotel in the picturesque, car-free village of St Wolfgang offers numerous opportunities to relax in beautiful surroundings. A very large pool in the lake, heated to 30°C all year round, a wellness studio offering beauty treatments, massages and special baths as well as indoor pool, Jacuzzi and sauna are also available. The elegant restaurant serves local dishes and an impressive selection of Austrian wines.

Ce magnifique hôtel se situe à St Wolfgang, un village pittoresque interdit aux voitures, sur les berges du lac du même nom, l'un des plus célèbres du Salzkammergut. Cette belle région forme un cadre enchanteur pour les nombreuses activités de détente. Sont disponibles une immense piscine aménagée dans le lac et chauffée à 30°C toute l'année, un centre de remise en forme proposant des soins de beauté, des massages, une piscine couverte, un Jacuzzi et un sauna. Des spécialités locales et des vins autrichiens sont servis dans l'élégant restaurant.

Direkt am Ufer des Wolfgangsees, eines der bekanntesten Seen des Salzkammerguts, liegt dieses zauberhafte Hotel mitten im malerischen, autofreien St. Wolfgang. Die herrliche Umgebung bietet zahlreiche Freizeitmöglichkeiten: Zur Verfügung stehen ein Seebad, ganzjährig auf 30°C beheizt, ein Wellness-Studio mit Schönheitsbehandlungen, Massagen und spezielle Bäder, Hallenbad und Whirlpool. Im eleganten Restaurant werden einheimische Gerichte und eine eindrucksvolle Auswahl an österreichischen Weinen serviert.

Directions: Beside St Wolfgang lake. **Price guide**: Single ATS977–1445; Double/twin ATS1568–2477; suites ATS2367–3137.

ANA GRAND HOTEL WIEN

KÄRNTNER RING 9, VIENNA 1010, AUSTRIA
TEL: +43 1 515 80 0 FAX: +43 1 515 13 13 E-MAIL: sales@anagrand.com

Spectacularly refurbished, yet still retaining its "Belle Epoque" ambience, the Ana Grand is one of the finest buildings in Vienna. The immense marbled foyer gives a hint of the pleasures to come, as one after another of the opulent public rooms vie for the visitors' favour. Food lovers are simply spoilt for choice with the French restaurant Le Ciel with a view over the city and the Unkai, where Japanese cuisine may be sampled.

Rénové de façon spectaculaire, tout en conservant son ambiance "Belle Epoque", l'Ana Grand est une des plus belles bâtisses de Vienne. L'immense hall habillé de marbre frappera le visiteur, ainsi que toutes les salles qui offrent leur opulence les unes après les autres. Les amoureux de la table auront l'embarras du choix entre le restaurant français Le Ciel avec sa vue sur la ville et l'Unkai, où l'art culinaire japonnais doit être essayé.

Das Ambiente der „Belle Epoque" ist in diesem eindrucksvoll renovierten Hotel allgegenwärtig. Es ist eines der glanzvollsten Gebäude Wiens, und bereits die riesige, in Marmor gehaltene Eingangshalle deutet auf ein opulentes Dekor in sämtlichen Räumen hin. Feinschmecker haben die Qual der Wahl zwischen dem französischen Restaurant Le Ciel mit Ausblick über die Stadt oder dem Unkai, das köstliche japanische Gerichte serviert.

Directions: On the Kärntner Ring, beside the Staatsoper. **Price guide:** Single ATS3900–4900; double/twin ATS4900–5900; suites ATS9000–40000.

HOTEL IM PALAIS SCHWARZENBERG

SCHWARZENBERGPLATZ 9, 1030 VIENNA, AUSTRIA
TEL: +43 1 798 4515 FAX: +43 1 798 4714 E-MAIL: palais@schwarzenberg.co.at

Redolent of imperial Austria, this grand baroque hotel stands in 18 acres private park with stunning sculptures and ornamental ponds. The friendly and intimate hotel offers a warm welcome, and the reception rooms, reflecting the hotel's rich history, are sumptuous, with the dome-ceilinged entrance hall and the frescoed Marble Hall particular attractions. The terrace restaurant, with views over the gardens, serves French and Austrian delights, accompanied by a choice of superb wines.

Réminiscence de l'Autriche impériale, cet hôtel grandiose et baroque est planté au milieu d'un parc privé de 7 ha avec d'étonnantes sculptures et des étangs ornementaux. L'hôtel est intime et accueillant, et les pièces communes, reflétant la riche histoire de l'hôtel, sont magnifiques avec une réception au plafond en dôme et un hall en marbre à fresques, qui sont ses principales attraits. Le restaurant Terrasse, avec ses vues sur le jardin, offre des délices français et autrichiens, accompagnés d'un choix de superbes vins.

Dieses phantastische Barockhotel erinnert an Österreichs Kaiserzeit und liegt inmitten eines 7 ha grossen Privatparks, der mit Skulpturen und Zierteichen gefüllt ist. Die Atmosphäre ist herzlich und familiär und die prachtvollen Empfangsräume spiegeln die Geschichte des Hotels wider, wobei die gewölbte Decke und die mit Fresken verzierte Marmorhalle besonders eindrucksvoll sind. Das Terrassenrestaurant mit Blick auf die Gärten serviert französische und österreichische Spezialitäten sowie eine Auswahl an erlesenen Weinen.

Directions: In the centre of Vienna. **Price guide**: Double/twin ATS3400–5600; suites ATS5600–12,000.

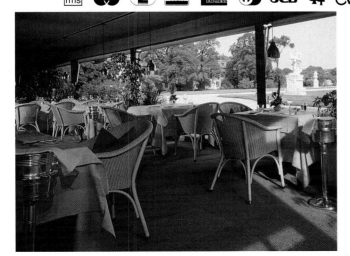

HOTEL GASTHOF GAMS

6870 BEZAU, AUSTRIA
TEL: +43 5514 2220 FAX: +43 5514 222024 E-MAIL: info@hotel-gams.at

Built in 1648, this delightful hotel is situated in natural and unspoilt surroundings and offers the warmest of welcome from its hosts, the Nenning family. Wood panelling and local antiques combine with modern amenities for maximum style and comfort, and the stylish banqueting hall is a wonderful setting for delicious local specialities. Cross-country skiing, walking and tennis are popular pastimes, as are the Bregenzer & Schubertiade summer music festivals.

Cet hôtel de charme construit en 1648 se dresse dans un cadre naturel et préservé, où la famille Nenning accueille chaleureusement ses hôtes. Style et confort sont au rendez-vous, des boiseries et des meubles anciens de la région côtoyant harmonieusement les commodités modernes. L'élégante salle de banquet permet de déguster les délicieuses spécialités locales dans un décor somptueux. Ski de randonnée, marche et tennis occupent les journées, remplies de musique l'été, durant le festival de Bregenz et la Schubertiade.

Dieses freundliche, im Jahre 1648 erbaute Hotel liegt inmitten von unberührter Natur, und die Eigentümer, die Familie Nenning empfängt Gäste mit herzlichster Gastfreundschaft. Holzvertäfelung und regionale Antiquitäten schaffen zusammen mit modernen Einrichtungen maximalen Komfort, und der elegante Bankettsaal bietet das ideale Umfeld, um einheimische Köstlichkeiten zu geniessen. Langlaufen, Wandern und Tennis sind beliebte Freizeitbeschäftigungen, und die Bregenzer Festspiele und die Schubertiade sorgen für kulturellen Genuss.

Directions: *A14 Bregenz-Arlberg, exit Dornbirn > BS200 via Egg to Bezau.* **Price guide:** *Single ATS710–1350; double/twin ATS630–880.*

SPORTHOTEL KRISTIANIA

OMESBERG 331, 6764 LECH AM ARLBERG, AUSTRIA
TEL: +43 5583 25 610 FAX: +43 5583 3550 E-MAIL: kristiania@lech.at

Set amidst the most stunning scenery – snow-clad mountains, pine forests and the picturesque mountain hamlet – this enchanting chalet-hotel offers winter sports aficionados a warm and friendly ambience. The bedrooms, furnished with deep-pile rugs, modern chairs and local antiques, are simply a delight. The restaurant, which serves hearty meals after a long day on the piste, houses a fine modern art collection on its pine walls.

Ce charmant hôtel positionné de façon merveilleuse est entouré de montagnes enneigées, de forêts de pins et d'un hameau pittoresque de montagne. Le chalet offre aux fanatiques de sports d'hiver une ambiance chaleureuse et accueillante. Les chambres, meublées avec d'épais tapis, des chaises modernes et des antiquités locales, sont un vrai plaisir. Le restaurant sert des plats généreux, appréciables après une longue journée sur les pistes et présente une collection d'art moderne raffinée sur ses murs en pin.

Schneebedeckte Berge, Kiefernwälder und ein malerisches kleines Bergdorf bilden die Umgebung dieses zauberhaften, freundlichen Chalethotels – ein wahres Paradies für Wintersportler. Die herrlichen Zimmer sind mit flauschigen Teppichen, modernen Sesseln und regionalen Antiquitäten ausgestattet. Im Restaurant, in dem auch eine Sammlung moderner Kunst zu bestaunen ist, werden deftige Mahlzeiten serviert – genau das richtige nach einem langen Tag auf der Piste!

Directions: Arlberg tunnel > hotel is on the left just before Lech village. **Price guide:** *Single ATS1600–3080; double/twin ATS3100–6060; suites ATS3900–7180.*

HOTEL GOLDENER BERG

PO BOX 33, 6764 LECH AM ARLBERG, AUSTRIA
TEL: +43 5583 22050 FAX: +43 5583 220513 E-MAIL: info@goldenerberg.com

Superb winter sports for the whole family are available until the end of April in car-free Oberlech, accessible only by cable car in the winter. The hotel is connected underground to the original 15th century building, which now houses a popular rustic restaurant and an extensive wine cellar, where exclusive tastings are held. Breathtaking views of the mountains can be enjoyed while dining in one of the five restaurants or from the spacious bedrooms. Free childcare available from 9am-1pm and 4-9pm.

Toute la famille peut profiter de superbes sports d'hiver jusqu'à fin avril dans le village piéton d'Oberlech. Celui-ci est accessible uniquement par téléphérique durant la saison. Par le sous-sol, l'hôtel est connecté à son bâtiment original du XVème siècle, qui loge de nos jours un restaurant rustique populaire et une superbe cave à vins, où des dégustations exclusives sont organisées. De spectaculaires vues sur les montagnes s'offrent à vos yeux lorsque vous dînez dans un des cinq restaurants ou depuis les chambres spacieuses. Crèche gratuite de 9h à 13h et de 16h à 21h.

Das autofreie Oberlech, in das man nur mit der Seilbahn gelangt, bietet bis Ende April hervorragende Wintersportmöglichkeiten für die ganze Familie. Das Hotel ist unterirdisch mit dem ursprünglichen Gebäude aus dem 15. Jahrhundert verbunden. Dort befinden sich heute ein rustikales Restaurant und ein umfassender Weinkeller, in dem exklusive Weinproben abgehalten werden. Die grosszügigen Zimmer und fünf Restaurants bieten einen herrlichen Ausblick auf die Lecher Bergwelt. Freie Kinderbetreuung von 9-13 Uhr und 16-21 Uhr.

Directions: Once in Lech, head towards the Seilbahn Oberlech. **Price guide**: *Single ATS1,695–2,295; double/twin ATS1,835–2,500; suites ATS2,195–2,850.*

ROMANTIK HOTEL GASTHOF HIRSCHEN

HOF 14, 6867 SCHWARZENBERG, AUSTRIA
TEL: +43 55 12 29 44 0 FAX: +43 55 12 29 44 20 E-MAIL: hirschen@romantikhotels.com

Situated at the heart of Schwarzenberg, one of the most picturesque villages in the Vorarlberg, the Gasthof Hirschen is a baroque-style hotel dating from the middle of the 18th century. The stylish interior has a spacious and elegant lounge and a stone-floored restaurant giving onto a pretty garden. The bedrooms, cosy and rustic, offer splendid views over the Arlberg. The Gasthof also has a sauna, steam room and underground parking.

Situé en plein coeur de Schwarzenberg, un des villages les plus pittoresques du Vorarlberg, le Gasthof Hirschen est un hôtel baroque dâtant du milieu du XVIIIème siècle. Spacieux et stylé, l'intérieur comporte un élégant salon. Le restaurant a un sol en pierre et donne sur un joli jardin. Les chambres, douillettes et rustiques, offrent des vues spectaculaires sur l'Arlberg. Le Gasthof dispose également d'un sauna, d'un hammam et d'un parking sous-terrain.

Dieser vom Holzbarockstil geprägte Gasthof aus dem 18. Jahrhundert liegt mitten in Schwarzenberg, einem der malerischsten Dörfer Vorarlbergs. Unter den stilvollen Räumen ist ein grosser, eleganter Salon sowie ein Restaurant mit Steinboden, von dem aus man auf einen schönen Garten blickt. Die gemütlichen, rustikal eingerichteten Zimmer bieten eine herrliche Sicht auf den Arlberg. Ausserdem besitzt der Gasthof Sauna, Dampfbad und eine Tiefgarage.

Directions: On the main square in Schwarzenberg. **Price guide:** Single ATS1150–1350; double/twin ATS1750–2000; suites ATS2600–2800.

THURNHERS ALPENHOF

6763 ZÜRS/ARLBERG, AUSTRIA

TEL: +43 5583 2191 FAX: +43 5583 3330 E-MAIL: mail@thurnhers–alpenhof.at

Situated high up in the Alps, Thurnhers Alpenhof is a luxury family-owned chalet hotel exclusively dedicated to ski enthusiasts. The interior is well designed, and the owner's interest in antiques is reflected in the plethora of knick-knacks that abound. The atmosphere is very convivial, with visitors mingling in the piano bar before dining in the restaurant. Other facilities include an indoor pool, sauna, steam room and solarium.

Situé dans les Hautes Alpes, Le Thurnhers Alpenhof est un chalet familial luxueux consacré exclusivement aux fanatiques de ski. L'intérieur est fort bien décoré et l'intérêt du propriétaire pour les antiquités se manifeste par le bric-à-brac environnant. L'atmosphère y est fort conviviale, et les clients pourront s'installer au piano bar avant de dîner au restaurant. D'autres équipements incluent une piscine couverte, un sauna, un bain turc et un solarium.

Der Thurners Alpenhof liegt, wie der Name schon sagt, hoch in den Alpen, ein luxuriöses Chalet-Hotel, das völlig auf den Skisport eingestellt ist. Die Räume sind hübsch gestaltet, und das Interesse der Besitzer an Antiquitäten wird anhand der Vielzahl von Kleinigkeiten deutlich. Die Atmosphäre ist herzlich, und die Gäste treffen sich in der Pianobar, bevor sie sich im Restaurant verwöhnen lassen. Zur Entspannung stehen Hallenbad, Sauna, Dampfbad und Solarium zur Verfügung.

Directions: *Follow signs to Zürs/Arlberg.* **Price guide:** *Single ATS2040–3700; double/twin ATS1980–3680; suites ATS2380–5200.*

Belgium

FIREAN HOTEL

KAREL OOMSSTRAAT 6, 2018 ANTWERPEN, BELGIUM
TEL: +32 3 237 02 60 FAX: +32 3 238 11 68 E-MAIL: hotel.firean@skynet.be

Set in a quiet residential street minutes away from the centre of picturesque Antwerp, this art deco hotel is a genuine original. Ideally suited for the traveller weary of homogeneous hotel chains, its suave style is all-pervasive, from the stunning entrance right through to the Tiffany enamel and glass in the bedrooms. Renowned for the courtesy of its staff, the Firean's restaurant combines excellent service with the finest of cuisine.

Situé dans une rue résidentielle calme à quelques minutes du centre de la pittoresque ville d'Anvers, cet hôtel art déco est très original. Situé idéalement pour le voyageur lassé des chaînes d'hôtels, son style est suave et partout présent, de l'entrée étonnante à l'émail de Tiffany et aux glaces des chambres. Renommé pour la courtoisie de son personnel, le restaurant du Firean combine un excellent service avec une cuisine raffinée.

In einer ruhigen Strasse, nur wenige Minuten vom Zentrum des malerischen Antwerpen entfernt, liegt dieses Art-Deco-Hotel, ideal für die Reisenden geeignet, die eintönigen Hotelketten entgehen wollen. Das stilvolle Ambiente reicht von dem beeindruckenden Eingang bis hin zu den Tiffany-Emaille- und Glaseinrichtungen in den Zimmern. Das hoteleigene Restaurant verbindet exzellenten Service mit köstlicher Küche.

Directions: From A14 – E17, exit 5. **Price guide:** *Single BF4500–4900; double/twin BF5400–5900; suites BF7950.*

HOTEL ACACIA

KORTE ZILVERSTRAAT 3A, 8000 BRUGES, BELGIUM
TEL: +32 50 34 44 11 FAX: +32 50 33 88 17 E-MAIL: info@hotel-acacia.com

An ideal base to explore the historic city of Bruges, this comfortable and functional yet elegant hotel has become synonymous with warm hospitality. The bedrooms are tastefully furnished, maintained to the highest standard and offer every modern convenience. After a hard day of sightseeing, visitors can relax in the hotel bar, or take refuge in the hotel's impressive leisure centre, which features a swimming pool, Jacuzzi, and sauna. Private parking facilities are also available.

Situé de façon idéale pour explorer la ville de Bruges, cet hôtel confortable et fonctionnel mais élégant est devenu synonyme de chaleureuse hospitalité. Les chambres, meublées avec goût et parfaitement entretenues, offrent tous les équipements modernes possible. A la suite d'une journée éprouvante de tourisme, les visiteurs peuvent se relaxer au bar de l'hôtel, ou trouver refuge au sein du centre de loisirs impressionnant qui propose piscine, Jacuzzi et sauna. Un parking privé est également disponible.

Dieses gemütliche, funktionelle und doch elegante Hotel ist ein idealer Ausgangspunkt, um die historische Stadt Brügge zu besichtigen. Es ist weithin für sein warmes Ambiente bekannt. Die Zimmer sind geschmackvoll eingerichtet und bieten jeglichen modernen Komfort. Nach einem erlebnisreichen Besichtigungstag können sich die Gäste in der Bar vergnügen oder im Fitnesszentrum entspannen, wo ein Hallenbad, Jacuzzi und Sauna zur Verfügung stehen. Das Hotel hat seinen eigenenen Parkplatz.

Directions: *Follow signs to Zilverpand public car park.* **Price guide:** *Single BF4450–4950; double/twin BF4950–6450; suites BF8950.*

HOTEL PRINSENHOF

ONTVANGERSSTRAAT 9, 8000 BRUGES, BELGIUM
TEL: +32 50 34 26 90 FAX: +32 50 34 23 21 E-MAIL: info@prinsenhof.be

This elegant 20th century Flemish mansion, hidden down a quiet side street, is a friendly and welcoming hideaway minutes from the pulsating heart of Bruges. The Burgundy style interior décor, rich with chandeliers, moulded ceilings and antiques, has a palpable air of opulence, which extends into the charming breakfast room. The bedrooms, elaborately decorated, have particularly elegant drapery.

Cet élégant manoir flamand du XXème siècle, caché au fond d'une rue calme, est une étape accueillante à quelques minutes du centre animé de Bruges. La décoration intérieure qui foisonne de chandelliers, de plafonds à moulures et d'antiquités dégage une atmosphère d'opulence, qui s'étend à la charmante salle du petit déjeuner. Les chambres, décorées avec soin, présentent des draperies particulièrement élégantes.

Dieses elegante flämische Herrenhaus aus dem 20. Jahrhundert liegt versteckt in einer ruhigen Seitenstrasse – ein freundliches Hotel, nur wenige Minuten vom pulsierenden Herzen Brügges entfernt. Das Interieur im Burgunder Stil ist reich an Lüstern, verzierten Decken und Antiquitäten, und vermittelt ein Gefühl von Opulenz, das sich bis zum Frühstücksraum erstreckt. Die Zimmer mit ihren herrlichen, eleganten Stoffdrapierungen, sind einfach exquisit.

Directions: *In the centre of Bruges.* **Price guide:** *Single BF4215–BF9197; double/twin BF4518–BF9500.*

HOSTELLERIE LE PRIEURÉ DE CONQUES

RUE DE CONQUES 2, 6820 FLORENVILLE, BELGIUM
TEL: +32 61 41 14 17 FAX: +32 61 41 27 03

Situated in magnificent surroundings far removed from the frenetic pace of modern day living, the Hostellerie is a peaceful rural hideaway offering some of most prized culinary delights in Belgium. The menu makes excellent use of seasonal specialities and the finest of local produce, and is complemented by over 200 vintage wine. The bedrooms, individually designed and decorated, offer a level of comfort which few hotels can equal.

Situé dans un environnement magnifique au loin du rythme frénétique des temps modernes, l'Hostellerie est une étape rurale paisible offrant une des meilleures tables de Belgique. Le menu combine à merveille les spécialités saisonnières et les produits locaux les plus fins, et est complété par une carte de plus de 200 vins. Les chambres, décorées de façon individuelles, offrent un niveau de confort que peu d'hôtels peuvent égaler.

Die Hostellerie liegt inmitten herrlicher Landschaft und fernab von der Hektik des modernen Lebens – ein friedliches Versteck auf dem Lande. Die Gäste können mit feinsten kulinarischen Genüssen rechnen, für die beste saisonbedingte einheimische Zutaten verwendet werden. Über 200 Jahrgangsweine runden die einfallsreichen Speisen perfekt ab. Die Zimmer sind individuell gestaltet und bieten ein Niveau an Komfort, mit dem nur wenige Hotels mithalten können.

Directions: Take exit 25 from E411, and follw signs to Herbeumont. **Price guide:** Single BF3600; double/twin BF4400–5700.

BELGIUM (Malmédy)

HOSTELLERIE TRÔS MARETS

ROUTE DES TRÔS MARETS, 4960 MALMÉDY, BELGIUM
TEL: +32 80 33 79 17 FAX: +32 80 33 79 10

Set at the foot of the Hautes Fagnes National Park and offering a panoramic view across the surrounding valleys, the Trôs Marets is the epitome of modern style and comfort. The elegant furnishings immediately catch the eye, but the spectacular views from the lounge and dining room are undoubtedly the hotel's chief attraction. In addition to an alfresco terrace, there is an outstanding restaurant, where succulent dishes are complemented by fine wines.

Hostellerie située au pied du Parc Naturel des Hautes Fagnes avec vue panoramique sur les vallées avoisinantes, le Trôs Marets est l'incarnation même du style moderne et du confort. Les meubles élégants attirent le regard, et les vues spectaculaires du salon et de la salle à manger forment indubitablement la principale attraction de l'hôtel. Outre la terrace alfresco, l'établissement a un restaurant exceptionnel, où des plats délicieux sont agrémentés de vins fins.

Das Trôs Marets, am Fusse des Nationalparks Hautes Fagnes gelegen und mit Panoramablick auf die umliegenden Täler, ist die Verkörperung modernen Stils und Komforts. Die elegante Einrichtung sticht sofort ins Auge, doch die Trumpfkarte des Hotels sind zweifellos die spektakulären Aussichten vom Aufenthaltsraum und Speisesaal. Neben einer Sonnenterrasse gibt es ein exquisites Restaurant, das mit köstlichen Speisen und erlesenen Weinen für das leibliche Wohl sorgt.

Directions: *Liège > E40 > Malmédy > 5 km.* **Price guide:** *Double/twin BF3900–8500; suites BF9000–18,000. Special mid-week price −25%.*

CHÂTEAU D'HASSONVILLE

ROUTE D'HASSONVILLE 105, 6900 MARCHE-EN-FAMENNE, BELGIUM
TEL: +32 84 31 10 25 FAX: +32 84 31 60 27

This turretted 17th century chateau, set in 140 acres of magnificent parkland, has the heady atmosphere of a fairy-tale. With peacocks on the lawn and sparkling chandeliers in the opulent salons and breathtaking views, the chateau extends a luxurious, yet homely welcome to its guests. Enjoy a stroll through the park, or simply relax in front of an open fire, basking in the quiet grandeur of antiques and gilt-framed paintings. The restaurant serves delicious award-winning cuisine and fine wines from the superb cellar.

Entouré d'un superbe parc de 55 hectares, ce château à tourelles du XVIIe siècle baigne dans une atmosphère féerique. Les paons sur la pelouse et les lustres scintillants des salons opulents donnent un cachet unique à ce château luxueux qui réserve un accueil cordial et des vues sensationnelles à ses visiteurs. Pour se détendre, rien ne vaut une promenade dans le parc ou une rêverie au coin du feu, dans un décor somptueux de meubles anciens et de beaux tableaux. Le restaurant sert une cuisine primée savoureuse et d'excellents vins de sa cave impressionnante.

Dieses Schloss aus dem 17. Jahrhundert ist von 55 ha Park umgeben und besitzt eine märchenhafte Atmosphäre. Mit Pfauen auf dem Rasen, glänzenden Kronleuchtern in den opulenten Salons und atemberaubenden Aussichten bietet das Schloss seinen Gästen einen luxuriösen und doch heimeligen Empfang. Geniessen Sie einen Spaziergang durch den Park, oder entspannen Sie sich vor dem Kamin, umgeben von feinen Antiquitäten und goldgerahmten Gemälden. Das Restaurant serviert köstliche, mit Preisen ausgezeichnete Küche und erlesenste Weine.

Directions: *Brussels>Marche>Aye*. **Price guide:** *Single BF4800; double/twin BF5200–BF7200.*

HOTEL CHÂTEAU DE PALOGNE

ROUTE DU PALOGNE 3, 4190 VIEUXVILLE, BELGIUM
TEL: +32 86 21 38 74 FAX: +32 86 21 38 76

Surrounded by rich and fruitful parkland and bordered by two brooding rivers, the Palogne is a rural retreat whose majesty and austere beauty most hotels can only dream of matching. With just 11 guestrooms – each named after a different flower – an intimate and homely atmosphere is guaranteed. The salon, crammed with antiques and bowls of freshly cut flowers, is ideal for a reposeful evening.

Entouré d'un superbe parc d'arbres fruitiers et bordé de deux rivières paisibles, le Palogne est un refuge rural dont la majesté et l'austère beauté peuvent être enviées de la plupart des hôtels. Avec tout juste 11 chambres, chacune nommée d'un nom de fleur, une atmosphère intime est garantie. Le salon, regorgeant d'antiquités et de vases de fleurs fraîchement coupées, est idéal pour une soirée tranquille.

Von üppiger Parklandschaft und zwei friedlichen Flüssen umgeben stellt das Palogne ein ruhiges Versteck auf dem Lande dar, dessen majestätische Eleganz und herbe Schönheit einfach unvergleichlich sind. Eine intime und heimelige Atmosphäre ist garantiert, da nur 11 Gästezimmer zur Verfügung stehen – alle nach unterschiedlichen Blumen benannt. Der Salon, mit Antiquitäten und Vasen mit frischen Blumen gefüllt, ist ein idealer Ort für einen ruhigen Abend.

Directions: *Brussels>Namur>Durbuy>Barvaux>Vieuxville.* **Price guide:** *Double/twin BF2500–5500.*

Cyprus

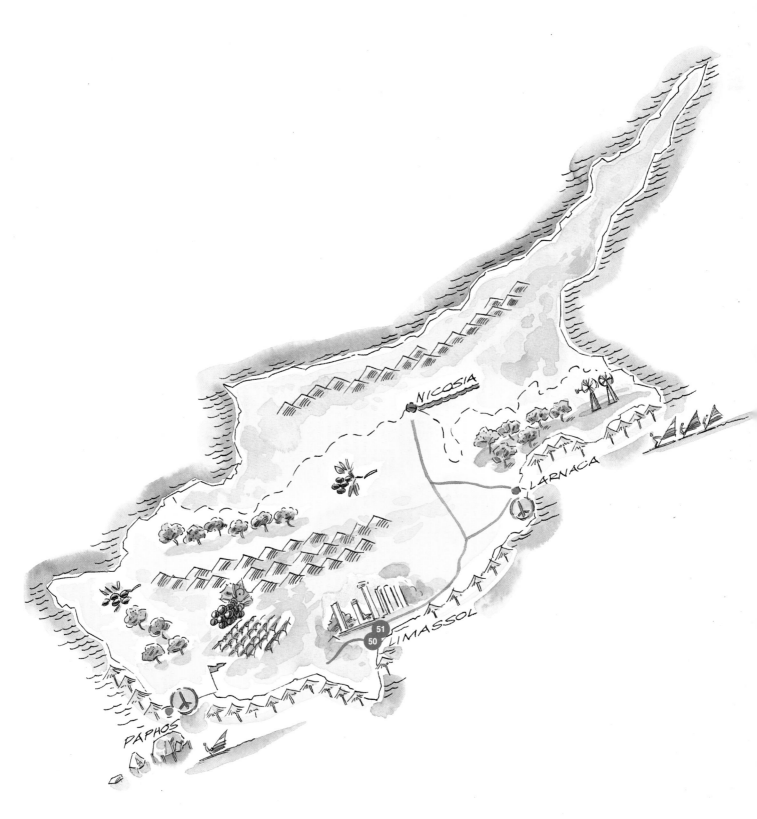

CYPRUS (Limassol)

FOUR SEASONS HOTEL

PO BOX 57222, LIMASSOL, CYPRUS
TEL: +357 5 310 222 FAX: +357 5 310 887

Luxurious amenities and elegant decor are the hallmarks of this superior hotel, located in the Amathus area on the outskirts of cosmopolitan Limassol. The beautiful bedrooms are airy, suffused with natural light and boast panoramic views. The three restaurants serve imaginative, eclectic fare, with a range of dishes certain to accommodate all tastes. Fitness fanatics will enjoy the indoor pool, high-tech gymnasium and Jacuzzi. The hotel's thalassotherapy spa provides total relaxation and rejuvenation.

Des équipements luxueux et élégants sont les principales caractéristiques de cet hôtel supérieur, situé dans la région d'Amathus, en bordure de la ville cosmopolite de Limassol. Les superbes chambres sont aérées, baignées de lumière naturelle et bénéficient de vues époustouflantes. Les trois restaurants proposent des plats créatifs, avec un menu éclectique, et un choix qui satisfera tous les goûts. Les amateurs de culture physique profitent de la piscine couverte, du gymnasium ultramoderne et du Jacuzzi. Le centre de thalassothérapie offre une totale relaxation.

Luxuriöse und elegante Ausstattung sind die Merkmale dieses vorzüglichen Hotels, das in der Amathus-Gegend etwas ausserhalb von Limassol gelegen ist. Die herrlichen Zimmer sind lichtdurchflutet und bieten traumhafte Aussichten. Die drei Restaurants servieren einfallsreiche eklektische Speisen, mit einer Auswahl an Gerichten für jeden Geschmack. Für Fitnessfanatiker gibt es Hallenbad, Jacuzzi und einen bestens ausgestatteten Fitnessraum. Das hoteleigene Thalassotherapie-Zentrum sorgt für totale Erholung und Verjüngung.

Directions: *Just outside Limassol.* **Price guide:** *Single CY£130–180; double/twin CY£178–188; studio room CY£157–193; garden studio CY£180–221; suites CY£340–850.*

Le Meridien Limassol Spa & Resort

PO BOX 56560, 3308 LIMASSOL, CYPRUS
TEL: +357 5 862 000 FAX: +357 5 634 222 E-MAIL: enquiries@lemeridien–cyprus.com

Combining European sophistication with welcoming Cypriot charm, Le Meridien is a large beach spa resort boasting all the amenities one would expect from a five-star hotel. There are gorgeously designed twin and double rooms and garden villas, Royal Spa rooms and suites. The cuisine consists of classical French meals and local specialities. 'Le Spa', a unique thalassotherapy health spa, with 7 sea water pools as well as 20 treatment rooms, is regarded as one of the best in the Eastern Mediterranean.

Mariant le meilleur du style européen à l'hospitalité cypriote, Le Meridien est un hôtel et spa de bord de mer offrant tous les services que l'on attend d'un hôtel 5 étoiles. Il offre des chambres twins et doubles superbement décorées, villas dans le jardin et des suites et chambres 'Royal Spa'. La cuisine offre des plats traditionaux français et des spécialités locales. 'Le Spa', un centre de thalassothérapie unique avec 7 piscines d'eau de mer et 20 salles de soins, est considéré comme l'un des meilleurs dans l'est méditérranéen.

Eine Mischung aus europäischem Stil und herzlicher zypriotischer Gastlichkeit macht das Strandresort und Spa Le Meridien zu einem perfekten 5-Sterne-Hotel. Es gibt zauberhaft eingerichtete Zweibett- und Doppelzimmer, Gartenvillen und 'Royal Spa' Zimmer und Suiten. Die Küche besteht aus köstlichen klassischen französischen Gerichten und einheimischen Spezialitäten. "Le Spa", ein einzigartiges Thalassotherapie-Gesundheitszentrum, ist mit 7 Salzwasserpools und 20 Behandlungsräumen eines der besten im östlichen Mittelmeerraum.

Directions: 15 km from Limassol. **Price guide:** *Single CY£100–130; double/twin CY£125–155; suites CY£225–750; garden villas CY£100–195.*

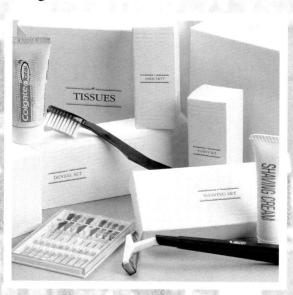

Czech Republic

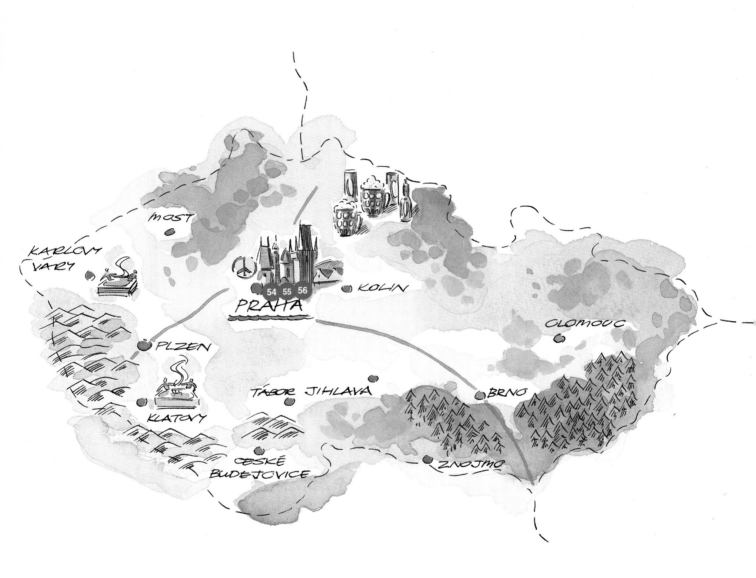

HOTEL HOFFMEISTER

POD BRUSKOU 7, KLÁROV, 11800 PRAGUE 1, CZECH REPUBLIC
TEL: +420 2 51017 111 FAX: +420 2 51017 100 E-MAIL: hotel@hoffmeister.cz

Located just below Prague's enchanting castle and commanding stunning views of the river, the Hoffmeister subtly blends the old and the new. An intriguing collection of paintings and portraits is one of the most interesting features, although visitors are equally impressed by the terrace café and the charming cellar bar. The chef serves a fascinating combination of local and international cuisine, complemented by delicious wines.

Situé juste au dessous du château enchanteur de Prague et proposant des vues époustouflantes sur la rivière, le Hoffmeister mélange l'ancien et le moderne de façon subtile. Une collection intrigante de peintures et de portraits est un des points clefs de l'hôtel, bien que les visiteurs seront également impressionnés par le café terrace et le charmant bar en sous sol. Le chef sert une combinaison fascinante de cuicine locale et internationale, agrémentée de vins délicieux.

Direkt unterhalb der zauberhaften Prager Burg gelegen und mit traumhaften Aussichten über den Fluss, bietet das Hoffmeister eine perfekte Mischung aus Alt und Neu. Eines der interessantesten Merkmale des Hotels ist eine einzigartige Sammlung von Gemälden und Portraits. Das Terrassencafe und die charmante Kellerbar servieren eine köstliche Mischung aus einheimischen und internationalen Speisen, die durch erlesene Weine ergänzt werden.

Directions: *Centre of the city.* **Price guide:** *Single U$125–170; double/twin U$165–230; suites U$205–330.*

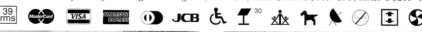

HOTEL U KRÁLE KARLA

NERUDOVA-ÚVOZ 4, 11800 PRAGUE 1, CZECH REPUBLIC
TEL: +420 2 57 53 12 11 FAX: +420 2 57 53 35 91 E-MAIL: ukrale@tnet.cz

Although modernised to cater for today's discerning visitors, this attractive, Baroque style hotel has retained its old charm and ambience. Standing on the hillside beneath the ancient Royal castle and surrounded by steep streets and stairs it is an ideal base from which to explore the city. Excellent meals are served in a small, romantic restaurant to the melodious strains of an old music box.

Modernisé pour répondre aux besoins des voyageurs d'aujourd'hui, ce bel hôtel de style baroque a su garder tout son charme et son atmosphère d'antan. Situé à flanc de coteau, en contrebas du château royal, dans un dédale de rues et d'escaliers escarpés, l'hôtel "Au Roi Charles" est un point de départ idéal pour explorer Prague. D'excellents repas se savourent dans le petit restaurant romantique aux sons mélodieux d'une vieille boîte à musique.

Obwohl dieses attraktive, barocke Hotel modernisiert wurde und nun den heutigen Anforderungen entspricht, konnte es viel von seinem ursprünglichen Charme und Ambiente behalten. Auf dem Hügel unterhalb der alten Burg gelegen und von engen Gassen und Treppen umgeben, ist es ein idealer Ausgangspunkt, um die Stadt zu erkunden. In einem kleinen, romantischen Restaurant geniesst man feinste Gerichte und die melodischen Klänge einer alten Jukebox.

Directions: *Centre of the city.* **Price guide:** *Single CZK4250–5800; double/twin CZK4600–6300; suites CZK6200–6900.*

CZECH REPUBLIC (Prague)

SIEBER HOTEL & APARTMENTS
SLEZSKÁ 55, 130 00 PRAGUE 3, CZECH REPUBLIC
TEL: +420 2 24 25 00 25 FAX: +420 2 24 25 00 27 E-MAIL: reservations@sieber.cz

Situated in a quiet side street near Wenceslas Square, the Sieber is an immaculate base for a visit to Prague. The beautifully designed bedrooms are spacious and comfortable and offer all the modern comforts one has come to expect. A charming and cosy bar leads into the restaurant where visitors can indulge in Czech specialities or more familiar international dishes – all imaginatively prepared by the renowned chef.

Situé dans une rue calme près de la Place Vanceslas, le Sieber est un pied à terre magnifique pour visiter Pargue. Les chambres sont superbement décorées, spacieuses et confortables et offrent tout le confort moderne auquel on s'attend. Un bar charmant et douillet vous mène au restaurant où vous pourrez goûter des spécialités tchèques ou des plats internationaux plus familiers – tous étant élaborés avec imagination par le fameux chef.

Das Sieber liegt in einer ruhigen Seitenstrasse in der Nähe des Wenzelsplatzes und ist ein perfekter Aufenthaltsort für Besucher Prags. Die wunderschön gestalteten Zimmer sind geräumig und bequem und bieten jeglichen modernen Komfort. Eine zauberhafte, gemütliche Bar führt in ein herrliches Restaurant, wo die Gäste sich tschechischen oder vertrauteren internationalen Gaumenfreuden hingeben können – alle einfallsreich von einem renommierten Küchenchef zubereitet.

Directions: *Near Jiriho Z Podebrad Metro.* **Price guide:** *Single CZK4480; double/twin CZK4780; suites CZK5480.*

Denmark

STEENSGAARD HERREGÅRDSPENSION

MILLINGE, STEENSGAARD, 5600 FAABORG, DENMARK
TEL: +45 62 61 94 90 FAX: +45 63 61 78 61 E-MAIL: steensgaard@herregaardspension.dk

Located on the delightful island of Fyn and surrounded by 24 acres of parkland and game reserve, this 14th century manor house has been tastefully restored. The interior, with its antiques, chandeliers and handsome oil paintings, is simply a delight. A grand mahogany staircase leads to the bedrooms, which are decorated in peaceful colours. The restaurant offers Danish and Finnish specialities and a selection of international wines.

Situé dans la superbe île de Fyn et entouré de 10 hectares de parc, ce manoir du XIVème siècle a été restauré avec goût. L'intérieur, avec ses antiquités, ses chandelliers et ses jolies peintures à l'huile, est un délice. Une grande cage d'escalier en acajou mène aux chambres, qui sont décorées avec des couleurs paisibles. Le restaurant propose des spécialités danoises et finlandaises et une sélection de vins internationaux.

Dieses perfekt restaurierte Herrenhaus aus dem 14. Jahrhundert liegt auf der Insel Fyn inmitten eines 10 ha grossen Parks mit Wildreservat. Das Interieur mit seinen Antiquitäten, Lüstern und kostbaren Ölbildern ist einfach traumhaft. Eine breite Mahagonitreppe führt zu den Zimmern, die alle in ruhigen Farben gehalten sind. Im Restaurant werden dänische und finnische Spezialitäten sowie eine Auswahl an internationalen Weinen serviert.

Directions: 2 hours from Copenhagen. **Price guide:** Single Kr815–1255; double/twin Kr990–1450.

HOTEL HESSELET

CHRISTIANSLUNDSVEJ 119, 5800 NYBORG, DENMARK
TEL: +45 65 31 30 29 FAX: +45 65 31 29 58 E-MAIL: hotel@hesselet.dk

Situated on the island of Funen and surrounded by woodland, the renowned Hesselet offers simply awe-inspiring views over the sea. The Japanese influenced architecture is one of the hotel's most outstanding features, and visitors are not disappointed by the tasteful interior and spacious airy rooms. More active guests will enjoy the indoor pool with fitness equipment or may prefer to swim from the hotel jetty or play tennis.

Situé sur l'île de Funen et entouré de bois, le fameux Hesselet offre des vues extraordinaires sur la mer. L'architecture d'influence japonaise est un des traits de caractères principaux de l'hôtel et les visiteurs ne seront pas déçus de l'intérieur superbe et des chambres aériennes et luxueuses. Les visiteurs les plus actifs pourront profiter de la piscine couverte avec ses équipements sportifs ou pourront préférer une nage depuis la jetée ou jouer au tennis.

Das renommierte Hotel Hesselet auf der Insel Funen ist von Waldlandschaft umgeben und bietet atemberaubende Aussichten über das Meer. Die japanisch beeinflusste Architektur ist eine seiner Besonderheiten, und die geschmackvolle Inneneinrichtung und die geräumigen, luftigen Zimmern sind nicht weniger beeindruckend. Sportliche Gäste können das Hallenbad und Fitnessgeräte nutzen, Tennis spielen oder vom hoteleigenen Steg aus schwimmen.

Directions: E20 > Exit 45 > Nyborg. **Price guide:** *Single Kr1090–1190; double/twin Kr1590–1690; suites Kr2200–2700.*

Estonia

PARK CONSUL SCHLÖSSLE

PÜHAVAIMU 13–15, 10123 TALLINN, ESTONIA
TEL: +372 699 7700 FAX: +372 699 7777

Situated in the centre of Tallinn's splendid old town, this attractive hotel dating from the middle ages has been restored to its former magnificence. With its cut-stone portals, small spiral staircases and irregular chambers, one is left with the impression that time has stood still. Notwithstanding its 13th century origins, the spacious bedrooms boast every modern convenience the discerning traveller now expects. In the "Great Hall" with its cosy fireplace, an extensive range of light meals and drinks are served.

Situé dans le centre de la splendide vieille ville de Tallinn, ce joli hôtel moyenâgeux a été restauré pour reproduire sa magnificence d'antan. Avec ses arches en pierre, son petit escalier en spirale et ses chambres irrégulières, il règne une ambiance où le temps s'arrête. Mis à part ses origines du XIIIème siècle, les grandes chambres offrent tout le confort moderne. Un grand choix de repas légers et de boissons est proposée dans le "Great Hall" avec sa cheminée reconfortante.

Dieses attraktive Hotel mitten im Zentrum von Tallinn's zauberhafter Altstadt stammt aus dem Mittelalter und erhielt durch Renovierung seine ehemalige Pracht wieder. Mit seinen Steinportalen, engen Wendeltreppen und unterschiedlich grossen Kammern bekommt man das Gefühl, die Zeit sei stehengeblieben. Trotz der ursprünglichen Merkmale aus dem 13. Jahrhundert sind die Zimmer mit jeglichem modernen Komfort ausgestattet. In der "Great Hall" wird eine grosse Auswahl an leichten Speisen und Gettränken serviert.

Directions: *Centre of Tallinn.* **Price guide:** *Single $176–$209; double/twin $220–$257; suites $290–350.*

CHATEAUX & HOTELS DE FRANCE

Getting to the heart of France

Look deep into France's soul - the balanced blend of historical drama and national unity, her sophisticated wit offset by unbridled daring, the delectable marriage of a ceaselessly changing culture and a timeless lifestyle. With the utmost authenticity and vivacity, the Châteaux & Hôtels de France characterise this unique cultural mix of pleasure and enjoyment. Staying in one of the group's 487 establishments means immersing oneself in a wealth of unforgettable emotions, inspired by fine cuisine, smiling hospitality and caring service.

Such is the soul of the world's most beautiful country, which the Châteaux & Hôtels de France have concentrated into a sole ambition: turning demanding clients into satisfied travellers.

Un certain Art de vivre

France

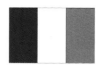

CHÂTEAU DE CANDIE

RUE DU BOIS DE CANDIE, 73000 CHAMBÉRY-LE-VIEUX, FRANCE
TEL: +33 4 79 96 63 00 FAX: +33 4 79 96 63 10 E-MAIL: candie@icor.fr

To stay in this comfortable and friendly 14th century chateau will not fail to impart a sense of rich history. A true connoisseur's paradise, the hotel is simply crammed with priceless antiques, collections of paintings and rare statues lurking in every corner. The lovely bedrooms and suites are named after historical personalities and furnished accordingly. The imaginative Savoyan dishes are simply divine.

Séjourner dans ce château du XIVème siècle confortable et acceuillant ne manquera pas de transmettre les charmes d'un riche passé historique. Paradis pour les vrais connaissseurs, l'hôtel regorge d'antiquités inestimables, de collections de peintures et de rares statues se nichant aux quatre coins du château. Les belles chambres et les suites sont dénommées en souvenir de personnalités historiques et meublées en conséquence. La cuisine savoyarde imaginative est tout simplement divine.

Ein Aufenthalt in diesem gemütlichen und freundlichen Chateau aus dem 14. Jahrhundert wird jedem Gast ein historisches Ambiente näherbringen. Es ist ein Paradies für den Kenner, verschwenderisch mit kostbaren Antiquitäten, Gemälden und seltenen Statuen in jeder Ecke gefüllt. Die zauberhaften Zimmer wie auch die Suiten sind nach historischen Persönlichkeiten benannt und entsprechend eingerichtet. Die einfallsreiche Savoyner Küche ist ein Hochgenuss.

Directions: *A43 > exit 15 > Chambert Le Haut.* **Price guide:** *Double/twin FF600–1200; suites FF1300.*

HÔTEL ANNAPURNA

73120 COURCHEVEL (1850), FRANCE
TEL: +33 4 79 08 04 60 FAX: +33 4 79 08 15 31 E-MAIL: hannapurna@aol.com

A sophisticated hotel in the middle of the Alps, the Annapurna has recognised the needs of its guests after a day on the piste. Its spacious and elegant interior and the soothing lounges assure complete relaxation. The luxurious wood-panelled bedrooms all have south-facing balconies. Boasting fine views of the mountainside, the panoramic restaurant serves exquisite French food accompanied by a delicious selection of wines.

Cet hôtel sophistiqué au milieu des Alpes est devenu une étape incontournable après une journée sur les pistes. Son intérieur spacieux et élégant, ses salons accueillants assurent une relaxation complète. Les chambres luxueuses et lambrissées ont toutes des balcons exposés au sud. Glorifié de vues magnifiques sur la montagne, le restaurant panoramique offre une cuisine française exquise accompagnée d'une délicieuse sélection de vins.

Das Annapurna, ein exquisites Haus inmitten der Alpen, hat sich ganz auf die Bedürfnisse seiner sportlichen Gäste eingestellt. Die weitläufigen und eleganten Innenräume sowie die bequemen Salons bieten nach einem Tag auf der Piste totale Entspannung. Die luxuriösen, holzgetäfelten Zimmer verfügen alle über einen Südbalkon. Das Panorama-Restaurant serviert vorzügliche französische Speisen und erlesene Weine und bietet eine herrliche Sicht auf die Berge.

Directions: *A43 > Montmelian > Moutiers > Courchevel.* **Price guide:** *Single FF1220–2910; double/twin FF1220–1890; suites FF3300–4140.*

LE DOMAINE DE DIVONNE

AVENUE DES THERMES, 01220 DIVONNE-LES-BAINS, FRANCE
TEL: +33 4 50 40 34 34 FAX: +33 4 50 40 34 24 E-MAIL: info@domaine-de-divonne.com

The Domaine de Divonne is one of the most exclusive French Resorts, the nearest to Geneva and the Swiss border, in sight of Mont Blanc and at the foot of the Jura Mountains. The magnificent estate consists of a 1930 art deco residence, the Grand Hotel, a challenging 18-hole golf course, a casino with 355 slot machines and gambling tables and a night club. The elegant guest rooms offer balconies overlooking the Alps and state-of-the-art technology. Five restaurants, including the 1 Michelin Star "La Terrasse", offer a diversity of cuisine.

Le Domaine de Divonne est un resort unique en France. C'est également le plus proche de Genève et de la frontièrer suisse, face au Mont Blanc et aux pieds du Jura. Cet établissement de grand luxe, dans un style Art Déco des années 30, réunit Le Grand Hotel, un superbe golf 18 trous, un casino avec 355 machines à sous et une salle de jeux traditionnels et une discothèque. Les chambres luxueuses disposent de balcons avec vue sur les Alpes et un équipement technique très complet. Il y a cinq restaurants, dont "La Terrasse" étoilé au guide Michelin.

Domaine de Divonne, eines der exklusivsten Resorts in Frankreich, liegt am Fusse des Jura-Gebirges nahe der Schweizer Grenze und Genf und mit Blick auf den Mont Blanc. Das luxuriöse Anwesen im 30er Jahre Art-Déco-Stil besteht aus dem Grand Hotel, einem anspruchsvollen 18-Loch Golfplatz, Casino mit 355 Spielautomaten und Spieltischen und einem Nightclub. Die eleganten Zimmer bieten Balkon mit Blick auf die Alpen und modernste Technologie. Fünf Restaurants stehen zur Auswahl, darunter das mit 1 Michelin-Stern ausgezeichnete "La Terrasse".

Directions: N1 from Geneva > Coppet/Divonne exit. **Price guide:** *Single FF1,000–1,550; double/twin FF1,500–2,900; suites FF2,750–15,000.*

CHALET HÔTEL LA MARMOTTE

74260 LES GETS, FRANCE

TEL: + 33 4 50 75 80 33 FAX: + 33 4 50 75 83 26 E-MAIL: marmotte@portesdusoleil.com

Situated amidst the beautiful alpine trails and ski slopes of the French Alps, the very family-orientated La Marmotte is friendly and cosy and the perfect base from which to explore this exciting region. Guests of all ages will appreciate the range of activities, including on-site gym, indoor swimming pool, spa and beauty facilities. Exhilarating ski slopes, golf courses and Lac de Baignade are nearby, and lively Les Gets with its shops and restaurants is within easy reach of other 'Portes du Soleil' ski resorts.

Au pied des pistes de ski et des sentiers pédestres des Alpes, vous attend un grand chalet convivial et confortable, la base parfaite pour explorer une région fascinante. Idéal pour les familles, cet hôtel offre des activités aux visiteurs de tout âge, qui peuvent profiter notamment du gymnase, de la piscine couverte, du spa et du centre de beauté. Pistes grisantes, golfs et lac de baignade ne sont qu'à deux pas. Et si l'animation des Gets, avec ses restaurants et ses magasins, ne vous suffit pas, vous pouvez facilement accéder aux autres stations des Portes du Soleil.

Umgeben von herrlichen Wanderwegen und Skipisten der französischen Alpen bietet das freundliche, familienorientierte Hotel La Marmotte den perfekten Ausgangspunkt, um diese faszinierende Gegend zu erforschen. Gäste aller Altersstufen nutzen das umfassende Freizeitangebot, wie Fitnessraum, Hallenbad, Spa und Schönheitsfarm. Traumhafte Abfahrten, Golfplätze und der Lac de Baignade sind in der Nähe, und vom lebhaften Les Gets mit seinen Restaurants und Geschäften sind auch andere 'Portes du Soleil' Skigebiete leicht erreichbar.

Directions: Leave the A40 exit Cluses. **Price guide (half-board):** *Double/twin FF515–1150.*

HÔTEL MONT-BLANC

PLACE DE L'ÉGLISE, 74120 MEGÈVE, FRANCE
TEL: +33 4 50 21 20 02 FAX: +33 4 50 21 45 28 E-MAIL: contact@hotelmontblanc.com

The rich alpine style in this recently refurbished hotel is the perfect complement to its dramatic surroundings of mountains and dense forests. It is truly delightful, with soft, deep fabrics and wooden furnishings creating a warm and convivial retreat for skiers of all ages at the Megève resort. Although there is no restaurant, breakfast and delicious afternoon teas are served in the breakfast room or the cosy lounge. A health centre with sauna, solarium and Jacuzzi completes the sense of total contentment and relaxation.

Le magnifique style alpin de cet hôtel est en parfaite harmonie avec le cadre spectaculaire formé par les montagnes et les forêts avoisinantes. Les étoffes moelleuses alliées au mobilier en bois créent une atmosphère conviviale idéale pour les skieurs séjournant dans cette station savoyarde. L'hôtel n'a pas de restaurant, mais le petit déjeuner et le thé sont servis dans la petite salle à manger ou le salon intime. Le centre de remise en forme comprenant un sauna, un solarium et un Jacuzzi, les visiteurs trouvent dans cet hôtel un bien-être absolu.

Der reiche Alpenstil passt perfekt zur atemberaubenden Berg- und Waldlandschaft, die dieses zauberhafte, erst kürzlich renovierte Hotel umgibt. Weiche, üppige Stoffe und Einrichtung aus Holz schaffen ein warmes und freundliches Ambiente – ideal für Skifreunde jeder Altersstufe, die das Gebiet um Megève besuchen. Zwar gibt es kein Restaurant, aber ein herzhaftes Frühstück und Kaffee und köstliche Kuchen sorgen täglich für Stärkung. Das Fitnesszentrum mit Sauna, Solarium und Jacuzzi vervollständigt das Gefühl völliger Erholung.

Directions: *Chamonix > Sallanches > Megeve.* **Price guide:** *Double/twin FF820–2100; suites FF1490–3470. Breakfast FF80 per person.*

LODGE PARK HÔTEL

100 RUE D'ARLY, 74120 MEGÈVE, FRANCE
TEL: +33 4 50 93 05 03 FAX: +33 4 50 93 09 52 E-MAIL: ldgepark@internet-montblanc.fr

Dating back to the early part of the century, this charming American lodge-style property is surrounded by striking mountains and forests. With log fires and soft furnishings, an ambience of cosy warmth pervades the lodge. The spacious bedrooms, most of which have balconies, are individually decorated and feature Ralph Lauren fabrics. The friendly restaurant serves traditional French cuisine and local cheese-based specialities.

Dâtant du début du siècle, ce charmant pavillon de style américain est entouré de superbes montagnes et de forêts. Avec ses feux de bois et ses tissus fins, une ambiance de chaleur douce caractérise le pavillon. Les chambres spacieuses, dont la plupart ont des balcons, sont décorées de manière individuelle avec notamment des tissus Ralph Lauren. Le restaurant chaleureux propose une cuisine traditonnelle française ainsi que des spécialités à base du fromage local.

Dieses charmante und im amerikanischen Stil gestaltete Gebäude stammt aus dem frühen 20. Jahrhundert und ist von beeindruckenden Bergen und Wäldern umgeben. Holzkaminfeuer und behagliche Einrichtung schaffen eine gemütliche Stimmung. Die geräumigen Zimmer sind individuell gehalten, die meisten verfügen über einen Balkon und sind mit Stoffen von Ralph Lauren gestaltet. Das freundliche Restaurant bietet traditionelle französische Küche und einheimische Käsespezialitäten.

Directions: Chamonix > Sallanches > Megève > Albertville. **Price guide:** Single FF1190–1560; double/twin FF790–1140; suites FF1550–1850.

CHÂTEAU DE COUDRÉE

DOMAINE DE COUDRÉE, BONNATRAIT, 74140 SCIEZ-SUR-LÉMAN, FRANCE
TEL: +33 4 50 72 62 33 FAX: +33 4 50 72 57 28 E-MAIL: chcoudree@aol.com

Perched on the edge of lake Geneva, this 12th century chateau with its turrets and pinnacles offers a truly fairy tale experience. With a mere nineteen guest rooms, all furnished with antiques, this is an elite hotel. Exquisite salons, and a big terrace overlooking the pool and gardens down to the water's edge all contribute to the visitors' overall pleasure. A memorable gastronomic experience is also guaranteed.

Niché sur les bords du lac de Genève, ce château du XIIème siècle avec ses 19 chambres meublées d'antiquités, offre une vision de conte de fée, avec ses tourrelles et ses donjons. Des salons raffinés, un bar accueillant, une grande terrasse avec vue sur la piscine et le jardin descendant jusqu'au bord du lac rendent les séjours encore plus agréables. Une mémorable expérience gastronomique est également garantie.

Am Ufer des Genfer Sees gelegen bietet dieses Chateau aus dem 12. Jahrhundert mit seinen Türmen und Zinnen einen märchenhaften Aufenthalt. Mit nur neunzehn Zimmern, alle mit erlesenen Antiquitäten möbliert, ist Exklusivität garantiert. Herrliche Salons, eine grosse Terrasse mit Blick über den Pool und ein Garten bis zum Seeufer schaffen ein Gefühl der totalen Entspannung. Die Küche verspricht gastronomischen Hochgenuss.

Directions: A40 - Annemasse/Thonon/Evian – Sciez Bonnatrait. **Price guide:** *Single from FF680; double/twin FF790–1945; apartments FF1525–2155.*

HÔTEL LES TÊTES

19, RUE DE TÊTES, 68000 COLMAR, FRANCE
TEL: +33 3 89 24 43 43 FAX: +33 3 89 24 58 34

Situated at the heart of this labyrinthine cathedral town, this beautiful renaissance hotel is truly unique. Covered by 105 grotesque masks, the baroque theme extends into the interior, where an intimate courtyard allows guests to relax over coffee and cool drinks in summer. The bedrooms, complete with ancient beamed ceilings and attractive stonework, are highly atmospheric. The hotel's welcoming owner, Marc Rohfritsch, prepares sumptuous dishes served under glittering chandeliers in the restaurant La Maison des Têtes.

Situé au coeur de cette ville tentaculaire avec sa cathédrale, ce magnifique hôtel Renaissance est vraiment exceptionnel. Décoré de 105 masques de style grotesque, le thème baroque s'étend à l'intérieur, où une cour intime permet aux clients de se détendre autour d'un café ou de boissons rafraîchissantes en été. Les chambres, avec leurs poutres anciennes et leurs beaux murs en pierre, dégagent une ambiance extraordinaire. L'accueillant maître des lieux, Marc Rohfritsch, prépare de sompteux repas dans son restaurant La Maison des Têtes.

Inmitten dieser labyrinthischen Domstadt liegt dieses einzigartige Renaissancehotel. Das Barockthema wird mit 105 grotesken Masken im Interieur fortgesetzt, wo ein intimer Innenhof die Gäste zu Kaffee oder einem kühlen Drink im Sommer einlädt. Die Zimmer, mit alten Balkendecken und attraktiven Steinarbeiten verziert, sind besonders stimmungsvoll. Marc Rohfritsch, der Besitzer des Hotels, bereitet köstliche Speisen, die im Restaurant La Maison des Têtes unter glänzenden Lüstern serviert werden.

Directions: *Colmar city centre.* **Price guide:** *Double/twin FF650–1230; suites FF1250–1500.*

HOSTELLERIE LES BAS RUPTS

88400 GÉRARDMER, VOSGES, FRANCE
TEL: +33 3 29 63 09 25 FAX: +33 3 29 63 00 40

Close to Lake Gérardmer, in the heart of Les Vosges Mountain region, the Hostellerie and its adjoining Chalet Fleuri is a magical retreat all year round. A homely and welcoming ambience is accompanied by warm hospitality – the bedrooms are comfortable and uniquely attractive, with hand-painted flowers adorning the walls and doors. The succulent dishes, an inspired interpretation of local specialities, are complemented by fine winesare and served in the panoramic restaurant.

Tout près du lac de Gérardmer, au coeur des Vosges, l'Hostellerie Les Bas Rupts et son annexe, le Chalet Fleuri, offrent une retraite idyllique tout au long de l'année. L'accueil cordial est complété par une atmosphère intime et chaleureuse - les chambres sont confortables et très jolies, avec des portes et des murs ornés de fleurs peintes à la main. Des plats succulents, une brillante interprétation des spécialités locales, accompagnés de vins exceptionnels sont servis dans le restaurant panoramique.

Nahe am Géradmer See und inmitten der Vogesen liegt die Hostellerie Les Bas Rupts und das dazugehörende Chalet Fleuri. Eine heimelige und warme Atmosphäre verbindet sich hier mit herzlicher Gastfreundschaft – die zauberhaften Zimmer sind gemütlich eingerichtet und die Wände und Türen mit Blumen handbemalt. Köstliche Speisen, eine gelungene Interpretation einheimischer Spezialitäten, und erlesene Weine werden im Panoramarestaurant serviert.

Directions: Paris > Nancy > Remiremont > Gérardmer. **Price guide**: Double/twin FF780–1200.

DOMAINE DE ROCHEVILAINE

POINTE DE PEN LAN, 56190 BILLIERS, FRANCE
TEL: +33 2 97 41 61 61 FAX: +33 2 97 41 44 85

Perched on the edge of the rocky Pointe de Pen Lan, this historic manor house affords a panoramic vista across the waterfront. The bedrooms are all designed in a stylish manner, while Aubusson tapestries adorn the walls of the comfortable lounge, where visitors enjoy pre-prandial drinks. After, they can revel in the delicious French cuisine that chef Patrice Caillaut crafts from the freshest of local produce.

Perché sur la pointe rocheuse de Pen Lan, ce manoir historique bénéficie d'une vue panoramique sur le bord de mer. Les chambres sont toutes décorées avec soin. Les tapisseries d'Aubusson décorent les murs du confortable salon et le visiteur se délectera d'apéritifs délicieux. Ensuite, il pourra évoluer vers la divine table française que le chef Patrice Caillaut concocte à partir des meilleurs produits locaux.

Dieses historische Herrenhaus liegt auf der Felspitze von Pen Lan und bietet eine traumhafte Sicht auf die Küste. Die Zimmer sind höchst elegant, Aubusson-Gobelins zieren die Wände des gemütlichen Aufenthaltsraums, in dem sich die Gäste auf einen Apéritif treffen. Für die herrlichen französischen Speisen verwendet Küchenchef Patrice Caillaut die frischesten und besten Zutaten der Region.

Directions: *From Nantes > E60 > Vannes > Billiers > Pen Lan.* **Price guide:** *Single FF590–1550; double/twin FF590–1550; suites FF1680–2500.*

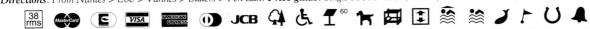

CHATEAU DE BONABAN

35350 LA GOUESNIÈRE, FRANCE

TEL: +33 2 99 58 24 50 FAX: +33 2 99 58 28 41 E-MAIL: chateau.bonaban@wanadoo.fr

Situated on a wooded estate in the midst of the Pays Malouin, this 17th century chateau offers best service in a friendly ambience. Boasting an opulently decorated chapel and a vast marble staircase, this idyllic country hideaway gives the impression of time standing still. The rooms are adorned with historical paintings, while the dining room invites guests to indulge in sumptuous traditional French fare. Five high quality golf courses are in close proximity.

Situé au coeur de la région boisée du Pays Malouin, ce château du XVIIème siècle offre le meilleur service dans une ambiance amicale. Exhibant une chapelle superbement décorée et une cage d'escalier en marbre, cette retraite idyllique campagnarde évoque une ambiance où le temps s'arrête. Les chambres sont ornées de peintures historiques et la salle à manger invite les clients aux plaisirs somptueux d'un menu français traditionnel. Cinq superbes parcours de golf sont situés à proximité.

Auf einem bewaldeten Gut inmitten des Pays Malouin bietet dieses Schloss aus dem 17. Jahrhundert anspruchsvollen Service in einem freundlichen Ambiente. Mit einer opulent gestalteten Kapelle und einer riesigen Marmortreppe erweckt dieses idyllische ländliche Versteck den Eindruck, als ob hier die Zeit stehengeblieben wäre. Die Zimmer sind mit historischen Gemälden geschmückt, und im Speisesaal werden köstliche traditionelle französische Gerichte serviert. Fünf hervorragende Golfplätze liegen in der Nähe.

Directions: N137 > St Malo > la Gouesniere > signposts. **Price guide:** *Single FF400–1000; Double/twin FF530–1000; suites FF1350–1800.*

MANOIR DE KERTALG

ROUTE DE RIEC SUR BELON, 29350 MOELAN-SUR-MER, FRANCE
TEL: +33 2 98 39 77 77 FAX: +33 2 98 39 72 07

Set in a huge park filled with a variety of trees, this country house offers tranquillity, discreet luxury and a truly warm welcome. The owner's paintings adorn the walls, and fresh flowers can be found everywhere. The bedrooms are individually and tastefully decorated, some with high class modern bathrooms. Breakfast is served in the conservatory or on the sun terrace overlooking the park. Although there is no restaurant at the hotel, numerous gastronomic restaurants can be found in the vicinity.

Blotti au milieu d'un parc peuplé de différentes espèces d'arbres, ce manoir vous accueille cordialement dans un cadre au luxe discret baigné d'une douce tranquillité. Les tableaux du propriétaire ornent les murs, et des fleurs fraîches égayent toute la demeure. Les chambres sont décorées individuellement et avec goût, certaines s'accompagnent de salles de bains modernes. Le petit déjeuner est servi dans le jardin d'hiver ou sur la terrasse avec vue sur le parc. L'hôtel n'a pas de restaurant, mais les environs regorgent d'établissements gastronomiques.

Dieses Landhaus liegt inmitten eines riesigen, mit verschiedensten Bäumen gefüllten Parks und bietet Ruhe, unaufdringlichen Luxus und warme Gastfreundschaft. Eigene Bilder des Besitzers zieren die Wände, und frische Blumen sind im ganzen Haus zu finden. Die Zimmer sind individuell und geschmackvoll eingerich-tet, einige haben hochmoderne Bäder. Das Frühstück geniesst man im Wintergarten oder auf der Terrasse mit Blick auf den Park. Zwar wird kein Abendessen serviert, aber zahlreiche Gourmetrestaurants liegen in nächster Nähe.

Directions: N165 exit Quimperlé centre. **Price guide:** *Single FF490–990; double/twin FF490–990.*

MANOIR DU VAUMADEUC

22130 PLEVEN, FRANCE
TEL: +33 2 96 84 46 17 FAX: +33 2 96 84 40 16

The magnificent Hunaudaye forest encompasses this luxurious former 15th century manor house, which fuses modern comfort and medieval grandeur. Sculpted beams, ornate fireplaces and wooden floors set the tone in the public rooms, while an imposing granite staircase leads to the individually decorated rooms. Only open during the summer, the restaurant offers an intriguing choice of traditional dishes and fine wines.

La somptueuse forêt de Hunaudaye abrite ce luxueux et ancien manoir du XVème siècle, qui allie un cadre médiéval authentique avec le confort moderne. Des poutres sculptées, des cheminées ornées et des parquets en bois plantent le décor des salons, alors qu'un magnifique escalier en granit vous amène aux chambres décorées de manière individuelle. Ouvert seulement l'été, le restaurant propose un choix fascinant de plats traditionnels et de vins fins.

Der herrliche Hunaudaye Forst umgibt dieses luxuriöse Herrenhaus aus dem 15. Jahrhundert, eine Mischung aus modernem Komfort und mittelalterlicher Opulenz. Zierbalken, prunkvolle Kamine und Holzböden verleihen den Empfangsräumen einen besonderen Charakter, und die Zimmer können über eine imposante Granittreppe erreicht werden. Das Restaurant, das nur während der Sommermonate geöffnet ist, bietet eine einfallsreiche Auswahl an traditionellen Gerichten und erlesenen Weinen.

Directions: N168 - Planceot - Lamballe - Pleven. **Price guide:** *Single FF590–1100; double/twin FF590–1100; suites FF590–1100.*

CHATEAU DU LAUNAY

56160 PLOERDÜT, FRANCE
TEL: +33 2 97 39 46 32 FAX: +33 2 97 39 46 31

Serene and sophisticated, Château de Launay offers a step back into a timeless and peaceful era. Its charming hosts have designed their hotel entirely with this purpose, and the tasteful, stylish décor and tranquil ambience testify their success. There is a well-stocked, cosy library, and musical evenings are held in the drawing room. Although there is no restaurant, table d'hôte is served on request. The hotel offers numerous outdoor pursuits such as tennis and riding; fishing is possible from a shady river bank within the grounds.

Paisible et élégant, le Château de Launay nous replonge dans le passé, vers une époque sereine. Les charmants propriétaires ont aménagé leur hôtel dans cet esprit, et le décor raffiné ainsi que la tranquillité des lieux témoignent de leurs efforts. Le château abrite une bibliothèque confortable et un salon accueillant des soirées musicales. L'hôtel n'a pas de restaurant, mais une table d'hôte est disponible sur demande. De nombreuses activités de plein air sont possibles telles que le tennis, l'équitation et la pêche sur la berge ombragée d'une rivière, dans le parc.

Das ruhige und elegante Château de Launay bietet eine Reise zurück in eine zeitlose und friedvolle Ära. Die Besitzer haben ihr Hotel in diesem Sinne gestaltet, und das geschmackvolle Dekor und die ruhige Atmosphäre zeugen von ihrem Erfolg. Eine gutbestückte, gemütliche Bibliothek steht zur Verfügung, und im Aufenthaltsraum finden musikalische Abende statt. Zwar gibt es kein Restaurant, aber auf Wunsch wird für die Gäste gekocht und zusammen gegessen. Das Freizeitangebot umfasst Tennis, Reiten und Angeln am Fluss innerhalb des Grundstücks.

Directions: Pontivy > Gourin, turn right after Toubahado. **Price guide:** *Single FF600; double/twin FF750.*

CHÂTEAU DE VAULT DE LUGNY

11 RUE DU CHÂTEAU, 89200 AVALLON, FRANCE
TEL: +33 3 86 34 07 86 FAX: +33 3 86 34 16 36 E-MAIL: hotel@lugny.com

Dating from the 16th century, this magical rural hideaway is surrounded by an authentic moat weaving its way through the verdant estate. The interior is no less dramatic, with its marvellous panelling, elaborate fireplaces and ornate ceilings. All of the splendid bedrooms have four-poster beds. The chateau is renowned for the variety of its food which is taken either around the kitchen table or in the magnificent garden.

Ce ravissant refuge d'un domaine de campagne dâte du XVIème siècle. Il est encerclé de ses douves authentiques et verdoyantes. L'intérieur est tout aussi impressionnant, avec ses lambris magnifiques, ses cheminées élaborées et ses plafonds à moulures. Toutes les chambres sont splendides et ont des lits à baldaquins. Le château est renommé pour la variété de sa table d'hôte qui peut être dégustée soit à la cuisine soit dans le magnifique jardin.

Dieses zauberhafte Landversteck aus dem 16. Jahrhundert liegt inmitten eines üppigen Parks und wird von einem echten Burggraben umgeben. Im Inneren sorgen herrliche Holzvertäfelung, opulente Kamine und reichverzierte Decken für ein dramatisches Ambiente. Jedes der prachtvollen Schlafzimmer besitzt ein Himmelbett. Das Chateau ist bekannt für seine grosse kulinarische Auswahl und Raffinesse, und die Gäste können entweder am Küchentisch oder im Garten dinieren.

Directions: A6 < Avallon < Vezelay > Pontaubert. **Price guide:** Double/twin FF1000–2900.

HOSTELLERIE DE LA POSTE

13 PLACE VAUBAN, 89200 AVALLON, FRANCE
TEL: +33 3 86 34 16 16 FAX: +33 3 86 34 19 19 E-MAIL: info@hostelleriedelaposte.com

Dating from the first decade of the 18th century, this former postal station is the ideal staging post between Paris and Lyon. Wonderfully refurbished, the Hostellerie is packed with priceless antiques and tastefully furnished. Offering every modern convenience, the en suite bedrooms are simply a dream. Befitting the ambience of the property, the cuisine is a delightful mixture of local dishes with a dash of modern refinement.

Cet ancien relais de poste, dont les origines remontent à la première décennie du XVIIIème siècle, constitue une étape paisible idéale entre Paris et Lyon. Superbement décorée, l'Hostellerie est fournie d'antiquités inestimables et de superbes meubles. Offrant tout le confort moderne, les chambres sont un vrai rêve. La table, en harmonie parfaite avec l'ambiance de la propriété, est un délicieux mélange de plats locaux et d'une pointe de raffinements modernes.

Diese ehemalige Poststation stammt aus der 1. Dekade des 18. Jahrhunderts und ist nach wie vor ein idealer Halt zwischen Paris und Lyon. Die Hostellerie wurde hervorragend restauriert, glänzt mit zahlreichen kostbaren Antiquitäten und ist geschmackvoll eingerichtet. Die traumhaften Zimmer verfügen über alle modernen Annehmlichkeiten. Die Küche spiegelt perfekt das Ambiente des Anwesens wider und bietet eine herrliche Mischung aus einheimischen Gerichten und einem Hauch moderner Raffinesse.

Directions: A6 > Avallon > centre of town. **Price guide:** *Single FF550; double/twin FF650; suites FF950.*

ERMITAGE DE CORTON

R.N. 74, 21200 CHOREY-LES-BEAUNE, FRANCE
TEL: +33 3 80 22 05 28 FAX: +33 3 80 24 64 51

Set in acres of glorious vineyards, this old burgundy-style mansion offers comfortable accommodation and warm hospitality in fine surroundings. The individually decorated rooms range from the grandiose to the simple yet elegant. The restaurant is undoubtedly the centre-point; the traditional French fare is prepared by a maître cuisinier de France, and is complemented by a fine selection of wines.

Entouré d'hectares de merveilleux vignobles, ce vieux manoir de style bourguignon offre des séjours confortables et une chaleureuse hospitalité dans un beau cadre. Les chambres décorées de manière individuelle varient d'un style grandiose au simple et élégant. Le restaurant est sans nul doute l'attraction centrale; la cuisine traditionnel le française est préparé par un Maître Cuisinier de France, et est complété par une fine sélection de vins.

Inmitten herrlicher Weinberge liegt dieses alte Haus im Burgunder Stil, das seinen Gästen ein herzliches Willkommen bietet. Die gemütlichen Zimmer sind in unterschiedlichen Stilen gestaltet, von prunkvoll bis einfach aber elegant. Das Restaurant, zweifellos Mittelpunkt des Hotels, serviert unvergleichliche französische Küche, kreiert von einem „Maître Cuisinier de France", und durch eine erlesene Auswahl an Weinen ergänzt.

Directions: *A6 > Beaune > exit 24 > Dijon.* **Price guide:** *Double/twin FF950–1500; suites FF950–1800.*

LE PETIT MANOIR DES BRUYÈRES

5 ALLEÉ DE CHARBUY-LES BRUYÈRES, 89240 VILLEFARGEAU, FRANCE
TEL: +33 3 86 41 32 82 FAX: +33 3 86 41 28 57 E-MAIL: infos@petit-manoir-bruyeres.com

In the heart of a 250 acre forest and amidst a fragrant garden lies this charming, welcoming and old-fashioned guesthouse with its glazed-tile roof typical of the Burgundy region. The individually decorated bedrooms and suites are equipped with period furniture and luxurious bathrooms, and overlook the park. Mrs Joullié lovingly prepares delicious meals in her splendid kitchen, and after an apéritif comprising a glass of the famous Chablis wine, guests can feast on local specialities.

Perdue au milieu de 100 hectares de forêt et entourée d'un jardin parfumé, cette demeure accueillante vous invite à découvrir le charme désuet qui se cache sous son toit en tuiles vernissées typique de la Bourgogne. Les chambres et les suites sont dotées de meubles d'époque et de salles de bains luxueuses et jouissent d'une vue sur le parc. Madame Joullié prépare des repas délicieux dans sa superbe cuisine et, après leur avoir offert un verre de Chablis, elle propose à ses hôtes de goûter d'excellentes spécialités locales.

Dieses charmante, freundliche und altmodische Haus mit seinem regionstypischen Ziegeldach liegt inmitten eines 100 ha grossen Waldes in einem duftenden Garten. Die individuell gestalteten Zimmer und Suiten sind mit Stilmöbeln und luxuriösen Badezimmern ausgestattet und haben Blick auf den Park. Madame Joullié bereitet köstliche Speisen in ihrer eindrucksvollen Küche, und nach einem Apéritif – meist ein Glass des berühmten Chablis – erfreuen sich die Gäste an einheimischen Spezialitäten.

Directions: A6 exit Auxerre-Sud or Auxerre-Nord. **Price guide:** *Double FF600–800; suites FF1000.*

HOSTELLERIE LA BRIQUETERIE
4 ROUTE DE SÉZANNE, 51530, VINAY – ÉPERNAY, FRANCE
TEL: +33 3 26 59 99 99 FAX: +33 3 26 59 92 10

Standing at the foot of the Côte des Blancs and surrounded by beautiful flower-filled gardens, this friendly family-owned hotel is ideal for the champagne lover. Elegant salons reflect the beauty of the surroundings whilst the newly refurbished bedrooms are simply stunning. Vintages from the Trouillard family's own Champagne House are among the prestigious champagnes enjoyed in the conservatory bar, before diners choose from an enticing range of succulent dishes in the handsome beamed restaurant.

Cet hôtel familial accueillant se dresse dans un beau jardin fleuri, au pied de la Côte des Blancs, un paradis pour les amateurs de champagne. Les salons élégants et les superbes chambres récemment rénovées reflètent la beauté du paysage environnant. La famille Trouillard produit son propre champagne, et ses millésimes figurent parmi les prestigieuses bouteilles que les visiteurs peuvent déguster dans le bar aménagé dans le jardin d'hiver avant de succomber au grand choix de plats savoureux proposé par le beau restaurant aux poutres apparentes.

Dieses freundliche Hotel liegt am Fusse der Côte des Blancs und ist von blumengefüllten Gärten umgeben. Elegante Salons und herrliche neue Zimmer spiegeln die Schönheit der Umgebung wider. Das Hotel ist ein Paradies für den Champagnerfreund – die Familie besitzt eine eigene Champagnerkellerei, und die Gäste können die erlesenen Jahrgänge in der Wintergarten-Bar geniessen, bevor sie sich im zauberhaften Restaurant von einer grossen Auswahl an köstlichen Speisen verlocken lassen.

Directions: *Route de Sézanne > Epernay > signposted.* **Price guide:** *Single FF650–820; double/twin FF750–940; suites FF1300.*

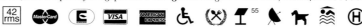

CHÂTEAU DE FÈRE

02130 FÈRE-EN-TARDENOIS, FRANCE
TEL + 33 3 23 82 21 13 FAX: +33 3 23 82 37 81 E-MAIL: chateau.fere@wanadoo.fr

Side by side with the impressive ruins of a medieval castle, this grand and exclusive 18th century château is situated in beautiful, wooded countryside just a one hour drive from Paris. The guestrooms are tastefully furnished, maintained to the highest standard and offer spectacular views. Excellent gourmet meals are served in three individual and stylishly designed dining rooms where the service is impeccable. The treasures of the champagne region can be enjoyed on a tour of the chateau's cellars.

Dominé par les ruines impressionnantes d'un château fort, cet hôtel de luxe occupe un magnifique château du XVIIIe siècle, au milieu d'un beau parc boisé, à une heure seulement de Paris. Des chambres de premier ordre, meublées avec goût, offrent des vues spectaculaires sur les environs. Trois salles à manger différentes proposent des menus gourmands dans un cadre élégant. Le service est d'une qualité irréprochable. Un tour des caves du château permet aux œnophiles de savourer les délices de la région champenoise.

Inmitten der imposanten Ruinen einer mittelalterlichen Burg und umgeben von herrlicher Waldlandschaft liegt dieses elegante und exklusive Schloss aus dem 18. Jahrhundert, nur eine Stunde Fahrt von Paris entfernt. Die Zimmer sind geschmackvoll eingerichtet und bieten höchstes Niveau und eindrucksvolle Aussichten. In drei unterschiedlichen, eleganten Speisesälen werden exzellente Gerichte serviert; der Service ist makellos. Champagnerfreunde werden sich über die Champagnerkeller des Schlosses freuen

Directions: From Paris on A4, exit Château-Thierry. **Price guide:** *Double/twin FF850–1900; suites FF1300–2300.*

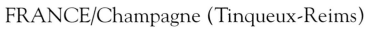

L'ASSIETTE CHAMPENOISE

40 AVENUE PAUL VAIFFANT COUTURIER, 51430 TINQUEUX, FRANCE
TEL: +33 3 26 84 64 64 FAX: +33 3 26 04 15 69

A truly warm welcome awaits visitors to this family-orientated hotel, highly reputed for its delicious modern and traditional cuisine. Complemented by a cosy and welcoming bar, a superb dining room opens out onto an amazing terrace. Guests may relax in the lawned gardens filled with trees and flowers, take advantage of the indoor swimming pool and sauna or visit Reims and some of the numerous champagne cellars in the vicinity, some of which house the finest bottles in the world.

Un accueil très chaleureux vous attend dans cet hôtel hautement réputé pour sa délicieuse cuisine moderne et traditionnelle. Complétée par un bar intime, l'élégante salle de restaurant s'ouvre sur une magnifique terrasse. Les visiteurs se reposent sur les pelouses du jardin rempli de fleurs et d'arbres, profitent de la piscine et du sauna ou visitent Reims et les innombrables caves à champagne des environs, dont certaines renferment les meilleures bouteilles du monde.

Ein herzlicher Empfang erwartet Besucher dieses familienorientierten Hotels, das für seine köstliche moderne und traditionelle Küche weithin bekannt ist. Es gibt eine gemütliche Bar und ein eleganter Speisesaal führt auf eine fantastische Terrasse hinaus. Die Gäste entspannen sich im gepflegten, mit Bäumen und Blumen gefüllten Garten, Hallenbad oder in der Sauna oder erkunden Reims und die zahllosen Champagnerkeller in der Umgebung, von denen einige die besten Champagnersorten der Welt beherbergen.

Directions: A4 exit Tinqueux. **Price guide:** *Double/twin FF585–770; suites FF970–1550.*

CHÂTEAU DE PRAY

ROUTE DE CHARGÉ, 37400 AMBOISE, FRANCE
TEL: +33 2 47 57 23 67 FAX: +33 2 47 57 32 50 E-MAIL: chateau.depray@wanadoo.fr

Nestled on the sunny terraced slopes overlooking the tranquil Loire river, Chateau de Pray is simply steeped in history. Surrounded by peaceful gardens, the imposing round towers bear witness to its Renaissance origins. The traditional ambience extends to the interior, where wood panelling, heavy beams and rich fabrics abound. The en suite bedrooms, many of which have stunning views, are tastefully furnished.

Niché sur les côteaux ensoleillés des collines des eaux tranquilles de la Loire, Le Château de Pray est imprégné d'histoire. Entouré de jardins paisibles, ses tours rondes sont témoins de son origine Renaissance. L'ambiance traditionnelle s'étend à l'intérieur où les boiseries, les lourdes poutres et riches étoffes abondent. Les chambres dont la plupart ont de superbes vues, sont meublées avec goût.

In die sonnigen, terrassenförmigen Hänge oberhalb der Loire schmiegt sich das geschichtsträchtige Chateau de Pray. Umgeben von ruhigen Gärten zeugen die imposanten runden Türme von seinen Ursprüngen aus der Renaissance. Das traditionsreiche Ambiente wird durch reichlich vorhandene Holzvertäfelung sowie schwere Balken und üppige Stoffe betont. Die Zimmer sind geschmackvoll eingerichtet und viele bieten einen herrlichen Ausblick.

Directions: *D31 > Blois.* **Price guide:** *Single FF490–990; double/twin FF490–990; suites FF880–1300.*

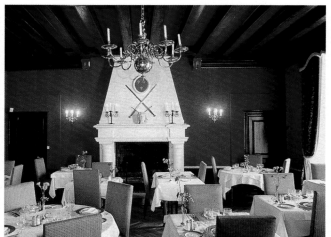

LE MANOIR LES MINIMES

34, QUAI CHARLES GUINOT, 37400 AMBOISE, FRANCE
TEL: +33 2 47 30 40 40 FAX: +33 2 47 30 40 77 E-MAIL: manoir-les-minimes@wanadoo.fr

This authentic 18th century manor house was built on the foundations of the ancient medieval Monastère des Minimes and is situated in proximity of the old town. It is the ideal place from which to explore the chateaux and vineyards of the Loire Valley. This selected stopping place offers its visitors comfort "à la française", a harmonious blend of sophistication and intimacy, whilst affording glorious views of the Château Royale d'Amboise and the river Loire. Air-conditioned rooms; private enclosed parking; no restaurant.

Authentique demeure du XVIIIème siècle, érigée sur les fondations de l'ancien monastère médiéval des Minimes, située à proximité immédiate de la vieille ville. Le Manoir les Minimes est un lieu de villégiature rêvé pour découvrir les châteaux et les vignobles de la Loire. Cette halte de choix offre à ses visiteurs ce confort "à la française", harmonieux dosage de délicatesse et d'intimité, avec une vue exceptionnelle sur le Château Royale d'Amboise et la Loire. Chambres climatisées et parking privé clos. Sans restaurant.

Dieses authentische Herrenhaus aus dem 18. Jahrhundert wurde auf dem Fundament des mittelalterlichen Klosters Monastère des Minimes erbaut und befindet sich in unmittelbarer Nähe zur Altstadt. Es liegt ideal, um die Schlösser und Weinberge des Loire-Tals zu erkunden und bietet typischen Komfort "à la française", eine harmonische Mischung aus Intimität und Raffinesse, mit atemberaubenden Blicken auf das Château Royale d'Amboise und die Loire. Klimatisierte Zimmer; private, abgeschlossene Parkplätze; kein Restaurant.

Directions: A10 exit Amboise, D751 on the South bank of the river. **Price guide (excl. breakfast):** Single/double/twin FF590–920; suites FF1180–1400. Breakfast FF65.

CHATEAU DE GOVILLE

14330 LE BREUIL EN BESSIN, FRANCE

TEL: +33 2 31 22 19 28 FAX: +33 2 31 22 68 74 E-MAIL: chateaugoville@mail.cpod.fr

Visitors to this charming chateau enjoy the warm welcome that has awaited famous guests in the past, such as The Duke of Orleans. Owner Jean-Jacques Vallée has honoured the chateau's fascinating history by restoring its 18th century grandeur, with antique furniture and elegant yet comfortable bedrooms providing unique character. An amazing dolls house collection can be marvelled at, and Le Baromètre restaurant serves fine food in a graceful setting.

L'accueil chaleureux dont bénéficiaient autrefois les invités célèbres, comme le duc d'Orléans, est réservé aujourd'hui à tous les visiteurs de ce beau château. Le propriétaire, Jean-Jacques Vallée, a honoré l'histoire fascinante de cette demeure ancestrale en lui rendant sa splendeur du XVIIIe siècle. Le mobilier d'époque et les chambres élégantes et confortables donnent au lieu un charme incomparable. Une impressionante collection de maisons de poupée peut être admirée, et Le Baromètre, un restaurant au décor raffiné, propose une excellente cuisine.

Besucher dieses bezaubernden Schlosses werden so herzlich willkommen geheissen wie einst berühmte Gäste wie z. B. der Herzog von Orleans. Eigentümer Jean-Jacques Vallée hält die faszinierende Geschichte des Schlosses in Ehren und hat es in seiner ursprünglichen Pracht des 18. Jahrhunderts restauriert, mit antiken Möbeln und eleganten, komfortablen Schlafzimmern. Eine einzigartige Puppenhaussammlung kann bestaunt werden, und das Restaurant Le Baromètre serviert erlesene Speisen in eleganter Atmosphäre.

Directions: D5 Bayeux-Le Molay Littry, 2km before Le Molay Littry. **Price guide:** Double/twin FF550–750; suites FF750–850.

LE DONJON

CHEMIN DE SAINT CLAIR, 76790 ETRETAT, FRANCE
TEL: +33 2 35 27 08 23 FAX: +33 2 35 29 92 24 E-MAIL: info@ledonjon-etretat.fr

The colour and character that abound within this ivy-clad chateau are as inspiring as those of its breathtaking coastal views. With individually decorated rooms, azure blue swimming pool and the warm glow of its log fires penetrating hidden corners, Le Donjon offers a memorable experience. After a delicious and sumptuous dinner in one of the three unique dining rooms, guests can retire to the cigar lounge, relax in the pretty covered courtyatd or enjoy a drink on the poolside terrace.

L'intérieur de ce château habillé de lierre rivalise de couleur et de charme avec les vues spectaculaires de la côte. Les chambres à la décoration personnalisée, la piscine azure et les feux de cheminée dont les flammes dansantes éclairent des recoins oubliés sont le secret d'un séjour inoubliable. Après un dîner somptueux dans l'une des trois remarquables salles à manger, les visiteurs peuvent savourer un cigare dans le salon privé, se détendre dans le joli patio intérieur ou déguster un digestif sur la terrasse, au bord de la piscine.

Farbe und Atmosphäre dieses von Efeu bewachsenen Schlosses sind ebenso faszinierend wie der atemberaubende Blick auf die Küste. Mit seinen individuell eingerichteten Zimmern, dem azurblauen Pool und dem warmen Schein von Kaminfeuer ist Le Donjon ein unvergessliches Erlebnis. Nach einem köstlichen luxuriösen Dinner in einem der drei einzigartigen Speisesäle können sich die Gäste in den Salon zurückziehen, im zauberhaften, überdachten Innenhof entspannen oder sich mit einem Drink auf der Terrasse am Swimmingpool niederlassen.

Directions: *Town centre, follow signs.* **Price guide:** *Single FF580; double/twin FF580–1080; suites FF1380.*

FOLIE DU BOIS DES FONTAINES

ROUTE DE DIEPPE, 76440 FORGES-LES-EAUX, FRANCE
TEL: +33 2 32 89 50 68 FAX: +33 2 32 89 50 67

Magnificent luxury surrounds every detail of this impeccably restored 19th century spa town villa. Its individually decorated rooms each have gorgeous spa bathrooms and are elegantly furnished. Guests are inspired by the exquisite restaurant where delectable food is accompanied by an exciting selection of fine wines. The beautiful Haute-Normandy region must be explored, and for leisure, riding, hunting, golf and tennis are available.

Située dans la ville thermale de Forges-les-Eaux, cette villa du XIXe siècle parfaitement restaurée baigne dans un luxe éclatant. Décorées toutes différemment, les chambres sont meublées avec élégance et dotées de formidables salles de bains avec spa. Le superbe restaurant provoque l'enthousiasme par sa cuisine savoureuse et son remarquable choix d'excellents vins. Les visiteurs, qui ne doivent pas manquer de découvrir les charmes de la Haute-Normandie, peuvent aussi s'adonner à l'équitation, à la chasse, au golf et au tennis.

Einzigartiger Luxus umgibt jedes Detail dieser in einem französischen Heilbad gelegenen, perfekt restaurierten Villa aus dem 19. Jahrhundert. Jedes der eleganten, individuell gestalteten Zimmer verfügt über ein eigenes Thermalbadezimmer. Ein hervorragendes Restaurant serviert vorzügliche Gerichte, die von einer aufregenden Auswahl erlesener Weine begleitet werden. Die landschaftlich einzigartige Haute Normandie ist auf jeden Fall eine Entdeckungsreise wert, und als Freizeitangebote stehen Reiten, Jagd, Golf und Tennis zur Verfügung.

Directions: On D915 Forges-les-Eaux to Dieppe Road. **Price guide**: *Double FF900–1500; suites FF2200–2900.*

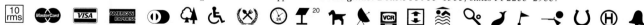

LA CHAUMIÈRE

ROUTE DU LITTORAL, 14600 HONFLEUR, FRANCE
TEL: +33 2 31 81 63 20 FAX: +33 2 31 89 59 23

A historic Norman chateau, la Chaumière has been transformed into an intimate hotel with spectacular sea views. The lounge is authentic old Normandy country house style, with its tiled floors and enormous fireplace, while the bedrooms, complete with period furniture, are a delight. Being beside the sea, the emphasis is on fresh fish, which is taken in a small but lively dining room.

Château historique normand, La Chaumière a été transformée en hôtel intime avec des vues superbes sur la mer. Le hall de réception est d'un style authentique normand campagnard, avec ses sols carrelés et son énorme cheminée, et les chambres, meublées d'époque, sont divines. Etant basé au bord de l'eau, l'accent est porté sur le poisson, qui peut être dégusté dans la salle à manger, petite mais vivante.

La Chaumière, ein historisches normannisches Chateau, wurde in ein kleines Hotel mit atemberaubender Aussicht auf das Meer umgewandelt. Der Salon ist in authentisch normannischem Landhausstil eingerichtet, mit gekacheltem Boden und riesigem Kamin, während die Gästezimmer mit zauberhaften Stilmöbeln aufwarten. Aufgrund der Meeresnähe stehen viele Fischgerichte auf der Speisekarte, die in dem kleinen, aber lebendigen Restaurant serviert werden.

Directions: *A13 > A19 > pont de Normandie > Trouville.* **Price guide:** *Double/twin FF990–2400.*

LA FERME SAINT-SIMÉON

RUE ADOLPHE–MARAIS, 14600 HONFLEUR, FRANCE
TEL: +33 2 31 81 78 00 FAX: +33 2 31 89 48 48

Guests at this glorious farmhouse enjoy today the beauty and charm that once attracted painters such as Monet and Boudin. Just a mile from delightful Honfleur, the hotel's decorative brickwork, fragrant gardens and spectacular views offer a feast equalled only by that served in its exquisite restaurant. Elegance combines with opulence throughout the welcoming, beamed salon, luxurious bedrooms with marble bathrooms, magnificent spa and Roman-style fitness area.

Les visiteurs séjournant dans cette splendide ferme découvrent la beauté et le charme qui séduisaient autrefois les peintres comme Monet et Boudin. Situé à 1½ km de Honfleur, l'hôtel se distingue par un briquetage décoratif, un jardin parfumé et des vues saisissantes, un spectacle dont la beauté n'a d'égal que le plaisir procuré par les festins servis dans le restaurant raffiné. Élégance rime avec opulence dans le salon aux poutres apparentes, les chambres de luxe dotées de salles de bains en marbre, le magnifique spa et le centre de remise en forme au style romain.

Die Besucher dieses phantastischen Bauernhauses begegnen heute der gleichen charmanten Schönheit, die einst Maler wie Monet und Boudin anzog. Das nur 1½ km vom Städtchen Honfleur entfernte Hotel mit seinen duftenden Gärten, seinem hübschen Mauerwerk und seiner spektakulären Aussicht wird nur von seinem exquisiten Restaurant übertroffen. Üppige Eleganz bestimmt den mit Balkendecke ausgestatteten Salon, die Schlafzimmer mit Marmorbädern, das einzigartige Thermalbad und das im römischen Stil gehaltene Fitnesszentrum.

Directions: *Honfleur > D15 > lighthouse.* **Price guide:** *Double/twin FF790–3510; suites FF4400–5400.*

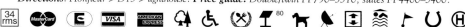

Le Manoir Du Butin

PHARE DU BUTIN, 14600 HONFLEUR, FRANCE
TEL: +33 2 31 81 63 00 FAX: +33 2 31 89 59 23

A short drive away from historic Honfleur, le Manoir du Butin is an idyllic rural retreat. A magnificent example of 18th century architecture, with distinctive half-timbering and graceful eaves, it is surrounded by beautiful gardens. The guest rooms are exquisite, with delicate fabrics on the walls and local period furniture. Traditional Normandy cooking, utilising freshly caught fish, is served in a romantic dining room.

A quelques km du port historique d'Honfleur, Le Manoir du Butin est un refuge campagnard idyllique. Magnifique exemple d'architecture du XVIIIène siècle, avec ses colombages typiques et ses superbes avants-toits, l'hôtel est entouré de magnifiques jardins. Les chambres sont exquises, avec des tentures précieuses et des meubles d'époque de la région. La cuisine traditionnelle et normande, proposant du poisson fraîchement pêché, est servie dans une salle à manger romantique.

Nur einige Kilometer vom historischen Honfleur entfernt liegt Le Manoir du Butin, eine idyllische ländliche Oase inmitten herrlicher Gärten. Mit seinem typischen Fachwerk und eleganten Dachgesims ist es ein prächtiges Beispiel für die Architektur des 18. Jahrhunderts . Die Zimmer sind exquisit und mit zarten Stoffen und regionalen Stilmöbeln eingerichtet. In einem romantischen Speisesaal werden traditionelle Gerichte der Normandie serviert – vor allem natürlich frisch gefangener Fisch.

Directions: A13 > A29 > D513 > *Phare du Butin.* **Price guide:** *Double/twin FF640–1970.*

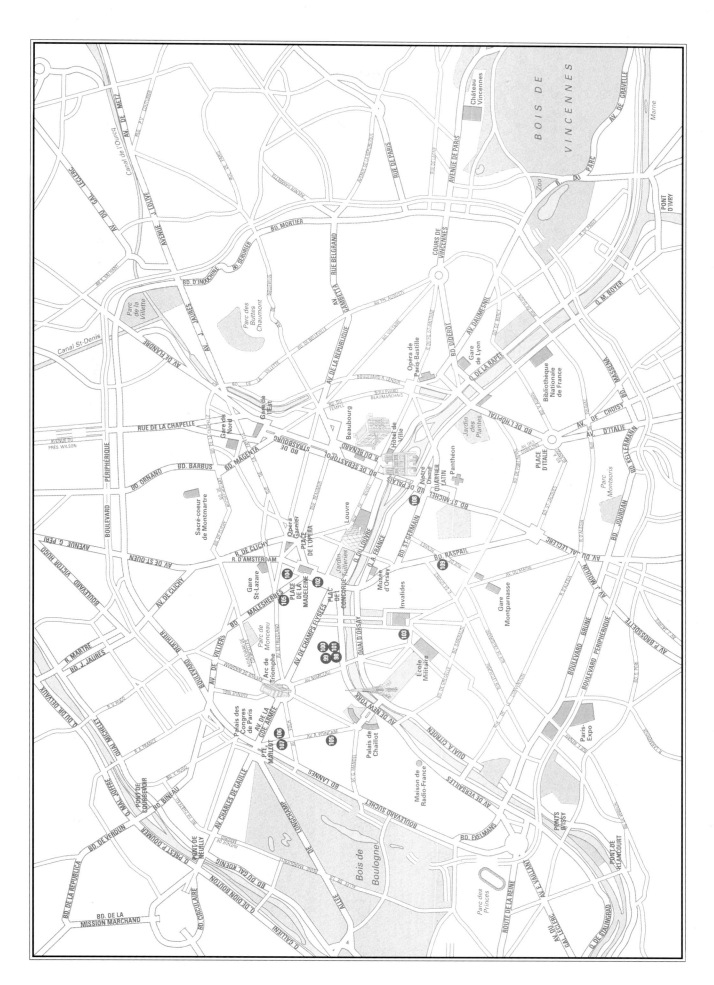

97

HÔTEL DE LA TRÉMOILLE

14 RUE DE LA TRÉMOILLE, 75008 PARIS, FRANCE
TEL: +33 1 56 52 14 00 FAX: +33 1 40 70 01 08

Those wishing to immerse themselves in the elegant and fashionable heart of Paris must visit this small, opulent hotel. Set between the glamorous Avenue George V and Avenue Montaigne, this sophisticated property is awash with works of art. Antique engravings and period décor feature in the individually decorated rooms. Authentic French dishes are created in the traditional restaurant. A multitude of theatres, boutiques and galleries are on the doorstep. **Closed for refurbishment from December 2000-April 2001.**

Cet hôtel luxueux est idéalement situé dans le quartier de l'élégance et de la mode. Niché entre l'Avenue George V et l'Avenue Montaigne, cet établissement sophistiqué est riche en oeuvres d'art. Les chambres, toutes décorées de manière différente, ont de nombreuses gravures anciennes et meubles de style. Une cuisine française, délicate et authentique, est servie dans le restaurant traditionnel. Une multitude de théâtres, boutiques et galeries se trouvent à proximité. **L'hôtel sera fermé pour renovation de décembre 2000 à avril 2001.**

Wer sich mitten ins elegante und modebewusste Herz von Paris stürzen will, darf sich dieses kleine, prachtvolle Hotel nicht entgehen lassen. Es liegt zwischen der eleganten Avenue George V und der Avenue Montaigne und prunkt mit unzähligen Kunstwerken. Antike Stiche und Stildekor zieren die individuell gestalteten Zimmer. Das Restaurant serviert traditionelle französische Küche, und zahlreiche Theater, Boutiquen und Galerien liegen in nächster Nähe. **Von Dezember 2000 bis April 2001 wegen Erneuerungsarbeiten geschlossen.**

Directions: Metro stations: Alma-Marceau or Franklin Roosevelt. **Price guide:** *Double/twin FF1990–3370; suites FF2910–8870.*

HOTEL FRANKLIN D. ROOSEVELT

18 RUE CLÉMENT MAROT, 75008 PARIS, FRANCE
TEL: +33 1 53 57 49 50 FAX: +33 1 47 20 44 30 E-MAIL: franklin@iway.fr

Located minutes away from the Champs Elysées and the Arc de Triomphe, this exquisite hotel epitomises Parisian style. Combining Anglo-Saxon refinement with French flair, the salons are as spacious as they are luxurious. The recently refurbished bedrooms are immaculately appointed in a traditional English style, with calico, cashmere and mahogany throughout. The bathrooms, all marble, will impress even the most exacting of travellers.

Situé à quelques minutes des Champs Elysées et de l'Arc de Triomphe, cet hôtel exquis exalte le style parisien. Combinant le raffinement anglo-saxon avec le style français, les salons sont aussi spacieux que luxueux. Les chambres récemment rénovées sont superbement décorées dans un style traditionnel anglais, avec calicot, cashmere et acajou de toutes parts. Les salles de bain, en marbre, impressionneront les voyageurs les plus exigeants.

Nur wenige Minuten von den Champs Elysées und vom Arc de Triomphe entfernt, verkörpert dieses exquisite Hotel perfekt die Eleganz von Paris. Mit einer Mischung aus angelsächsischer Raffinesse und französischem Flair sind die Salons geräumig und luxuriös. Die kürzlich renovierten Zimmer sind makellos im englischen Stil eingerichtet, und voll von Kaliko, Kaschmir und Mahagoni. Die Bäder, ganz in Marmor gehalten, werden selbst den anspruchsvollsten Gast beeindrucken.

Directions: The Right Bank. **Price guide:** *Double/twin FF945–2200; suites FF2500–3500.*

HÔTEL PLAZA ATHÉNÉE

25 AVENUE MONTAIGNE, 75008 PARIS, FRANCE
TEL: +33 1 53 67 66 65 FAX: +33 1 53 67 66 66

Since opening in 1911 this elegant hotel has become synonymous with luxury and charm. Situated on the exclusive Avenue Montaigne in the heart of Paris, the Hôtel Plaza Athénée has undergone a complete renovation, preserving and combining classical French and art deco styling on the top two floors with 21st century facilities in all rooms. Alain Ducasse opened his gastronomic restaurant at the Plaza Athénée, and also supervises the kitchens of the Relais Plaza, the summer courtyard restaurant and the new bar.

Depuis son ouverture en 1911, cet élégant hôtel est devenu un symbole de luxe et de charme. Il se dresse au coeur de Paris, sur l'avenue Montaigne, une des rues les plus chics de la capitale. Entièrement remis à neuf, le Plaza Athénée a su garder son style français classique et innover avec le style art déco aux deux derniers étages, tout en intégrant les commodités du XXIe siècle. Alain Ducasse a ouvert son restaurant gastronomique au Plaza Athénée; il supervise également les cuisines du Relais Plaza, de la Cour Jardin l'été, et du nouveau bar.

Seit seiner Eröffnung 1911 ist das elegante Hotel Plaza Athénée der Inbegriff von Luxus und Charme. Es liegt in der exklusiven Avenue Montaigne mitten in Paris und wurde völlig renoviert. Dabei wurde klassischer französischer Stil mit Art-Déco-Ausstattungen auf den zwei oberen Etagen kombiniert, die sich perfekt mit den Annehmlichkeiten des 21. Jahrhunderts in allen Zimmern vereinen. Alain Ducasse eröffnete hier sein Gourmetrestaurant, und leitet daneben auch die Küche des Relais Plaza, des Cour Jardin im Sommer und der neuen Bar.

Directions: *Centre of Paris, 5 minutes walk from Champs-Elysées.* **Price guide:** *Upon Application*

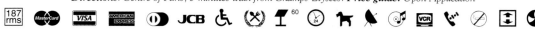

HÔTEL SAN REGIS

12 RUE JEAN GOUJON 75008 PARIS
TEL: +33 1 44 95 16 16 FAX: +33 1 45 61 05 48 E-MAIL: message@hotel–sanregis.fr

Deep in the heart of Paris's fashion district lies this small, intimate and beautifully appointed hotel. Opened in the early 1920s, the interior charmingly combines modern comforts with 17th, 18th and 19th century furniture and antiques. Each of the 44 bedrooms has been individually decorated and boasts a marble bathroom and all modern conveniences. The restaurant, set in an old library, is an oasis of tranquillity, and serves simply impeccable fare.

Ce luxueux petit hôtel parisien à l'atmosphère intime jouit d'une situation privilégiée au coeur du quartier de la mode. Ouvert au début des années 20, le San Régis marie à merveille des meubles et des objets d'art du XVIIe, XVIIIe et XIXe siècle avec un confort des plus modernes. Chacune des 44 chambres a son propre charme et dispose d'une salle de bains en marbre et des dernières commodités. Le restaurant, aménagé dans une ancienne bibliothèque, est un havre de paix propice à la dégustation de mets exquis.

Dieses persönliche und attraktive Hotel eröffnete Anfang der 20er Jahre und liegt mitten im Pariser Modeviertel. Moderner Komfort verbindet sich perfekt mit Möbeln und Antiquitäten aus dem 17., 18. und 19. Jahrhundert. Die 44 Zimmer sind individuell gestaltet und besitzen Marmorbäder und jegliche moderne Annehmlichkeit. Das herrlich ruhige Restaurant liegt in einer alten Bibliothek und serviert hervorragende Gerichte.

Directions: *Rue Goujon is off the Champs-Elysées and Avenue Montaigne.* **Price guide:** *Single FF1,850, double/twin FF2,450–3,300, suites FF6,300.*

The Leading Hotels of the World®

HÔTEL DE CRILLON

10, PLACE DE LA CONCORDE, 75008 PARIS, FRANCE
TEL: +33 1 44 71 15 00 FAX: +33 1 44 71 15 02

Built during the reign of Louis XV, this superior hotel is a landmark on Paris' Place de la Concorde. The interior is quintessentially French, with parquet floors, Aubusson carpets, magnificent tapestries and period furniture. Sumptuously decorated and furnished with antiques, the bedrooms are no less striking. In the legendary restaurant Les Ambassadeurs, meals of imagination and flair are served with an extensive choice of wines.

Construit durant le règne de Louis XV, cet hôtel exceptionnel est une figure de la Place de la Concorde à Paris. L'intérieur est resté fondamentalement français, avec parquets, tapis d'Aubusson, magnifiques tâpisseries et meubles anciens. Les chambres, somptueusement décorées et meublées d'antiquités, sont tout aussi frappantes. Dans le légendaire restaurant Les Ambassadeurs, des plats imaginatifs et fins sont proposés avec un choix exhaustif de vins.

Dieses prächtige Hotel an der Place de la Concorde wurde zur Regierungszeit Louis XV. erbaut. Das Intérieur ist in seinem Kern französisch geblieben, mit Parkettböden, Aubusson-Teppichen, herrlichen Gobelins und erlesenem Stilmobiliar. Die luxuriösen Zimmer sind üppig eingerichtet und mit kostspieligen Antiquitäten ausgestattet. Im legendären Restaurant Les Ambassadeurs werden einfallsreiche und köstliche Speisen serviert, ergänzt von einer beeindruckenden Auswahl an Weinen.

Directions: *Place de la Concorde.* **Price guide:** *Single FF2950; double/twin FF3500–3750; suites from FF4950.*

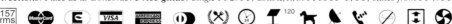

HÔTEL LE TOURVILLE

16 AVENUE DE TOURVILLE, 75007 PARIS, FRANCE
TEL: +33 1 47 05 62 62 FAX: +33 1 47 05 43 90 e-mail: hotel@tourville.com

Though located in the heart of Paris, close to the Eiffel Tower, this neo-classical hotel enjoys a unique atmosphere of refined tranquillity. Soft pastel colours form a warm ambience and ideal background for the wealth of antique furniture and paintings that grace its salons and bedrooms. Guests are cosseted by the fine breakfasts served in the vaulted cellar room and the large range of toiletries that are thoughtfully provided in the marble bathrooms.

Bien qu'il se situe au coeur de Paris, à deux pas de la Tour Eiffel, cet hôtel néoclassique jouit d'une tranquillité raffinée. Les couleurs pastel créent une ambiance chaleureuse et soulignent à merveille la beauté des nombreux meubles et objets d'art anciens qui ornent les salons et les chambres. Les visiteurs choyés dégustent d'excellents petits déjeuners dans la cave voûtée et profitent du vaste choix d'articles de toilette gracieusement mis à leur disposition dans les salles de bains en marbre.

Trotz seiner Lage im Herzen von Paris und in der Nähe des Eiffelturms geniesst dieses neoklassische Hotel eine Atmosphäre herrlicher Ruhe. Sanfte Pastellfarben schaffen ein warmes Ambiente und einen idealen Hintergrund für die Vielfalt antiker Möbel und Gemälde, welche die Salons und Schlafzimmer schmücken. Die Gäste werden durch das erlesene Frühstück im Gewölbekeller verwöhnt, des Weiteren durch das grosse Angebot an Toilettenartikeln, die sorgfältig ausgewählt in den Marmorbadezimmern bereitstehen.

Directions: *Beside Les Invalides.* **Price guide**: *Double/twin FF890–1390; suites FF1990.*

HÔTEL DE L'ARCADE

9 RUE DE L'ARCADE, 75008 PARIS, FRANCE
TEL: +33 1 53 30 60 00 FAX: +33 1 40 07 03 07

Situated at the heart of Paris's business district, this charming 19th century townhouse has been lovingly restored to its erstwhile elegance. Decorated in subtle colours, the salon rooms create an atmosphere of tranquillity. Thoughtful planning is evident in the furnishings and accessories, and the marble bathrooms have windows opening into the bedrooms to catch daylight. Although only breakfast is served, the vicinity abounds with bars, cafes and bistros.

Situé en plein coeur du centre d'affaires de Paris, cette maison de ville du XIXème siècle a été rénovée avec goût avec son élégance ancienne. Décorés en couleurs subtiles, les salons créent une atmosphère de tranquillité. Les chambres ont été conçues intelligemment; les salles de bain en marbre ont des fenêtres donnant sur les chambres, ce qui ajoute de la luminosité. Seul le petit déjeuner y est servi mais les environs abondent de bars, de cafés et de bistrots.

Dieses charmante Stadthaus aus dem 19. Jahrhundert liegt im Herzen von Paris und ist mit viel Liebe zu seiner ehemaligen Eleganz renoviert worden. Die Salons, in gedämpften Farben gehalten, schaffen ein ruhiges Ambiente. Einrichtung und Details zeugen von überlegter Planung, und die Marmorbäder haben Fenster, die sich zu den Zimmern hin öffnen lassen und so das Tageslicht hereinlassen. Zwar wird nur Frühstück angeboten, doch eine Vielzahl von Bars, Cafes und Bistros befinden sich in nächster Nähe.

Directions: Off Place de Madeleine. **Price guide:** *Single FF820–920; double/twin FF1040; duplex apartment FF1230.*

HÔTEL LE LAVOISIER

21 RUE LAVOISIER, 75008 PARIS, FRANCE
TEL: +33 1 53 30 06 06 FAX: +33 1 53 30 23 00 E-MAIL: info@hotellavoisier.com

One of the most chic hotels in Paris, Hotel le Lavoisier is mere minutes away from Place de la Concorde and the famous shops of the Boulevard Haussman. Well-chosen antique furniture and warm, elegant colour schemes compose a refinement that makes this hotel an ideal retreat from the busy streets of Paris. The intimacy of communal areas such as the cellar breakfast room, and the attentive service of the staff are suggestive of comforts from outside the city.

L'Hôtel Le Lavoisier, l'un des plus chics de Paris, n'est qu'à quelques minutes de la place de la Concorde et des célèbres magasins du boulevard Haussmann. Les meubles anciens choisis avec soin et les couleurs élégantes et chaleureuses du décor créent une ambiance raffinée qui fait de cet hôtel un refuge idéal pour échapper à la fébrilité des rues parisiennes. L'intimité des salles communes, telles que la petite salle à manger occupant la cave, et la prévenance du personnel évoquent le charme des hôtels provinciaux.

Dieses nur wenige Minuten vom Place de la Concorde und den Geschäften des Bouldeward Haussman entfernt gelegene Hotel ist eines der elegantesten von Paris. Geschmackvolles, antikes Mobiliar und warme, elegante Farben schaffen eine erlesene Atmosphäre, die dieses Hotel zu einer Oase inmitten der geschäftigen Straßen von Paris macht. Die Abgeschiedenheit der Aufenthaltsräume, z. B. des Frühstücksraums im Kellergewölbe, sowie aufmerksamster Service bieten einen Komfort, wie man ihn sonst nur ausserhalb der Stadt erwarten würde.

Directions: *Near Place Saint-Augustin.* **Price guide:** *Double/twin FF1290–1490; suites FF1690–2500.*

DESIGN HOTELS

L'HÔTEL PERGOLÈSE

3 RUE PERGOLÈSE, 75116 PARIS, FRANCE
TEL: +33 1 53 64 04 04 FAX: +33 1 53 64 04 40 E-MAIL: hotel@pergolese.com

Originally a 19th century bourgeois town house, this vibrant hotel, designed by Rena Dumas-Hermès, is the height of sophistication. The light, warmth and colour of the elegant interior leave an immediate impression on visitors, while the parquet floors and stylish leather chairs create a charismatic ambience. The colourful bedrooms combine serene comfort with cutting edge furnishings. Breakfast and drinks are served in the foyer, with glass walls opening onto the courtyard.

Cet hôtel particulier du XIXe siècle est aujourd'hui le comble de l'élégance. Dans cet établissement éblouissant, décoré par Rena Dumas-Hermès, les visiteurs sont d'emblée frappés par la chaleur, la clarté et les couleurs qui règnent dans les pièces distinguées et par la note charismatique apportée par le parquet et les beaux fauteuils en cuir. Confort et sérénité caractérisent les chambres aux couleurs gaies et au mobilier dernier cri. Le petit déjeuner et des rafraîchissements sont servis dans le hall dont les murs en verre s'ouvrent sur une cour intérieure.

Dieses charmante, von Rena Dumas-Hermès gestaltete Hotel war ursprünglich ein Stadthaus im 19. Jahrhundert, und ist heute der Inbegriff von Eleganz. Licht, Wärme und Farbe durchfluten das Interieur und fallen sofort ins Auge, während die Parkettböden und herrlichen Ledersessel ein gemütliches Ambiente schaffen. Die farbenfrohen Schlafzimmer verbinden Komfort und modernste Ausstattung. Frühstück und Drinks werden im Foyer serviert, dessen Glaswände den Blick auf den Innenhof freigeben.

Directions: *Close to Porte Maillot terminal.* **Price guide:** *Single FF1100–1500; double/twin FF1200–1700; suites FF1800–2000.*

LA VILLA MAILLOT

143 AVENUE DE MALAKOFF, 75116 PARIS, FRANCE
TEL: +33 1 53 64 52 52 FAX: +33 1 45 00 60 61 E-MAIL: villa.maillot@wanadoo.fr

A short walk from the Champs-Elysées, the Villa Maillot is a charming, elegant and discreet haven in the centre of Paris. Behind the façade of this unique historic residence lies an art deco interior, with the subtlety of the pastel colours creating an atmosphere of warmth and hospitality. The bedrooms are all well-appointed, and have rose-coloured marble bathrooms. Breakfast, selected from the enticing buffet, may be enjoyed in the garden conservatory.

A deux pas des Champs-Elysées, la Villa Maillot est un havre de charme, élégant et discret au coeur de la capitale. La façade de cet ancien hôtel particulier cache un hôtel "style Art Déco", avec de subtiles nuances de pastels créant une atmosphère chaleureuse et conviviale. Les chambres sont toutes bien équipées et offrent des salles de bains en marbre rose. Un superbe buffet petit déjeuner dressé dans les salons est servi dans la verrière nichée dans un jardin.

Nur einen kurzen Spaziergang von den Champs-Élysées entfernt liegt die charmante Villa Maillot, die Eleganz und Diskretion mitten im Stadtzentrum bietet. Hinter der Fassade dieses aussergewöhnlichen alten Hotels versteckt sich ein Art-Deco Interieur, das mit feinen Pastellfarben ein behagliches und einladendes Ambiente schafft. Die Zimmer sind alle bestens ausgestattet und verfügen über Marmorbäder in Rosétönen. Ein herrliches Frühstücksbuffet steht im Salon bereit und wird im Wintergarten serviert.

Directions: *Close to Porte Maillot*. **Price guide:** *Double/twin FF1800–2050; suites FF2600–2800.*

HOTEL BUCI LATIN

34, RUE DE BUCI, 75006 PARIS, FRANCE
TEL: +33 1 43 29 07 20 FAX: +33 1 43 29 67 44 E-MAIL: hotel@bucilatin.com

Set in a maze of narrow streets in the Latin Quarter, this intimate hotel is tailor-made for those francophiles intrigued by Paris' literary heritage. The atmosphere is vibrant, and visitors will enjoy relaxing in the coffee bar, with its quirky plant-filled pond. The art deco interior is adorned with wrought iron and eclectic furnishings. In the bedrooms, all immaculately maintained, the doorknobs are made from boules!

Situé dans un labyrinthe de rues étroites du Quartier Latin, cet hôtel intime est cousu-main pour les francophiles intéressés par l'héritage littéraire de Paris. L'atmosphère est vibrante et les visiteurs se relaxeront dans le bar café, et son bassin de plantes bizarres. L'intérieur art déco est orné de fer forgé et de tentures éclectiques. Dans les chambres, toutes immaculées, les poignées de porte sont de boules de pétanque!

Dieses bezaubernde Hotel liegt in einem Gewirr enger Strassen im Quartier Latin und ist wie geschaffen für Gäste, die das literarische Erbe von Paris fasziniert. Die Atmosphäre sprüht vor Leben und man kann sich in der Kaffee-Bar hervorragend entspannen. Ausgefallene Pflanzen zieren einen kleinen Teich, die Art-Deco-Inneneinrichtung ist erstklassig und bietet viel Schmiedeeisen und ausgewähltes Mobiliar. In den makellosen Zimmern dienen Boulekugeln als Türgriffe!

Directions: *Saint-Germain-des-Prés is nearest metro.* **Price guide:** *Double/twin FF1100–1400; suites FF1850–1950.*

HÔTEL LE SAINT-GRÉGOIRE

43 RUE DE L'ABBÉ GRÉGOIRE, 75006 PARIS, FRANCE
TEL: +33 1 45 48 23 23 FAX: +33 1 45 48 33 95 E-MAIL: hotel@saintgregoire.com

Set at the heart of the Rive Gauche, this small 18th century hotel offers guests refined elegance in a tranquil environment. Overlooking the interior garden, the charming lobby with an open fire becomes a cosy retreat during winter. Twenty unique bedrooms are adorned with period paintings and antiques and offer every modern amenity. Guests enjoy an imaginative breakfast in the stonewall cellar before exploring the Saint Germain quarter.

Situé en plein coeur de la Rive Gauche, cet hôtel du XVIIIème siècle offre à ses visiteurs une élégance raffinée dans un environnement tranquille. Surplombant le jardins intérieur, le charmant hall de réception est encore plus attrayant en hiver avec son feu de cheminée. Les vingt chambres, toutes uniques, sont décorées de peintures d'époques et d'antiquités et offrent tout le confort moderne. Les hôtes peuvent déguster un petit déjeuner imaginatif dans la salle voutée aux murs de pierre, avant de s'explorer le quartier Saint-Germain.

Mitten im Herzen des rechten Seine-Ufers gelegen bietet dieses kleine Hotel aus dem 18. Jahrhundert subtile Eleganz in einer ruhigen Umgebung. Der auf den Garten blickende Empfangsraum sorgt mit seinem offenen Kaminfeuer im Winter für Behaglichkeit. 20 einzigartige Zimmer sind mit Bildern und Antiquitäten des 18. Jahrhunderts geschmückt und bieten modernsten Komfort. Im Kellergeschoss mit seinen Steinwänden geniesst man ein einfallsreiches Frühstück, bevor Saint Germain mit seinen vielen Attraktionen lockt.

Directions: Near Rue de la Bac. Price guide: Single FF890; double/twin FF1090; suitesFF1490.

Domaine De Belesbat

COURDIMANCHE-SUR-ESSONNE, 91820 BOUTIGNY-SUR-ESSONNE, FRANCE
TEL: +33 1 69 23 19 00 FAX: +33 1 69 23 19 01 E-MAIL: domaine.de.belesbat@wanadoo.fr

Surrounded by its own moat and occupying 120 acres of gardens and woodland, this sumptuous chateau dates back to the 15th century. The rooms are all elegantly furnished in Louis XV, Louis XVI and more contemporary styles. The gastronomic restaurant delivers food fit for any lord, offering a myriad of pleasures to the senses. The golf course that surrounds the chateau provides a stern challenge for beginners and experts alike.

Entouré de douves et au milieu d'un jardin et d'une forêt de 50 hectares, ce somptueux château date du XVème siècle. Les chambres sont toutes élégamment meublées en Louis XV, Louis XVI et en style plus contemporain. Le restaurant gastronomique propose des mets délicats, offrant une myriade de plaisirs des sens. Le golf entourant le domaine est un véritable challenge autant pour les débutants que pour les joueurs avertis.

Dieses herrliche, von einem Graben umgebene Chateau aus dem 15. Jahrhundert liegt inmitten von 50 Hektar Park und Wald. Die Zimmer sind alle elegant im Louis XV. und Louis XVI. oder im zeitgenössischen Stil eingerichtet. Das Gourmet-Restaurant bietet eine fürstliche Küche, die Genuss für alle Sinne verspricht. Der an das Chateau angrenzende Golfplatz ist sowohl für Anfänger als auch für Experten eine Herausforderung.

Directions: A6 > Exit 11 > Auvernaux > Milly la Forêt > Golf de Belesbat. **Price guide:** Double/twin FF1250–2100; suites FF2500–3500.

LE MAS CANDILLE

BOULEVARD CLEMENT REBUFFEL, 06250 MOUGINS, FRANCE
TEL: +33 4 92 28 43 43 FAX:+33 4 92 28 43 40

Based on the judgement of our regional inspector and on the reputation of the owner, we have no hesitation in recommending this hotel due to open in 2001. A peaceful retreat, this tastefully refurbished 18th century farmhouse belies its nearness to vibrant Cannes. It cossets its guests with luxurious bedrooms, peaceful gardens and parkland and a glorious spa with beauty facilities. Delicious regional specialities are served in the restaurant or on the terrace, which enjoys stunning views of nearby Grasse and the mountains beyond.

La réputation du propriétaire et l'avis de notre inspecteur régional nous incitent à recommander cet hôtel, dont l'ouverture est prévue pour 2001. Devant la tranquillité de cette ferme du XVIIIe siècle réaménagée avec goût, on a peine à croire que Cannes est si proche. Le mas gâte les visiteurs avec des chambres luxueuses, des jardins paisibles et un merveilleux spa avec centre de beauté. Des spécialités régionales sont servies dans le restaurant ou sur la terrasse, qui offre une vue magnifique de Grasse et des montagnes au loin.

Wir empfehlen dieses Hotel aufgrund des Rufes seines Besitzers und der Begutachtung unseres regionalen Inspektors. Es wird im Jahr 2001 eröffnen. Man glaubt kaum, dass sich dieses geschmackvoll wiederhergerichtete, ruhige Landhaus aus dem 18. Jahrhundert so nahe am lebendigen Cannes befindet. Die Gäste geniessen luxuriöse Zimmer, friedliche Gärten und ein Spa mit Schönheitsfarm. Köstliche regionale Gerichte werden im Restaurant oder auf der Terrasse serviert, von der sich eine herrliche Sicht auf Grasse und die Berge bietet.

Directions: Leave A8 exit Cannes/Mougins Junction 42; follow signs to Mougins; hotel is signposted. **Price guide:** Single/double/twin from FF1875.

LA FERME D'AUGUSTIN

PLAGE TAHITI, 83350 RAMATUELLE, FRANCE NR SAINT-TROPEZ
TEL: +33 4 94 55 97 00 FAX: + 33 4 94 40 30 E-MAIL: vallet.ferme.augustin@wanadoo.fr

This delightful, family-run hotel combines traditional French charm with modern hospitality to create an idyllic retreat from the buzzing pace of the southern coast. The pretty bedrooms and suites are furnished with antiques and have Jacuzzi baths – some even have private gardens. A hydrotherapy pool in the charming gardens and wonderful home-made cooking create a sense of luxury and complement the impeccable standards set by the Vallet family owners.

La famille Vallet a complété le charme français traditionnel de cet hôtel séduisant par un accueil moderne pour créer un havre de paix idyllique, à l'écart de la vie trépidante de la Côte d'Azur. Les jolies chambres et suites sont pourvues de meubles anciens et d'un jacuzzi, parfois même d'un jardin privatif. La piscine hydrothérapique aménagée dans le ravissant parc et la cuisine maison succulente soulignent le caractère luxueux et la qualité exceptionnelle de cet établissement.

Dieses freundliche, familiengeführte Hotel , das traditionelles französisches Flair mit moderner Gastfreundschaft verbindet, liegt idyllisch fernab vom geschäftigen Treiben der Südküste. Die hübschen Zimmer und Suiten sind mit Antiquitäten ausgestattet und haben Jacuzzibäder. Einige bieten auch einen privaten Garten. Ein Hydrotherapie-Pool im Garten und köstliche Hausmannskost schaffen ein Gefühl von Luxus und spiegeln perfekt das hohe Niveau wider, das sich die Eigentümer, die Familie Vallet, zum Ziel gesetzt haben.

Directions: . ***Price guide:*** *Double/twin FF650–1200; suites FF1700–1900.*

LA GRANDE BASTIDE

ROUTE DE LA COLLE, 06570 SAINT-PAUL-DE-VENCE, FRANCE
TEL: +33 4 93 32 50 30 FAX: +33 4 93 32 50 59 E-MAIL: stpaullgb@lemel.fr

This charmingly renovated 18th century 'bastide' is a gem from which to experience the beautiful Provençal region. Perfectly located for the vibrant towns of Nice, Monaco and Cannes, the hotel also offers the treasures of Provence on a more local scale, whether as the stunning views from many of its delightful, individually styled bedrooms or its closeness to the famous village of Saint Paul. The owners have decorated with an exquisite attention to comfort and authenticity throughout, and their warm hospitality ensures a truly memorable stay.

Rénovée de façon attrayante, cette bastide du XVIIIe siècle est un vrai bijou, qui met tous les charmes de la Provence à votre portée. Très bien située pour aller absorber l'atmosphère animée de Nice, Monaco ou Cannes, la Bastide permet aussi de savourer des plaisirs plus locaux, tels que les superbes vues offertes par les ravissantes chambres ou la visite du célèbre village de Saint-Paul. Dans tout l'hôtel, les propriétaires ont mis l'accent sur le confort et l'authenticité du décor. Combiné à un accueil chaleureux, ce cadre exquis est la clé d'un séjour inoubliable.

Diese zauberhaft renovierte 'Bastide' aus dem 18. Jahrhundert ist ein Kleinod, von dem aus man diese schöne Region erkunden kann. Die pulsierenden Städte Nizza, Monaco und Cannes liegen in der Nähe, doch auch auf lokaler Ebene bietet das Hotel provenzalische Schätze. Die Aussichten von vielen der individuell gestalteten Zimmer sind atemberaubend, und der berühmte Ort Saint-Paul ist nicht weit entfernt. Überall findet man Komfort und Authentizität, und die herzliche Gastfreundschaft der Besitzer gewährt einen wahrhaft unvergesslichen Aufenthalt.

Directions: . *Price guide:* Double/twin FF750–1200; suites FF1200–1800.

CHÂTEAU DES ALPILLES

ROUTE DÉPARTEMENTALE 31, ANCIENNE ROUTE DU GRÈS, 13210 SAINT RÉMY DE PROVENCE, FRANCE
TEL: +33 4 90 92 03 33 FAX: +33 4 90 92 45 17 E-MAIL: chateau.alpilles@wanadoo.fr

Surrounded by verdant grounds in which rare old trees offer a touch of the exotic, this elegant 19th century chateau offers wonderful seclusion. The salons reflect its age-old grandeur, with moulded ceilings, mosaic floors, tapestries and enormous gilt mirrors. Many bedrooms reflect this ancient splendour, while some are more contemporary. Adjoining the cosy bar is the dining room, where visitors can enjoy simple regional dishes.

Entouré de terrains verdoyants où de vieux arbres offrent une touche exotique, cet élégant château XIXème siècle offre une merveilleuse occasion de retraite. La salon reflète la grandeur d'époque, avec moulures, sols en mosaïque, tâpisseries et d'énormes miroirs dorés. La plupart des chambres reflète cette grandeur ancienne, alors que certaines sont plus contemporaines. A côté du bar chaleureux se trouve le restaurant, où les visiteurs peuvent déguster des plats régionaux simples.

Umgeben von einer Parkanlage mit seltenen alten Bäumen bietet dieses elegante Chateau aus dem 19. Jahrhundert herrliche Abgeschiedenheit. Die Salons spiegeln mit ihren Stuckverzierungen, Mosaikböden, Gobelins und riesigen vergoldeten Spiegeln eine Erhabenheit aus vergangenen Zeiten wider. Einige Zimmer zeigen die gleiche ehrwürdige Pracht, andere sind modern gestaltet. Neben der behaglichen Bar können die Gäste einfache, regionale Gerichte im Speisesaal geniessen.

Directions: *D31 – Tarascon.* **Price guide:** *Single FF1000; double/twin FF1000–1250; suites FF1520–1790; chapelle FF1630–2150.*

HÔTEL SUBE

15 QUAI SUFFREN, 83990 SAINT-TROPEZ, FRANCE
TEL: +33 4 94 97 30 04 FAX: +33 4 94 54 89 08

A warm welcome awaits guests to this charming small hotel – the only one in Saint-Tropez overlooking the port. The bedrooms are simply charming, some with a balcony or terrace, some opening onto a lovely courtyard patio. Breakfast is a croissant in the sun, while soaking in the multi-national atmosphere of this vibrant port. There is no restaurant, but a variety of bistros to explore nearby. In the evenings, the famous English bar with its appropriate nautical ambience is a fashionable rendez-vous for visitors and locals alike.

Cet hôtel charmant, le seul à St-Tropez à jouir d'une vue sur le port, réserve un accueil chaleureux à ses hôtes. Certaines des chambres exquises donnent sur un balcon ou une terrasse privés, d'autres s'ouvrent sur un joli patio. Au petit déjeuner au soleil, les visiteurs s'imprègnent de l'atmosphère cosmopolite du port. L'hôtel n'a pas de restaurant, mais les environs offrent un grand choix de bistrots. Le célèbre bar anglais avec son ambiance nautique est un lieu de rendez-vous populaire apprécié tant par les visiteurs que par les habitants du coin.

Ein herzlicher Empfang erwartet die Gäste dieses kleinen Hotel – dem einzigen in St Tropez mit Blick auf den Hafen. Die Zimmer sind bezaubernd, einige mit Balkon oder Terrasse, andere mit Blick auf den hübschen Innenhof. Beim Frühstück in der Sonne kann man die multi-nationale Atmosphäre des lebendigen Hafens geniessen. Es gibt kein Restaurant, aber zahlreiche Bistros liegen in nächster Nähe. Abends trifft man sich in der englischen Bar mit ihrem nautischen Ambiente, die bei Gästen und Einheimischen gleichermassen beliebt ist.

Directions: On quay at port. **Price guide:** *Single from FF390; double/twin FF590–1200; rooms with sea view FF990–1500.*

RÉSIDENCE DE LA PINÈDE

PLAGE DE LA BOUILLABAISSE, 83990 SAINT-TROPEZ, FRANCE
TEL: +33 4 94 55 91 00 FAX: +33 4 94 97 73 64 E-MAIL: Residence.PINEDE@wanadoo.fr

Basking in Mediterranean sunshine, this de luxe hotel is set on the edge of the waterfront in the glamorous Gulf of Saint Tropez. Cosy fires, fine paintings, plush fabrics and other opulent touches feature throughout. The restaurant has one Michelin Star, and gastronomes will be delighted with the sumptuous dishes created with delicate Provençal flavours. Guests frolic in the beautiful outdoor pool, laze on sunny terraces or on the private beach and hire boats from the hotel.

Baigné du soleil méditerranéen, cet hôtel de luxe se dresse au bord de l'eau dans le merveilleux golfe de Saint Tropez. Des cheminées intimes, de beaux tableaux, des étoffes somptueuses et d'autres touches d'opulence abondent de toutes parts. Le restaurant a une étoile Michelin, et les gourmets seront ravis des plats somptueux élaborés à partir de délicates saveurs provençales. Les visiteurs peuvent également gambader autour de la superbe piscine, lézarder sur les terrasses ensoleillées et la plage privée ou encore louer des bateaux depuis l'hôtel.

Im Schein der Mittelmeersonne und direkt am Ufer des berühmten Golfs von Saint Tropez liegt dieses luxuriöse Hotel, das mit seinen Kaminfeuern, edlen Gemälden und üppigen Stoffen eine opulente Atmosphäre ausstrahlt. Das Restaurant besitzt 1 Michelin Stern, und Feinschmecker werden sich über die köstlichen Speisen freuen, die eine feine provenzalische Note tragen. Zur Entspannung kann man in einem herrlichen Pool schwimmen, sich auf einer der Sonnenterrassen oder am Strand sonnen oder sich ein hoteleigenes Boot mieten.

Directions: *Leave St Rémy on D31 towards Tarascon.* **Price guide:** *Double/twin FF950–6300; suites FF2645–9450.*

HOTEL LE BEAUVALLON

BAIE DE SAINT-TROPEZ, BEAUVALLON-GRIMAUD, 83120 SAINTE-MAXIME, FRANCE
TEL: +33 4 94 55 78 88 FAX: +33 4 94 55 78 78

Majestic Hotel Le Beauvallon looks upon the Bay of St Tropez from its 10 hectares of lush Mediterranean garden. The irresistible azure blue ocean is brought to guests while they dine in the waterfront restaurant or upon the white sands of the hotel's private beach. An adjacent 18 hole golf course and Stefan Edberg's tennis centre form part of a variety of activities, whilst the sauna, gymnasium, spa and Jacuzzi provide a more relaxing option.

L'hôtel Le Beauvallon s'étend majestueusement dans un beau parc de 10 ha à la végétation méditerranéenne luxuriante, d'où il domine la baie de Saint-Tropez. D'un bleu azur fascinant, l'océan vient charmer les visiteurs faisant bombance dans le restaurant au bord de l'eau ou sur la plage de sable blanc privée de l'hôtel. Le Beauvallon permet de pratiquer divers sports, dont le golf sur un terrain voisin de 18 trous et le tennis au centre de Stefan Edberg. Et qui préfère les activités plus délassantes trouvera son bonheur dans le spa, le sauna et le Jacuzzi.

Das majestätische Hotel Le Beauvallon ist inmitten 10 Hektar üppiger Mittelmeergärten gelegen und bietet einen einladenden Blick auf die Bucht von St. Tropez. Während die Gäste im Meerblick-Restaurant oder auf den privaten, weissen Sandstränden des Hotels dinieren, erstreckt sich unwiderstehlich vor ihnen das azurblaue Meer. Ein benachbarter 18-Loch-Golfplatz, das Stefan-Edberg-Tenniszentrum und ein Fitnessraum sind nur einige der vielen Sportmöglichkeiten, während Sauna, Dampfbad und Whirlpool zum Entspannen einladen.

*Directions: On the coast midway between St Tropez and Sainte-Maxime. **Price guide:** Double/twin FF1800–3150; suites FF4300–13000.*

L'Auberge Du Choucas

05220 MONETIER-LES-BAINS, SERRE-CHEVALIER, HAUTES-ALPES, FRANCE
TEL: +33 4 92 24 42 73 FAX: +33 4 92 24 51 60

Situated at the centre of a genuine Alpine village and next to an imposing 15th century church, this is a warm and charming family-run hotel. The friendly ambience is enhanced by big log fires in the winter and the aroma of high living – herbs, flowers, wines and cooking. Many of the light and airy bedrooms, with their Alpine-style decor, have balconies. The Auberge restaurant is simply a delight.

Situé au coeur d'un authentique village haut-alpin et près d'une imposante église du XVème siècle, il s'agit d'un charmant hôtel chaleureux tenu par une famille. L'ambiance amicale est renforcée par des grands feux de bois en hiver et par l'essence d'une excellente qualité de vie; herbes, fleurs, vins et table. Nombre de chambres sont non seulement lumineuses et aérées, avec une décoration d'un style alpin, mais bénéficient de surcroît de balcons. Le restaurant de l'Auberge est un délice.

Dieses charmante, familiengeführte Hotel befindet sich im Zentrum eines traditionellen Alpendorfes neben einer Kirche aus dem 15. Jahrhundert. Das freundliche Ambiente wird durch grosse Kaminholzfeuer im Winter sowie das Aroma eines üppigen Lebens – Kräuter, Blumen, Weine und Küchengerüche – gebührend verstärkt. Viele der hellen und luftigen Zimmer bieten einen Balkon und sind im Alpenstil eingerichtet. Das Restaurant Auberge ist einfach ein Genuss.

Directions: N91 - Briancon - Monetier-les-Bains. **Price guide:** *Single FF570–770; double/twin FF770–970; suites FF1070–1570.*

CHÂTEAU D'ARPAILLAGUES

HÔTEL MARIE D'AGOULT, 30700 UZÉS, FRANCE
TEL: +33 4 66 22 14 48 FAX: +33 4 66 22 56 10 E-MAIL: SavryCHATEAU30@aol.com

Protected by thick stone walls, this chateau offers a warm welcome and all the charm and authenticity of a Provençal stately home. The bedrooms and apartments are elegantly furnished, and the superb dining rooms with their vaulted ceilings are warmed by crackling fires in autumn. In fine weather, delicious meals are served in the lovely courtyard. Guests may relax on the huge terrace, play tennis or swim in the fantastic swimming pool surrounded by a beautiful park. Golf can be arranged nearby.

Protégé par d'épais murs en pierre, ce château accueillant cache le charme et l'authenticité d'un logis seigneurial de Provence. Les chambres et les appartements sont aménagés dans un style élégant. En automne, des feux de cheminée crépitent dans les belles salles à manger aux plafonds voûtés. Par beau temps, des repas savoureux sont servis dans la jolie cour. Les visiteurs lézardent sur la terrasse, jouent au tennis ou se baignent dans la fabuleuse piscine entourée d'un beau parc. Golf possible à proximité.

Von dicken Steinmauern umgeben verkörpert dieses freundliche Chateau den Charme und die Authentizität der Provence. Die Zimmer und Appartements sind elegant ausgestattet, und die herrlichen Speisesäle mit ihren gewölbten Decken werden im Herbst von offenem Kaminfeuer gewärmt. Bei gutem Wetter werden im zauberhaften Innenhof köstliche Gerichte serviert. Die Gäste können sich auf der grossen Terrasse entspannen, Tennis spielen oder im eindrucksvollen Pool schwimmen. Auch Golf ist in der Nähe möglich.

Directions: A9 exit Remoulins, follow signs to Uzès. **Price guide:** *Single FF500–750; double/twin FF600–950; suites FF850–1200.*

HÔTEL LE MAQUIS

BP 94, 20166 PORTICCIO-CORSICA, FRANCE
TEL: +33 4 95 25 05 55 FAX: +33 4 95 25 11 70

The setting for this luxurious and extremely hospitable hotel is truly breathtaking, with each window offering a stunning view of its verdant gardens and white sand. The 20 bedrooms and five suites are well appointed with interesting and authentic family furnishings. Seafood and Corsican dishes are among the mouthwatering specialities served at the L'Arbousier restaurant, located on a terrace by the pool.

La situation de ce luxueux hôtel, outre son accueil extraordinaire, est d'une beauté à vous couper le souffle. Chaque fenêtre permet d'admirer les jardins verdoyants et la plage de sable fin. Les 20 chambres et 5 suites sont très bien arrangées avec des meubles de famille authentiques et dignes d'interêt. Les fruits de mer et les plats corses font partie des specialités savoureuses proposés au restaurant L'Arbousier, situé sur la terrasse près de la piscine.

Die Lage dieses luxuriösen und gastfreundlichen Hotels ist wahrhaft atemberaubend, jedes Fenster bietet einen herrlichen Ausblick über dichte Gärten und weissen Sand. Die 20 Zimmer und fünf Suiten sind mit interessanten und familieneigenen Gegenständen eingerichtet. Fisch, Meeresfrüchte und korsische Gerichte sind nur einige der köstlichen Spezialitäten, die im Restaurant L'Arbousier auf einer Terrasse neben dem Pool serviert werden.

Directions: 10 km south of Ajaccio airport. **Price guide:** *Single FF700–2700; double/twin FF800–2700; suite FF1400–5400.*

MANOIR DE LA ROSERAIE

ROUTE DE VALRÉAS, 26230 GRIGNAN, FRANCE
TEL: +33 4 75 46 58 15 FAX: +33 4 75 46 91 55 E-MAIL: roseraie.hotel@wanadoo.fr

Surrounded by five acres of lush, fragrant lawns and gardens that seem to explode into a riot of colours, this is a luxurious and welcoming 19th century manor. Fusing past and contemporary decor, the interior has been appointed in stylish fabrics and comfortable furnishings. The fresh taste of home-grown vegetables and fruit entices visitors towards the restaurant, where the inspired dishes are complemented by a selection of fine wines.

Entouré de 2 hectares d'un magnifique parc, de pelouses et de jardins qui semblent exploser dans une fête colorée, il s'agit ici d'un accueillant et luxueux manoir du XIXème siècle. Mariant le passé et le présent, la décoration a été arrangée avec de fins tissus et de confortables meubles. Les légumes frais, cultivés sur place et les fruits de la maison ajoutent à l'authenticité du restaurant, où les plats inspirés sont complétés par une sélection de vins fins.

Dieses luxuriöse und einladende Herrenhaus aus dem 19. Jahrhundert liegt inmitten von 2 ha üppig grünem Rasen und farbenfrohen Gärten. Vergangenheit vermischt sich mit zeitgenössischem Dekor, die Innenräume sind mit stilvollen Stoffen und bequemem Mobiliar eingerichtet. Der köstliche Geschmack von selbst angebautem Gemüse und Obst lockt die Gäste ins Restaurant, wo einfallsreiche Gerichte von einer Auswahl erlesener Weine ergänzt werden.

Directions: A7 > Montelimar Sud > Nyons Sud. **Price guide:** *Double/twin FF900–1180; suites FF1700–1900.*

LA TOUR ROSE

22 RUE DE BOEUF, 69005 LYON, FRANCE
TEL: 33 4 78 37 25 90 FAX: 33 4 78 42 26 02 E-MAIL: chavent@asi.fr

Boasting a Tuscan garden with terraces, waterfalls and ornamental pools, this striking collection of three Renaissance buildings is perhaps Lyon's most luxurious hotel. Each of the suites has been designed by one of Lyon's most famous silk manufacturers. A former chapel, leading onto a terrace, the restaurant serves classically-inspired nouvelle cuisine. Afterwards, visitors can relax in the stylish bar or one of the sunlit gardens.

La Tour Rose a pour cadre un jardin toscan avec terrasses, cascades et bassins d'agrément. Ses trois bâtiments Renaissance composent probablement l'un des hôtels les plus luxueux de Lyon. Chaque suite a été décorée par de célèbres fabricants de soie. Le restaurant, jadis une chapelle, mène à la terrasse et sert une nouvelle cuisine teintée de classicisme. Les visiteurs pourront également se relaxer dans le bar stylé ou dans un des jardins ensoleillés.

Mit seinem toskanischen Garten, herrlichen Terrassen, Wasserfällen und farbenfrohen Teichen ist dieser eindrucksvolle Komplex aus drei Renaissancebauten das wohl luxuriöseste Hotel in Lyon. Jede der Suiten wurde von einem bekannten Lyoner Seidenfabrikanten entworfen. Das Restaurant, eine ehemalige Kapelle, führt auf eine Terrasse und serviert moderne und doch klassisch inspirierte Gerichte, und die Gäste können sich in der eleganten Bar oder in einem der sonnigen Gärten vergnügen.

Directions: *Vieux-Lyon*. **Price guide:** *Single FF1200–1650; double/twin FF1350–1850; suites FF1850–3200.*

The Leading Hotels of the World®

HÔTEL DU PALAIS

AVENUE DE L'IMPÉRATRICE, 64200 BIARRITZ, FRANCE
TEL: +33 5 59 41 64 00 FAX: +33 5 59 41 67 99 E-MAIL: reception@hotel–du–palais.com

The auspicious history of this exceptional waterfront residence echoes proudly today. Marble pillars and glistening chandeliers adorn its palatial foyer and exquisite antique furniture is set throughout the sophisticated bars and luxurious bedrooms. Built by request of Napoleon III for his wife Eugénie in 1855, the hotel offers a dazzling range of entertainment. The elegance of its 1 Michelin Star restaurant is worthy of the many notable guests who have chosen this magnificent hotel as their summer retreat.

Cadeau impérial de Napoléon III à son épouse Eugénie, cette somptueuse demeure, construite sur le front de mer en 1855, témoigne d'un riche passé. Des colonnes de marbre et des lustres scintillants ornent le hall grandiose, et des meubles anciens raffinés agrémentent les bars élégants et les chambres luxueuses. L'hôtel offre en outre un choix impressionnant de loisirs. Quant à l'élégant restaurant une étoile Michelin, il est digne des nombreux hôtes prestigieux qui ont fait de ce palais leur résidence d'été.

Dieses prächtige, direkt am Wasser gelegene Anwesen ist reich an Geschichte – Napoleon III. baute es 1855 für seine Gemahlin Eugénie. Marmorsäulen und glänzende Lüster zieren das palastartige Foyer, und die eleganten Bars und luxuriösen Schlafzimmer sind mit erlesenen antiken Möbeln gefüllt. Umfassende Freizeitmöglichkeiten stehen zur Verfügung, und das elegante 1 Michelin Stern Restaurant begeistert die zahlreichen Gäste, die sich dieses superbe Hotel als "Sommerresidenz" ausgewählt haben.

Directions: *Centre of Biarritz.* **Price guide**: *Single FF1250–2150; double/twin FF1600–2950; suites FF2100–6350.*

CHÂTEAU D'AIGUEFONDE
81200 AIGUEFONDE, FRANCE
TEL: +33 5 63 98 13 70 FAX: +33 5 63 98 69 90 E-MAIL: chateau.daiguefonde@wanadoo.fr

Buried deep in the forested National Park of the Montagne Noire, this magnificent chateau has recently been restored to its 18th century splendour. Each of the eight bedrooms has been individually furnished, contains wonderful antiques, and has en suite bathrooms. The cuisine is a revelation, with hearty breakfasts served on a sunny terrace, while guests can enjoy beautifully prepared dinners around the fountains and pool.

Perdu au milieu du parc national de la Montagne Noire, ce château magnifique a été recemment restauré pour retrouver sa splendeur du XVIIIème siècle. Chacune des huit chambres est meublée de manière individuelle et est parée de merveilleuses antiquités et des salles de bain privées. La cuisine est une révélation, les petits déjeuners sont servis sur la terrasse ensoleillée et les délicieux dîners se dégustent autour des fontaines et du bassin.

Tief im bewaldeten Nationalpark der Montagne Noire liegt dieses herrliche Chateau, das seine Pracht aus dem 18. Jahrhundert durch Renovierung wiedererlangt hat. Jedes der acht Zimmer ist individuell eingerichtet und verfügt über herrliche Antiquitäten. Die Küche ist eine Offenbarung, Gäste nehmen das üppige Frühstück auf der Terrasse zu sich, während exquisit zubereitete Dinner um den Springbrunnen und das Becken serviert werden.

Directions: From Toulouse > Castres > Mazamet. **Price guide:** *Single FF800; double/twin FF1000; suites FF1250.*

Germany

HOTEL RÖMERBAD

SCHLOSSPLATZ 1, 79410 BADENWEILER, GERMANY
TEL: +49 7632 700 FAX: +49 7632 70200 E-MAIL: info@hotel-roemerbad.de

Set at the foot of the Black Forest, the Römerbad enjoys panoramic views of the surroundings vineyards towards the Vogesen. Dating from the 19th century, the furnishings are exquisite, with many antiques and beautiful accessories adorning the salons. The dining room serves succulent fare, employing fresh local produce, and an extensive wine list. Music festivals are held every year in the octagonal, dome-roofed "Hofsaal".

Situé au pied de la Forêt Noire, le Römerbad bénéficie de vues panoramiques sur les vignobles environnants des Vosges. Dâtant du XIXème siècle, l'ameublement est exquis, avec nombre d'antiquités et de magnifiques accessoires décorants les salons. La salle à manger propose un menu succulent utilisant des produits frais locaux et offre une superbe carte de vins. Des festivals de musique sont organisés chaque année dans le salon à plafond en dôme octagonal, le "Hofsaal".

Das Römerbad liegt am Fusse des Schwarzwalds und bietet traumhafte Aussichten auf die umliegenden Weinberge und die Vogesen. Das aus dem 19. Jahrhundert stammende Mobiliar ist exquisit, und zahlreiche Antiquitäten und zauberhafte Kleinigkeiten zieren die Aufenthaltsräume. Im Speisesaal wird neben köstlichen Speisen, für die beste einheimische Zutaten verwendet werden, auch eine grosse Auswahl an Weinen serviert. Jedes Jahr finden unter dem Kuppeldach des achteckigen "Hofsaals" Musikfestspiele statt.

*Directions: A5 > exit Neuenburg > Müllheim > Badenweiler-West. **Price guide:** Single DM260–300; double/twin DM380–410; suites DM580–610.*

HOTEL KÖNIGSHOF

KARLSPLATZ 25, 80335 MUNICH, GERMANY
TEL: +49 89 551 360 FAX: +49 89 5513 6113 E-MAIL: koenigshof–muenchen@geisel–hotels.de

In the heart of Munich and overlooking the spectacular fountain on Stachus square, this hotel is one of the most prestigious hotels in the city. Dating back to the 19th century, it has undergone major refurbishment and provides stunning accommodation and excellent service. The rooms are decorated differently on each floor, and the Royal Suite has accommodated Queens and Prime Ministers. The sophisticated 1 Michelin star restaurant serves exquisite classical gourmet cuisine and is complemented by an intimate piano bar.

Situé au coeur de Munich, avec vue sur la spectaculaire fontaine de la place Stachus, l'hôtel Königshof est l'un des plus prestigieux de la ville. Cet établissement du XIXe siècle entièrement rénové offre un hébergement de grande classe accompagné d'un excellent service. Les chambres sont décorées différemment à chaque étage. La suite royale peut se vanter d'avoir accueilli des reines et des premiers ministres. L'élégant restaurant 1 étoile Michelin sert une cuisine gastronomique classique savoureuse, complétée à merveille par un verre dans le piano-bar intime.

Im Herzen von München gelegen und mit Blick auf den spektakulären Brunnen auf dem Karlsplatz zählt dieses Hotel zu den besten der Stadt. Das aus dem 19. Jahrhundert stammende Hotel wurde gründlich renoviert und bietet erstklassige Unterkunft und exzellenten Service. Die Zimmer sind auf jeder Etage unterschiedlich gestaltet, und die Royal Suite beherbergte bereits königliche Gäste und Premierminister. Das elegante Restaurant besitzt 1 Michelin Stern und serviert köstliche klassiche Speisen, die mit einem Drink in der gemütlichen Pianobar abgerundet werden.

Directions: Centre of Munich. **Price guide:** *Single DM365–410; double/twin DM400–470; suites DM700–1200.*

BURGHOTEL AUF SCHÖNBURG

55430 OBERWESEL/RHEIN, GERMANY
TEL: +49 67 44 93 930 FAX: +49 67 44 16 13 E-MAIL: huettl@hotel–schoenburg.com

High up on the Schönburg overlooking the Rhine, this romantic secluded hotel dates from the 10th century. Many of the original features still remain, including stone walls and pillars, archways and old beams which have been carefully restored so that history and luxury effortlessly co-exist. With opulent bathrooms and traditional furniture, the bedrooms are a delight. Dinner is served either in the 'Ritterstube' – the knights' dining room – or on the Rhine Terrace.

Perché sur le Schönburg et surplombant le Rhin, cet hôtel romantique intime dâte du Xème siècle. Bon nombre de caractéristiques originelles ont été conservées, telles que les murs et les pilliers en pierre, les voûtes et les vieilles poutres. L'hôtel a été savamment restauré afin de mettre en valeur son histoire et son luxe. Les chambres sont charmantes, avec des salles de bain luxueuses et des meubles traditionnels. Le dîner est servi soit à la 'Ritterstube' – la salle à manger des chevaliers – soit sur la Terrace du Rhin.

Hoch auf der Schönburg, mit Blick über den Rhein, steht dieses romantische und exclusive Hotel, das zum Teil aus dem 10. Jahrhundert stammt. Ursprüngliche Merkmale wie Steinmauern, Säulen, Torbögen und alte Balken sind behutsam restauriert worden, so dass sich Geschichte und luxuriöser Komfort perfekt verbinden. Mit grosszügigen Bädern und traditionellen Stilmöbeln sind die Zimmer einfach zauberhaft. Gourmetmenues werden entweder in der Ritterstube oder auf der Rheinterrasse serviert.

Directions: *A61 - Oberwesel exit - follow signs.* **Price guide:** *Single DM115–150; double/twin DM270–370; suites DM370–390.*

HOTEL EISENHUT

HERRNGASSE 3-7, 91541, ROTHENBURG OB DER TAUBER, GERMANY
TEL: +49 9861 7050 FAX: +49 9861 70545 E-MAIL: hotel@eisenhut.com

Situated in the middle of the unspoilt medieval town of Rothenburg, the Eisenhut is an attractive hotel created from four 14th century town houses. Its historic origins are reflected in the interior, which is adorned with gleaming suits of armour, marvellous antiques and relics of imperial armies. The bedrooms are luxurious and spacious, with gorgeous flowered bedcovers and big gilt mirrors adding to their charm. Sophisticated international menus also include local specialities, and are complemented by fine wines from the cellar.

Composé de quatre demeures du XIVème, le Eisenhut est un bel hôtel situé au coeur de la ville médiévale préservée de Rothenburg. Ses origines historiques sont reflétées à l'intérieur, qui est agrémenté par de superbes armures, de belles antiquités et des reliques des armées impériales. Le charme des chambres, luxueuses et spacieuses, est accentué par de magnifiques dessus-de-lit fleuris et de grands miroirs dorés. Les menus sophistiqués de cuisine internationale proposent également des spécialités régionales agrémentées de bons vins.

Dieses attraktive Hotel im Zentrum der mittelalterlichen Stadt Rothenburg besteht aus vier Patrizierhäusern aus dem 14. Jahrhundert. Die historischen Ursprünge zeigen sich in der Einrichtung: schimmernde Rüstungen, eine Hinterlassenschaft der kaiserlichen Armee, und herrlichste Antiquitäten zieren die Räume. Die grossen Zimmer sind luxuriös, und vergoldete Spiegel und zauberhafte geblümte Bettdecken sorgen für Persönlichkeit. Auf der Speisekarte stehen exquisite internationale Gerichte sowie regionale Spezialitäten und erlesene Weine.

Directions: A7 - Rothenburg - Marktplatz. **Price guide:** Single DM215–235; double/twin DM300–395; suites DM540–660.

CHRISTIAN VIII

HELEEKER 1, 25980 ARCHSUM, SYLT, GERMANY
TEL: +49 4651 97070 FAX: +49 4651 970777 E-MAIL: christianVIII@royal-companie.de

Situated within a splendid, extensive park, this friendly hotel is a superb mixture of history and modern comfort. Its three houses offer generously furnished suites, individually designed with excellent bathrooms; some have open fireplaces and private terraces. Service is caring and attentive, and offers such as personalised stationery and E-mail, fruit baskets and afternoon tea with delicious, homemade cake guarantee an unforgettable stay.

Situé dans un magnifique vaste parc, cet hôtel convivial marie élégamment cachet historique et confort moderne. Les trois demeures qui le composent renferment des suites richement meublées, décorées dans un style individuel et dotées de belles salles de bains. Certaines disposent également de cheminées et de terrasses privatives. Le service se teint de mille attentions : papier à lettres personnalisé, e-mail, corbeilles de fruits et thé accompagné de délicieux gâteaux faits maison sont la garantie d'un séjour inoubliable.

In einem herrlichen, weitläufigen Park gelegen bietet dieses freundliche Hotel eine eindrucksvolle Mischung aus Geschichte und modernem Komfort. In drei Häusern befinden sich grosszügig eingerichtete und individuell gestaltete Suiten mit exzellenten Bädern. Einige haben offene Kamine und private Terrassen. Der Service ist aufmerksam und freundlich, und Extras wie persönliches Briefpapier und E-mail, Obstkörbe und Nachmittagstee mit köstlichem selbstgebackenen Kuchen machen den Aufenthalt unvergesslich.

Directions: On left hand side when driving into Archsum. *Price guide*: Suites DM430–720.

HOTEL UND RESTAURANT LANDHAUS NÖSSE

NÖSISTIEG 13, 25980 MORSUM, SYLT, GERMANY
TEL: +49 4651 97220 FAX: +49 4651 891658 E-MAIL: noesse.sylt@t–online.de

Situated in the Morsum nature conservation area, splendidly isolated and with spectacular views over the moorland and tidal area, the Landhaus Nösse is renowned for its welcoming atmosphere and flawless elegance. The rooms are decorated with fine furnishings and fabrics, and most enjoy splendid views of the surroundings. Exquisite regional cuisine is served in the elegant restaurant, and guests can choose from over 200 fine wines from the cellar. The energetic visitor may hire a bicycle to explore this beautiful island.

Situé dans la réserve naturelle de Morsum, cet hôtel paisible jouit de vues spectaculaires sur les landes et la Watt. Son atmosphère chaleureuse et son élégance sans faute en font un établissement de renom. Les chambres sont ornées de beaux meubles et de jolis tissus. La plupart d'entre elles offrent des vues magnifiques sur les environs. Une cuisine régionale raffinée est servie dans l'élégant restaurant, où les visiteurs peuvent choisir parmi plus de 200 excellents vins de la cave. Il est possible de louer des vélos pour explorer l'île.

Mitten im Naturschutzgebiet Morsum und mit atemberaubendem Blick auf Heidelandschaft und Wattenmeer liegt das Landhaus Nösse, das weithin für seine herzliche Atmosphäre und Eleganz bekannt ist. Die Zimmer sind mit hübschen Stoffen und Möbeln eingerichtet und die meisten haben eine herrliche Sicht auf die Landschaft. Im eleganten Restaurant werden regionale Köstlichkeiten serviert, und man hat die Qual der Wahl bei über 200 Weinen aus dem Weinkeller. Aktive Gäste können diese zauberhafte Insel per Fahrrad erkunden!

Directions: K117 > Morsum > Terpstieg > Nösistieg. **Price guide:** *Double/twin DM250–499; suites DM425–499.*

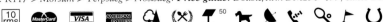

HOTEL-RESTAURANT JÖRG MÜLLER

SÜDERSTRASSE 8, 25980 WESTERLAND, SYLT, GERMANY
TEL: +49 4651 27788

Built in traditional Frisian style using old timber and tiles, this charming hotel offers personal and friendly service. The bright and spacious rooms are tastefully decorated and have en suite bathrooms. Guests may feast on delicious award-winning cuisine in the elegant 1 Michelin Star Restaurant Jörg Müller, which is considered to be the best on the island and achieved the Wine Spectators "Grand Award" for its wine cellar and selection. The more informal cosy Pesel restaurant serves regional fare, whilst the attractive bar provides snacks and cocktails.

Construit dans un style frison traditionnel, avec de vieilles poutres et tuiles, ce charmant hôtel offre un service cordial et personnalisé. Spacieuses et claires, les chambres avec salles de bains sont décorées avec goût. La cuisine servie dans le restaurant Jörg Müller a rapporté une étoile Michelin à cet établissement élégant considéré comme la meilleure table de l'île. Le restaurant est aussi primé pour sa cave et son choix de vins. Plus intime, le Pesel propose des spécialités de la région, et le beau bar, des cocktails et des collations.

Dieses zauberhafte Hotel wurde im friesischen Stil mit traditionellen alten Ziegeln und Balken erbaut und besticht durch persönlichen und freundlichen Service. Die hellen, grosszügigen Zimmer sind geschmackvoll eingerichtet und haben En-Suite Bäder. Das elegante Restaurant Jörg Müller gilt als das beste der Insel und wurde bereits mit 1 Michelin Stern und dem "Grand Award" für Weinkeller und -auswahl ausgezeichnet. Das gemütliche Pesel serviert regionale Küche in lockerer Atmosphäre und die Bar sorgt für Snacks und Cocktails.

Directions: *Westerland > Randum > 300m from the city on right hand side.* **Price guide:** *Double/twin DM240–380; suites DM390–590.*

       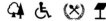

THE ROCK HOTEL

EUROPA ROAD, GIBRALTAR

TEL: +350 73000 FAX: +350 73513 E-MAIL: rockhotel@gibnynex.gi

Built over 60 years ago by the Marquis of Bute, The Rock has maintained its feeling of colonial elegance and affords spectacular views over the Strait of Gibraltar with the Spanish mainland on one side and the Rif mountains of Morocco on the other. The courteous staff provide unobtrusive service and the recently refurbished bedrooms provide all the expected amenities alongside many thoughtful extras. The menu in the Rib Room Restaurant consists of an eclectic mix of British, Iberian and Moorish flavours.

Construit il y a plus de 60 ans par le Marquis de Bute, Le Rock a conservé son ambiance coloniale et bénéficie de vues spectaculaires sur le détroit de Gibraltar. Il est environné de terres espagnoles d'un côté et des montagnes marocaines de Rif de l'autre. Le personnel courtois fournit un service hors-pair et les chambres récemment redécorées offrent toutes les équipements nécessaires avec des extras fort ingénieux. Le menu de le Rib Room Restaurant propose un mélange éclectique de saveurs britanniques, ibériques et maures.

The Rock, vor über 60 Jahren von Marquis de Bute erbaut, ist immer noch geprägt von der Eleganz der Kolonialzeit und bietet traumhafte Blicke auf die Meerenge von Gibraltar, mit Spanien auf der einen und dem Rif-Gebirge in Marokko auf der anderen. Der Service ist höflich und unaufdringlich, und die kürzlich renovierten Zimmer sind mit jedem erdenklichen Komfort und vielen Extras ausgestattet. Im Rib Room Restaurant wird eine interessante Mischung aus britischer, iberischer und maurischer Küche serviert.

Directions: From airport, 5 minute taxi drive. **Price guide:** Double/twin £160–£165; suites £195–£290.

the preferred
champagne
of johansens

Great Britain & Ireland

ADARE MANOR HOTEL & GOLF RESORT

ADARE, CO LIMERICK, IRELAND
TEL: +353 61 396 566 FAX: +353 61 396 124

A wonderful example of 18th century gothic architecture, Adare Manor is set in 840 acres of majestic parkland. Splendour is evident throughout the estate, from the elegant lobby to the luxurious bedrooms, which are decorated with soft fabrics and individually designed wood panels. Enjoy a fireside drink in the library or sample some of the European haute cuisine in one of the enchanting restaurants. Activities include a championship golf course designed by Robert Trent Jones, Sr, an equestrian centre, an indoor swimming pool, sauna and fitness centre.

Bel exemple de l'architecture gothique du XVIIIe siècle, cet hôtel entouré d'un vaste parc ouvre sur un luxe éblouissant, qui règne aussi bien dans l'élégante entrée que dans les chambres confortables, parées d'étoffes soyeuses et de boiseries. La bibliothèque est idéale pour boire un verre au coin du feu avant de déguster des spécialités culinaires européennes dans l'un des ravissants restaurants. L'hôtel offre un parcours de golf de championnat conçu par Robert Trent Jones, Senior, un centre équestre, une piscine couverte, sauna et centre de remise en forme.

Dieses herrliche Beispiel für Architektur des 18. Jahrhunderts liegt inmitten eines 340 ha grossen Parkes. Die prächtige Einrichtung reicht vom eleganten Foyer bis hin zu den luxuriösen, mit weichen Stoffen und Holzvertäfelung ausgestatteten Zimmern. In der Bibliothek kann man am Kamin einen Drink zu sich nehmen, bevor man in einem der bezaubernden Restaurants europäische Haute Cuisine geniesst. Das Hotel bietet einen von Robert Trent Jones Senior gestalteten Championship Golfplatz, einen Reitstall, ein Hallenbad, Sauna und Fitness-Center.

Directions: 20 miles from Shannon airport on N21. **Price guide:** Double/twin from IR£150–500.

WAREN HOUSE HOTEL

WAREN MILL, BAMBURGH, NORTHUMBERLAND NE70 7EE
TEL: +44 1668 214581 FAX: +44 1668 214484 E-MAIL: enquiries@warenhousehotel.co.uk

Situated in six acres of gardens and woodland on the edge of the Budle Bay Bird Sanctuary, the Waren House Hotel offers discerning visitors peace and quiet even during the frenetic summer months. Throughout the hotel, the antique furnishings and the immaculate and well-chosen décor evoke a warm and friendly ambience. In the intimate candle-lit dining room, guests can choose from an eclectic menu and extensive wine list.

Situé dans un parc et une forêt de $2\frac{1}{2}$ hectares sur le bord de la Baie de Budle Bird Sanctuary, le Waren House offre à ses visiteurs une paix et une tranquillité inégalables même durant les mois estivaux. Dans l'hôtel, les meubles anciens et la décoration extrêment soignés évoquent une ambiance chaleureuse et amicale. Dans la salle à manger intîme éclairée aux bougies, les visiteurs pourront se régaler d'un menu éclectique et d'une superbe liste de vins.

Das Waren House Hotel liegt in $2\frac{1}{2}$ ha Park- und Waldlandschaft am Rande des Budle Bay Vogelschutzgebietes und bietet anspruchsvollen Gästen selbst während der geschäftigen Sommermonate völlige Ruhe. Im ganzen Hotel befinden sich Antiquitäten und geschmack-volle Einrichtungen, die ein behagliches und freundliches Ambiente schaffen. Im intimen und mit Kerzenlicht beleuchteten Speisesaal erfreuen sich die Gäste an abwechslungsreichen Speisen und einer ausführlichen Weinkarte.

Directions: B1342 > Waren Mill > south-west of Budle Bay. **Price guide:** Single £57.50–£67.50; double/twin £115–£135; suites £155–£185.

RISLEY HALL COUNTRY HOUSE HOTEL

DERBY ROAD, RISLEY, DERBYSHIRE DE72 3SS
TEL: +44 115 V939 9000 FAX: + 115 939 7766

Dating from Elizabethan times, Risley Hall has been splendidly restored to its former glory. Its peaceful atmosphere is enhanced by spectacular, colourful gardens. The décor inside features oak beams, ornate fireplaces and individually decorated bedrooms. The cosy Drawing Room is a convivial place to enjoy afternoon tea, whilst the Cocktail Lounge serves lunchtime drinks or apéritifs. The hotel is ideal for corporate meetings or special occasions, and guests are free to explore the wealth of historic buildings in the vicinity.

Datant de l'époque élisabéthaine, Risley Hall a retrouvé sa splendeur d'origine grâce à une restauration soignée. Un beau parc fleuri accentue l'atmosphère paisible des lieux. L'hôtel ouvre sur des pièces dotées de poutres en chêne et de cheminées richement ornées et des chambres au style individuel. Le salon convivial est l'endroit indiqué pour prendre le thé, et le bar vous attend pour l'apéritif. Risley Hall est idéal pour organiser des réunions d'affaires ou des réceptions et découvrir les nombreux monuments historiques de la région.

Risley Hall stammt aus der Zeit Elizabeths I. und erlangte durch ausführliche Renovierung seine ursprüngliche Pracht wieder. Die friedliche Atmosphäre verstärkt sich noch durch prachtvolle, bunte Gärten. Eichenbalken und verzierte Kamine schmücken die Innenräume und die Zimmer sind individuell gestaltet. Der Aufenthaltsraum lädt zum Nachmittagstee ein, und in der Cocktail Lounge werden Drinks und Apéritifs serviert. Das Hotel ist ideal für Geschäftstreffen, und zahlreiche historische Bauten können in der Nähe erforscht werden.

Directions: M1 exit at junction 25 towards Sandiacre. **Price guide:** *Single £75–£95; double/twin £95–£115.*

BEAUFORT HOUSE APARTMENTS

45 BEAUFORT GARDENS, KNIGHTSBRIDGE, LONDON SW3 1PN
TEL: +44 20 7584 2600 FAX: +44 20 7584 6532 E-MAIL: beauforthouse.co.uk

Situated in a quiet tree-lined Regency cul-de-sac in the heart of Knightsbridge, Beaufort House comprises 22 self-contained apartments of five star standard. Each has been individually and traditionally decorated, with direct dial telephones and voice mail. Every apartment has a fully fitted kitchen. A concierge is on duty 24 hours a day. Complimentary membership to two health clubs is also offered to all guests during their stay.

Situé dans une impasse calme et longée d'arbres dans Knightsbridge, Beaufort House comprend 22 appartements indépendants de catégorie cinq étoiles. Chacun est décoré de manière individuelle et traditionnelle et possède téléphone direct et messagerie vocale. Tous sont équipés de cuisine. Un concierge est à votre disposition 24h/24. Une adhésion complémentaire à deux clubs de remise en forme est également offerte à tous les visiteurs durant leur séjour.

In einer ruhigen, von Bäumen eingefassten Strasse im Herzen von Knightsbridge liegt Beaufort House, das aus 22 abgeschlossenen 5-Sterne Appartements besteht. Jedes ist individuell und traditionell eingerichtet und bietet neben Telefon mit Direktdurchwahl und Voicemail auch eine voll ausgestattete Küche. Ein Pförtner ist rund um die Uhr im Dienst. Während des Aufenthalts haben die Gäste freie Mitgliedschaft in zwei Fitnessclubs.

Directions: *Off Brompton Road in Knightsbridge*. *Price guide:* *Apartments £180–£550.*

CANNIZARO HOUSE

WEST SIDE, WIMBLEDON COMMON, LONDON SW19 4UE
TEL: +44 20 8879 1464 FAX: +44 20 8879 7338 E-MAIL: cannizaro.house@thistle.co.uk

An elegant Georgian country house, Cannizaro House commands spectacular views of Wimbledon Common. Its eighteenth century origins are reflected in the ornate fireplaces, gilt mirrors and antiques that adorn every room. All bedrooms have been individually designed, and several intimate rooms are available for meetings and private dinners. The spacious summer terrace is ideal for afternoon tea and early evening cocktails.

Elégant manoir georgien, Le Cannizaro House jouit de vues spectaculaires sur le parc de Wimbledon. Le style du XVIIIème siècle se reconnaît dans les cheminées ornées, les miroirs dorés et les nombreuses antiquités. Chaque chambre a été décorée de manière différente, et plusieurs pièces intimes sont disponibles pour des réunions et des dîners privés. La grande terrasse estivale est idéale pour prendre le thé ou des cocktails le soir.

Cannizaro House, ein elegantes georgianisches Herrenhaus, bietet einen traumhaften Ausblick auf den Park von Wimbledon. Aufwendige Kamine, vergoldete Spiegel und Antiquitäten zieren sämtliche Räume und verraten seinen Ursprung aus dem 18. Jahrhundert. Alle Zimmer sind individuell gestaltet, und es stehen auch einige Räume für Tagungen sowie für private Anlässe zur Verfügung. Die grosse Südterrasse lädt zum Nachmittagstee oder Abendcocktail ein.

*Directions: Nearest tube is Wimbledon. **Price guide:** Double/twin from £211; suites from £335.*

THE COLONNADE, THE LITTLE VENICE TOWN HOUSE

2 WARRINGTON CRESCENT, LONDON W9 1ER
TEL: +44 20 7286 1052 FAX: +44 20 7286 1057 E-MAIL: res_colonnade@etontownhouse.com

Situated at the heart of London's Little Venice, the Colonnade is a tall, elegant Victorian house that simply exudes charm and sophistication. Dating from the middle of the 19th century it has been refurbished to the very highest of standards. Each of the 43 bedrooms has been individually designed with sumptuous fabrics and antiques, and the intimate drawing room completes the feeling of a true "home away from home". In contrast, the contemporary breakfast room serves an unforgettable town house breakfast.

Situé en plein coeur de la Petite Venise à Londres, le Colonnade est une grande et élégante maison victorienne qui dégage une ambiance de charme et de sophistication. Dâtant du milieu du XIXème siècle, l'hôtel a été superbement rénové. Chacune des 43 chambres a été décorée de manière individuelle et est agrémentée de somptueux tissus et d'antiquités. L'intimité du salon complète le sentiment d'être "comme à la maison". Un succulent petit déjeuner "Town House" inoubliable est servi dans la petite salle à manger contemporaine.

Das Colonnade, im Herzen von Londons Little Venice gelegen, ist ein hohes, elegantes viktorianisches Haus mit Charme und Raffinesse. Es wurde Mitte des 19. Jahrhunderts erbaut und in exklusivem Stil renoviert. Jedes der 43 Zimmer ist individuell gestaltet und mit herrlichsten Stoffen und erlesenen Antiquitäten eingerichtet, und der heimelige Aufenthaltsraum sorgt dafür, dass man sich wie zu Hause fühlt. Im zeitgenössischen Frühstücksraum wird morgens ein unvergessliches "Town House" Frühstück serviert.

Directions: Near Warwick Avenue tube. **Price guide (excl. VAT):** *Single £120; suites £220.*

THE DORCHESTER

PARK LANE, MAYFAIR, LONDON W1A 2HJ
TEL: +44 20 7629 8888 FAX: +44 20 7409 0114 E-MAIL: reservations@dorchesterhotel.com

Recently restored to its original splendour, the Dorchester is quite plainly one of the finest hotels in the world . Each of the bedrooms and suites has been luxuriously designed, and benefits from marble bathrooms. Apart from the renowned Grill Room, there is an exquisite Chinese restaurant. Specialised health and beauty treatments are available in the Dorchester Spa, impressive with its statues and glass and water fountain.

Récemment restauré, le Dorchester est tout simplement un des hôtels les plus raffinés du monde. Chaque chambre et suite a été luxueusement conçue avec des salles de bain en marbre. Outre la fameuse rotisserie, l'hôtel dispose d'un exquis restaurant chinois. Le Spa du Dorchester propose des traitements spéciaux de beauté et de santé. Il se distingue par ses impressionnantes statues, ses fontaînes et ses miroirs.

Vor kurzem zu seiner ursprünglichen Pracht renoviert, ist das Dorchester eines der besten Hotels der Welt. Jedes Zimmer sowie jede Suite ist luxuriös gestaltet und verfügt über ein Marmorbad. Ausser dem renommierten Grill Room gibt es auch ein herrliches kantonesisches Restaurant. Besondere Schönheits- und Gesundheitsanwendungen werden im Dorchester Spa angeboten, das die Gäste mit Statuen und Glas- und Wasser-Springbrunnen beeindruckt.

Directions: Hyde Park Corner end of Park Lane. **Price guide:** Single £285–£305; double/twin £315–£345; suites £475–£1950.

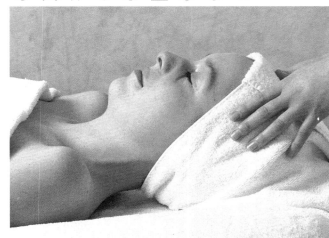

THE MILESTONE AND APARTMENTS

1 KENSINGTON COURT, LONDON W8 5DL

TEL: +44 20 7917 1000 FAX: +44 20 7917 1010 FROM THE USA: 1 800 223 6800 E-MAIL: reservations@milestone.redcarnationhotels.com

Situated opposite Kensington Palace and offering unparalleled views over Kensington Gardens, the Milestone is a Victorian masterpiece. Combining 19th century splendour with modern convenience, the Milestone abounds with antiques and elegant furnishings. Magnificent fare is served in a delightful restaurant with an elaborately carved ceiling and ornate walls. The health and fitness centre offers a Jacuzzi, sauna and gymnasium.

Situé en face de Kensington Palace et offrant des vues imprenables sur Kensington Gardens, le Milestone est un joyau de l'époque victorienne. Mariant la splendeur du XIXème siècle avec le confort moderne, le Milestone regorge d'antiquités et de beaux meubles. Un succulent menu est proposé au restaurant agrémenté d'un plafond voûté élaboré et de murs décorés. Le centre de culture physique et de remise en forme comprend un Jacuzzi, un sauna et un gymnasium.

Das Milestone, gegenüber des Kensington Palace gelegen und mit unvergleichlicher Aussicht auf die Kensington Gardens, ist ein viktorianisches Meisterwerk. Mit Antiquitäten und eleganten Einrichtungen reichlich bestückt bietet das Hotel eine Mischung aus der Pracht des 19. Jahrhunderts und modernsten Annehmlichkeiten. Das bezaubernde Restaurant mit seiner kunstvoll geschmückten Decke und üppig verzierten Wänden serviert verlockende Gerichte. Im Freizeitzentrum stehen Jacuzzi, Sauna und Fitnessraum bereit.

Directions: Kensington High Street. **Price guide:** Single from £250; double/twin £270; suites from £430.

NUMBER ELEVEN CADOGAN GARDENS

11 CADOGAN GARDENS, SLOANE SQUARE, KNIGHTSBRIDGE, LONDON SW3 2RJ
TEL: +44 20 7730 7000 FAX: +44 20 7730 5217 E-MAIL: reservations@number–eleven.co.uk

In a quiet tree-lined street between Harrods and the King's Road, Number Eleven is an elegant town house with a reputation for first class service. The well-appointed bedrooms are covered with antiques and oriental rugs, while the Garden Suite has a spacious drawing room overlooking attractive gardens. Pre-dinner drinks and canapés are served in the Drawing Room or the Library, which can also be reserved for private parties.

Situé dans une paisible rue bordée d'arbres entre Harrods et King's Road, le Number Eleven est un élégant établissement citadin avec une réputation hors pair. Les merveilleuses chambres sont meublées d'antiquités et de tapis orientaux, et la suite Garden a un salon avec vue sur de superbes jardins. Les apéritifs et canapés sont servis dans le salon ou dans la bibliothèque, également disponibles pour des réunions privées.

In einer ruhigen, von Bäumen umsäumten Strasse zwischen Harrods und der King's Road steht Number Eleven, ein elegantes Stadthaus, das für seinen erstklassigen Service bekannt ist. Die schön eingerichteten Zimmer sind mit Antiquitäten und Perserteppiche ausgestattet, und die Garden Suite verfügt über ein geräumiges Wohnzimmer mit Ausblick auf herrliche Gärten. Apéritifs und Canapés werden im Drawing Room oder der Bibliothek serviert, die auch für private Anlässe reserviert werden kann.

Directions: Off Sloane Street. **Price guide (excl. VAT):** *Single from £140; double/twin from £177; suites from £250.*

NUMBER SIXTEEN

16 SUMNER PLACE, LONDON SW7 3EG

TEL: +44 20 7589 5232 US TOLL FREE: 1 800 553 6674 FAX: +44 20 7584 8615 E-MAIL: reservations@numbersixteenhotel.co.uk

On entering Number Sixteen, with its beautifully pillared façade, one is immediately struck by the atmosphere of seclusion and comfort that has remained virtually unaltered from its early Victorian origins. The relaxed atmosphere of the bar extends to the drawing room where a blazing fire greets guest during colder months. Each of the spacious bedrooms is subtly decorated with both antiques and traditional furnishings.

Au Number Sixteen, une atmosphère de calme et de confort domine. Celle-ci, maintenue depuis sa construction à l'époque victorienne, est accentuée par la magnifique façade à pilliers. La douce ambiance du bar s'étend au salon où un superbe feu de cheminée accueille les clients durant les mois d'hiver. Chacune des grandes chambres est subtilement décorée avec des antiquités et des meubles traditionnels.

Schon beim Betreten von Number Sixteen mit seiner schönen Säulenfassade befindet man sich in einer Atmosphäre von Abgeschiedenheit und Komfort, die sich seit dem frühen viktorianischen Ursprung des Hotels so gut wie nicht verändert hat. Die lockere Atmosphäre der Bar erstreckt sich auch auf den Salon, wo ein Kaminfeuer in der kühleren Jahreszeit für Behaglichkeit sorgt. Jedes der geräumigen Zimmer ist raffiniert mit Antiquitäten und traditionellen Gegenständen ausgestattet.

*Directions: Sumner Place is of Brompton Road. Nearest tube: South Kensington. **Price guide:** Single from £100; double/twin from £175; junior suites from £225.*

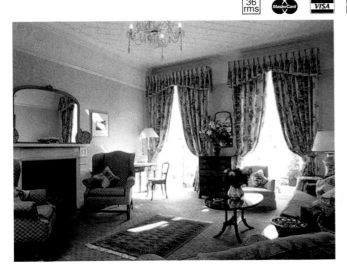

PEMBRIDGE COURT HOTEL

34 PEMBRIDGE GARDENS, LONDON W2 4DX
TEL: +44 20 7229 9977 FAX: +44 20 7727 4982 E-MAIL: reservations@pemct.co.uk

Beautifully restored to its nineteenth century origins, this gracious Victorian town house offers the high level of service demanded by today's discerning traveller. The well-appointed bedrooms are individually decorated with pretty fabrics and the walls are adorned with a collection of framed Victorian fans. It is situated at the heart of Notting Hill, renowned for its vibrant night-life and one of the largest antiques markets in the world.

Superbement restauré en fonction de ses origines du XIXème siècle, cette jolie maison de ville victorienne offre un grand standing de service. Les jolies chambres sont toutes individuellement décorées avec de superbes tissus et les murs sont ornés d'une collection d'évantails victoriens. Il est situé au coeur de Notting Hill, renommé pour sa vie nocturne animée et pour être un des plus grands marchés aux puces du monde.

Dieses elegante viktorianische Herrenhaus aus dem 19. Jahrhundert wurde perfekt restauriert und bietet dem anspruchsvollen Gast von heute höchsten Standard an Service. Die gutausgestatteten Zimmer sind individuell mit hübschen Stoffen gestaltet, und eine Sammlung von viktorianischen Fächern ziert die Wände. Das Pembridge Court liegt im Herzen von Notting Hill, das für sein reges Nachtleben und einen der weltgrössten Antiquitätenmärkte bekannt ist.

Directions: 2 minutes from Portobello Road. **Price guide:** *Single £125–£160; double/twin £185–£200.*

THE ROOKERY

PETER'S LANE, COWCROSS STREET, LONDON EC1M 6DS
TEL: +44 20 7336 0931 FAX: +44 20 7336 0932 E-MAIL: reservations@rookery.co.uk

The wonderful 18th century Rookery is a stylish and historic find. Its stunningly restored buildings belie its lawless heritage that once attracted villains such as Charles Dickens' Fagin. The bedrooms show amazing attention to detail and have beautiful furnishings. Guests can relax in the welcoming drawing room and conservatory overlooking the garden. A popular business meeting venue, the Rookery attracts with its superb oak-panelled library and stone flagged floors, although it is said to be populated by ghosts!

Le magnifique Rookery, datant du 18ème siècle, est une véritable découverte historique de style. Ses superbes bâtiments restaurés cachent l'histoire d'un quartier autrefois fréquenté par les brigands tels que Fagin de Charles Dickens. Les chambres parées de somptueuses étoffes mettent en valeur un impressionnant souci du détail. Les hôtes peuvent se relaxer dans l'accueillant salon ou dans la véranda qui s'ouvre sur le jardin. La salle de réunion est renommée, avec son sol dallé et sa superbe bibliothèque en chêne, mais on l'a dit peuplée de fantômes!

Die Rookery stammt aus dem 18. Jahrhundert und ist ein phantastischer historischer Fund. Die herrlich renovierten Gebäude kaschieren ein 'kriminelles' Erbe – einst trieben hier Unholde wie Charles Dickens' Fagin ihr Unwesen. Die Zimmer sind wunderschön mit Liebe zum Detail eingerichtet, und die Gäste können sich im Aufenthaltsraum oder im Wintergarten mit Blick auf den Garten entspannen. Das Hotel ist beliebt für Geschäftstreffen und besitzt Steinböden und eine eindrucksvolle Bibliothek mit Eichenvertäfelung. Allerdings soll es hier spuken!

Directions: Near Farringdon tube. **Price guide (Room only excl. VAT):** *Single £160–£180; double/twin £195; suites £250–£450.*

SHAW PARK PLAZA

100–110 EUSTON ROAD, LONDON NW1 2AJ
TEL: +44 20 7666 9000 FAX: +44 20 7666 9100 E-MAIL: sppinfo@parkplazahotels.co.uk

Combining four star standard and a prime location, this modern hotel is stylish and vibrant with a glass-fronted restaurant, relaxing lounge and colourful bar. The exhilarating atmosphere is followed through to the extensive conference facilities and the air-conditioned, comfortable bedrooms with Internet access, which offer skyline views and 24 hour service. Guests enjoy a delicious selection of dishes from the international menu in the lively restaurant The hotel has a health club providing sauna, gym, steam room and solarium.

Cet hôtel 4 étoiles moderne et distingué jouit d'une situation privilégiée et d'une ambiance gaie qui transcende tout, le restaurant à verrière, les salons reposants, le bar animé et même les salles de conférence et les chambres confortables. Ces dernières sont climatisées et offrent accès à l'Internet ainsi qu'une belle vue sur la ville. Le service des chambres est assuré 24h/24. Le menu comprend un choix alléchant de plats internationaux. L'hôtel compte aussi un club de remise en forme avec sauna, gymnase, bain de vapeur et solarium.

Dieses moderne und stylishe 4-Sterne Hotel ist einzigartig gelegen und besticht durch sein von Glaswänden eingefasstes Restaurant, die gemütliche Lounge und lebendige Bar. Die heitere Atmosphäre reicht bis in die umfassenden Konferenzeinrichtungen und klimatisierten, komfortablen Zimmer, die neben Internetzugang herrliche Blicke auf die Stadt und 24-Stunden Zimmerservice bieten. Auf der Speisekarte stehen verlockende internationale Köstlichkeiten. Ausserdem gibt es ein Fitnesszentrum mit Sauna, Fitnessraum, Dampfbad und Solarium.

Directions: *Adjacent to British Library, between King's Cross and Euston tube stations.* **Price guide:** *Double/twin £145–£195; suites £325–£550.*

THE SLOANE HOTEL

29 DRAYCOTT PLACE, CHELSEA, LONDON SW3 2SH
TEL: +44 20 7581 5757 FAX: +44 20 7584 1348 E-MAIL: sloanehotel@btinternet.com

The Sloane is a delightful and unique hotel situated in the heart of fashionable Chelsea. The air-conditioned rooms are beautifully furnished and antique treasures abound, all of which can be purchased by guests. Each room has an en suite marble bathroom. The rooftop terrace and sun room is popular for breakfast, light meals, afternoon tea or evening cocktails. The business visitor is catered for with a fully equipped business centre complete with technical and secretarial support, translation and courier service.

Le Sloane est un hôtel d'exception situé au coeur du quartier chic de Chelsea. Les chambres climatisées sont très belles et regorgent de trésors anciens que les visiteurs peuvent acquérir. Les salles de bains attenantes sont habillées de marbre. Le toit en terrasse et la véranda sont parfaits pour prendre le petit déjeuner, des repas légers, le thé et des cocktails. Un centre d'affaires très bien équipé, offrant support technique et services de secrétariat, de traduction et de messagerie rapide, est également disponible.

Das freundliche Sloane Hotel liegt mitten im Herzen des attraktiven Chelsea. Die klimatisierten Zimmer sind wunderschön eingerichtet und haben En-suite Marmorbäder. Überall sind antike Kostbarkeiten zu finden, die von den Gästen erworben werden können. Die Dachterrasse und das Sonnenzimmer sind beliebte Orte, um Frühstück, leichte Mahlzeiten, Nachmittagstee und -kaffee oder einen Cocktail am Abend einzunehmen. Geschäftsreisenden steht ein mit Sekretariats- und Übersetzungsdienst ausgerüstetes Business-Zentrum zur Verfügung.

Directions: *Draycott Place is off Sloane Square, behind Peter Jones store.* **Price guide:** *Double £140; suites £225.*

MILLER HOWE

RAYRIGG ROAD, WINDERMERE, CUMBRIA LA23 1EY
TEL: +44 15394 42536 FAX: +44 15394 45664 E-MAIL: lakeview@millerhowe.com

Boasting one of the finest views in the Lake District, Miller Howe is a magnificent hotel perched on the shore of Lake Windermere. Lawned gardens bedded with mature shrubs, trees and borders of colour sweep down to the water's edge. All 12 en suite bedrooms are luxuriously furnished, with most benefiting from spectacular views. Chef Susan Elliot's traditional fare will surprise even the most discerning of visitors.

Jouissant d'une des plus belles vues sur le Lake District, le Miller Howe est un magnifique hôtel perché sur les bords du lac Windermere. Des pelouses bordées de plate-bandes fleuries et de divers arbres descendent jusqu'au bord de l'eau. Les 12 suites sont luxueusement meublées, et la plupart bénéficient de vues spectaculaires. Le menu du chef Susan Elliot surprendra même les visiteurs les plus exigeants.

Das prächtige Hotel Miller Howe liegt am Ufer des Lake Windermere und geniesst eine der schönsten Aussichten im ganzen Lake District. Die weitläufige Gartenanlage mit altem Baumbestand und Sträuchern, umrahmt von farbenfrohen Blumenbeeten, reicht bis zum Ufer hinab. Alle 12 Zimmer sind luxuriös gestaltet und die meisten bieten atemberaubende Aussichten. Die traditionelle Küche von Susan Elliot wird auch die anspruchsvollsten Gäste überraschen.

Directions: M6 - A592 - Windermere - Bowness. **Price guide (incl. 4-course dinner):** *Single £95–£175; double/twin £140–£260.*

Greece

HOTEL PENTELIKON

66 DILIGIANNI STREET, 14562 ATHENS, GREECE
TEL: +30 1 62 30 650-6 FAX: +30 1 80 10 314

Set in a peaceful residential area of Athens, this impressive, discreet small hotel is the essence of style. Fine antiques, silk curtains and immaculate staff contribute to its select ambience. The luxurious bedrooms are individually decorated in French fabrics with harmonising wall coverings. Cuisine is a delight with the informal La Terrasse and the gourmet Vardis restaurant, the only restaurant in Greece boasting one Michelin star.

Situé dans un quartier calme d'Athènes, ce petit hôtel impressionnant et discret est une figure de style. Des antiquités raffinées, des rideaux de soie et un personnel impeccable contribuent à son ambiance sélective. Les chambres luxueuses sont décorées individuellement avec des tissus français coordonnés aux papiers muraux. La table est divine tant sur la Terrace détendue qu'au restaurant gastronomique le Vardis, qui est le seul restaurant en Grèce ayant une étoile Michelin.

In einer ruhigen Wohngegend von Athen gelegen bietet dieses vortreffliche kleine Hotel Diskretion und einzigartigen Stil. Kostbare Antiquitäten, seidene Vorhänge und tadelloses Personal tragen zu diesem exklusiven Ambiente bei. Die luxuriösen Zimmer sind individuell mit französischen Stoffen und damit harmonisierenden Tapeten gestaltet. Köstliche Gerichte werden im informellen La Terrasse oder im Gourmetrestaurant Vardis serviert, das als einziges Restaurant in Griechenland mit einem Michelin-Stern glänzt.

Directions: Set in the suburb of Kifissia. **Price guide:** *Single Dr82,000; double/twin Dr96,000; suites Dr120,000–230,000.*

St Nicolas Bay Hotel

72100 AGIOS NIKOLAOS, CRETE, GREECE
TEL: +30 841 25041/2/3 FAX: +30 841 24556 E-MAIL: stnicolas@otenet.gr

Glorious gardens scented with flowers and bedecked with olive, lemon and orange trees surround this elegant Mediterranean bungalow hotel. With its own sandy beach in a tranquil seafront location, it offers excellent accommodation, mouth-watering cuisine and superb service. All rooms and suites enjoy stunning views from their balconies or terraces, whilst the suites have marble bathrooms with Jacuzzi, and some boast a private heated pool. Activities include watersports, scuba diving, gym, sauna, steambath, Jacuzzi and massage.

De magnifiques jardins remplis de fleurs et parsemés d'oliviers, de citronniers et d'orangers entourent cet élégant hôtel méditerranéen formé de plusieurs pavillons. Outre sa plage privée sur ce site tranquille de front de mer, l'hôtel offre un excellent logement, une table savoureuse et un service impeccable. Les chambres et suites possèdent des balcons ou des terrasses offrant une vue imprenable. Les suites, certaines avec piscine privée chauffée, ont des salles de bain en marbre avec Jacuzzi. Loisirs: sports nautiques, plongée, gymnase, sauna, hammam, Jacuzzi et massage.

Herrliche, mit Blumen und Oliven-, Zitronen- und Orangenbäumen gefüllte Gärten umgeben dieses elegante mediterrane Bungalow-Hotel. Ein eigener ruhiger Sandstrand steht zur Verfügung, und die köstliche Küche sorgt für kulinarische Genüsse. Service und Unterkunft sind hervorragend; die Zimmer und Suiten bieten vom Balkon oder der Terrasse aus traumhafte Ausblicke. Die Suiten, einige mit eigenem beheizten Pool, haben Marmorbad mit Jacuzzi. Freizeitaktivitäten sind Wassersport, Tauchen, Fitness, Sauna, Dampfbad, Whirlpool und Massage.

Directions: *Heraklion > Agios Nikolas*. **Price guide:** *Single Dr50,000–90,000; double/twin Dr70,000–120,000; suites Dr120,000–360,000.*

HOTEL CLUB MONTANA

36100 KARPENISI, GREECE
TEL: +30 237 80400/7 FAX: +30 237 80409

This idyllic hotel is situated in picturesque mountain surroundings sprinkled with the dark greens of high rising pine trees. It is perfect for summer leisure seekers, winter skiers and all those who enjoy an active break. With its sparkling white frontage, traditional décor and comfortable furnishings, the hotel offers a cosy ambience. Guests relax in lounges beside fireplaces or venture outdoors for trekking, rafting and canoeing.

Cet hôtel idyllique se dresse dans des montagnes pittoresques habitées de grands pins verts foncés. C'est l'étape idéale pour les visiteurs estivaux, les skieurs et tous ceux qui sont à la recherche d'un break actif. Une douce ambiance émane de l'hôtel, avec sa façade blanche éclatante, sa décoration traditionnelle et ses meubles confortables. Les clients peuvent se relaxer dans le salon avec ses cheminées ou s'aventurer à l'extérieur pour faire du trekking, du rafting et du canoe.

Dieses idyllische, von hohen Kiefern umsäumte Hotel liegt in einer malerischen Berg-umgebung. Es ist ein idealer Ort für Gäste, die sich erholen und aktiv betätigen wollen, und das sowohl im Sommer als auch im Winter. Mit einer weissen Aussenfassade, traditioneller Ausstattung und gemütlichem Mobiliar bietet das Hotel eine behagliche Atmosphäre. Die Gäste entspannen sich in den Salons mit offenen Kaminen oder geniessen sportliche Aktivitäten wie Wandern, Floss- oder Kanufahrten.

Directions: Athens-Lamia road > Athens-Karpenisi. **Price guide:** *Single Dr29,300; double/twin Dr38,800–45,700; suites Dr45,700–147,000.*

GRAND HOTEL COCUMELLA

VIA COCUMELLA, 7, 80065 SANT'AGNELLO, SORRENTO, ITALY
TEL: +39 081 878 2933 FAX: +39 081 878 3712 E-MAIL: hcocum@tin.it

This former Jesuit monastery was transformed into a hotel in 1822. Traces of the past remain; the elegant hall was once the cloisters and the chapel is still used for weddings and concerts. Many of the guest rooms have magnificent antique furnishings and the bridal suite has an exquisite painted ceiling. Guests feast on aromatic Mediterranean dishes, and in summer, light buffet lunches are enjoyed by the pool.

Cet ancien monastère jésuite a été transformé en hôtel en 1822. Les traces du passé sont encore présentes, le hall élégant occupe l'ancien cloître et la chapelle continue d'être utilisée pour des mariages ou des concerts. De magnifiques meubles anciens agrémentent les chambres et une peinture raffinée orne le plafond de la suite nuptiale. Les visiteurs dégustent des plats méditerranéens aux saveurs aromatiques l'été et des buffets légers sont proposés au bord de la piscine.

Dieses ehemalige Jesuitenkloster wurde 1822 zu einem Hotel umgebaut, und Spuren der Vergangenheit sind immer noch vorhanden. Die elegante Halle war einst der Kreuzgang und die Kapelle wird noch heute für Hochzeiten und Konzerte genutzt. Viele der Zimmer sind mit prächtigen Antikmöbeln eingerichtet und die Hochzeitssuite ziert eine beeindruckend bemalte Decke. Die Gäste erfreuen sich an köstlichen mediterranen Gerichten, und in den Sommermonaten sind leichte Buffetlunches am Pool zu geniessen.

Directions: *Naples>Castellammare di Stabia>Sorrento*. **Price guide:** *Single L350,000–470,000; double/twin L520,000–680,000; suites L700,000–1150,000.*

GRAND HOTEL EXCELSIOR VITTORIA

PIAZZA TASSO 34, 80067 SORRENTO (NAPLES), ITALY
TEL: +39 081 807 1044 FAX: +39 081 877 1206 E-MAIL: exvitt@exvitt.it

Built at the turn of the century and set on the Sorrento waterfront with its own moorings, the architecture of this fine hotel is graceful fin de siècle. The grounds are beautiful, filled with exotic subtropical plants and scented from the orange groves and olive trees. Guests can dine al fresco in the Restaurant Panoramico or enjoy the ambience in the grand Sala Vittoria restaurant, with its impressive marble pillars. The hotel boasts new health and fitness facilities.

Construit au début du siècle, l'Exelsior Vittoria se dresse sur le front de mer de Sorrente et dispose de ses propres mouillages. Cet hôtel raffiné se distingue par son élégante architecture de fin de siècle. Le parc est magnifique, rempli de plantes subtropicales et parfumé par des orangers et des oliviers. Les clients peuvent dîner alfresco au restaurant Panoramico ou profiter de l'ambiance du restaurant le Sala Vittoria avec ses piliers en marbre impressionnants. L'hôtel est fier de posséder un nouveau centre de santé et remise en forme.

Dieses herrliche Hotel im eleganten Fin-de-siècle-Stil wurde um die Jahrhundertwende erbaut und hat seinen eigenen Anlegeplatz direkt am Meer von Sorrento. Die herrlichen Gärten sind voll von exotischen subtropischen Pflanzen und dem zarten Duft von Orangen- und Olivenbäumen. Die Gäste können im Restaurant Panoramico im Freien oder im prachtvollen Sala Vittoria mit seinen beeindruckenden Marmorsäulen dinieren. Neue Gesundheits- und Fitnesseinrichtungen stehen ebenfalls zur Verfügung.

Directions: *A3>Castellammare di Stabia>Sorrento*. **Price guide**: *Single L370,000; double/twin L450,000–655,000; suites L840,000–2,900,000.*

TOSCO ROMAGNOLO

PIAZZA DANTE ALIGHIERI 2, 47021 BAGNO DI ROMAGNA TERME, ITALY
TEL: +39 0543 911260 FAX: +39 0543 911014 E-MAIL: hotel.tosco@comm2000.it

Situated in a small, ancient village and surrounded by fascinating landscape only a few miles from the Adriatic Sea, this traditional, family-run hotel offers pure relaxation. Friendly and welcoming, it provides comfortable, modern accommodation and refined cuisine. Guests can choose between two restaurants, the Tosco Romagnolo and the Paolo Teverini, which has received many awards for its exquisite cuisine and wide selection of fine wines. For those wishing to be pampered, there is an extensive beauty farm and health centre.

Situé dans un vieux village, au milieu d'une contrée fascinante, à quelques kilomètres à peine de l'Adriatique, cet hôtel familial traditionnel est une invitation à la douceur de vivre. Dans un cadre accueillant, les visiteurs découvrent des chambres modernes confortables et une cuisine raffinée, proposée par deux restaurants différents, le Tosco Romagnolo et le Paolo Teverini. Ce dernier a obtenu maintes distinctions pour ses plats exquis et son grand choix d'excellents vins. Des soins attentifs sont dispensés par un vaste centre de beauté et de remise en forme.

In einem kleinen, alten Dorf nur wenige km von der Adria entfernt gelegen und von faszinierender Landschaft umgeben bietet dieses traditionelle, familiengeführte Hotel reinste Erholung in freundlicher Umgebung. Die Unterkunft ist komfortabel und modern, die Küche hervorragend. Man hat die Wahl zwischen zwei Restaurants, dem Tosco Romagnolo und dem Paolo Teverini, das mehrfach für seine exquisiten Gerichte und erlesenen Weine ausgezeichnet wurde. Eine umfassendes Schönheits- und Gesundheitszentrum steht ebenfalls zur Verfügung.

Directions: E45 from Cesena towards Perugia; exit Bagno di Romagna. **Price guide:** *Single L190,000–260,000; junior suites L280,000–450,000; suites L490,000–800,000.*

PALAZZO VIVIANI – CASTELLO DI MONTEGRIDOLFO

VIA ROMA, 38, 47837 MONTEGRIDOLFO (RN), ITALY
TEL: +39 0541 855350 FAX: +39 0541 855340 E-MAIL: montegridolfo@montegridolfo.com

This is an enchanting stone walled hotel standing majestically in a medieval village on top of a green hill which slopes gently down to the Adriatic sea. Surrounded by a beautiful garden, it commands panoramic views over a countryside sprinkled with abandoned fortresses, towers, ancient churches and innumerable historical sites. This is an ideal venue for those seeking a historical ambience amidst comfort and tranquillity.

Cet hôtel magique, protégé par un mur en pierre, est perché de façon imposante sur un village médiéval dont les vertes collines se jettent doucement dans la mer Adriatique. Entouré d'un superbe jardin, il domine des vues panoramiques sur le paysage parsemé de forteresses abandonnées, de tours, de vieilles églises et d'innombrables monuments historiques. Il s'agit là d'un endroit parfait pour le visiteur en quête d'ambiance historique, de confort et de paix.

Dieses märchenhafte, von einer Steinmauer umgebene Hotel liegt in einem mittelalterlichen Dorf majestätisch auf einem Hügel, der sanft bis zur Adria hinabführt. Von einem herrlichen Garten umgeben bietet es traumhafte Aussichten auf eine Landschaft, die mit Türmen, Festungen, alten Kirchen und unzähligen historischen Stätten gespickt ist. Ein idealer Ort für diejenigen, die ein historischen Ambiente sowie Komfort und Ruhe suchen.

Directions: *A14>Cattolica.* **Price guide:** *Single L250,000–300,000; double/twin L360,000–400,000; suites L450,000.*

ALBERGO ANNUNZIATA

PIAZZA REPUBBLICA 5, 44100 FERRARA, ITALY
TEL: +39 0532 201111 FAX: +39 0532 203233 E-MAIL: annunziata@tin.it

It is believed that Casanova stayed at this hotel over two centuries ago, and, as the Visitor Book testifies, it is now patronised by several artists and musicians. Whilst the interior is largely decorated in a contemporary fashion, the building preserves all its 18th century beams, providing a superb contrast with the modern nuances. The hotelier is an engineer with artistic talents, and the walls of the entrance hall are adorned with his creations.

On raconte que Casanova a séjourné dans cet hôtel il y a plus de deux siècles, et que, comme le précise le livre des visiteurs, l'hôtel est à présent fréquenté par divers artistes et musiciens. L'intérieur est décoré en style contemporain et le bâtiment a conservé ses poutres du XVIIIème siècle, qui offrent un superbe contraste avec les nuances modernes. L'hôtelier est un ingénieur à talents artistiques, et les murs du hall d'entrée sont ornés de ses créations.

Dieses Hotel, in dem sich angeblich Casanova vor über zwei Jahrhunderten aufhielt, beherbergt nun laut Gästebuch hauptsächlich Künstler und Musiker. Das Gebäude besitzt immer noch sein Balkenwerk aus dem 18. Jahrhundert und steht so in faszinierendem Kontrast zum Interieur, das weitgehend modern gehalten ist. Der Hotelier ist ein Ingenieur mit künstlerischer Neigung, und die Wände der Eingangshalle sind mit seinen Werken verziert.

Directions: A13 exit Ferrara Sud or Nord > town centre> follow signs. **Price guide:** Single L150,000–230,000; double/twin L250,000–330,000; suites L350,000–450,000.

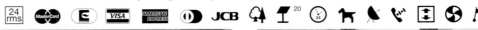

RIPAGRANDE HOTEL

VIA RIPAGRANDE 21, 44100 FERRARA, ITALY
TEL: +39 0532 765250 FAX: +39 0532 764377 E-MAIL: ripahotel@mbox.4net.it

This superbly restored XV century palace features a Renaissance interior, appropriate to the history of the hotel, and the entrance hall is spectacular with its marble staircase and pillars, wrought iron banisters and beamed ceiling. The attractive Ripa restaurant serves many traditional Ferrarese specialities. Two enchanting courtyards make wonderful settings for banquets. Guests relax in the cool salons or upon terraces, some of which are privately adjoined to the spacious bedrooms.

Ce palais du XVème siècle superbement restauré est agrémenté d'un intérieur Renaissance. Le hall d'entrée est spectaculaire en raison de sa cage d'escalier orné d'une rampe en fer forgé, de ses colonnes en marbre et de son plafond orné de poutres. Le charmant restaurant Ripa sert nombre de spécialités traditionnelles de Ferrare. Enfin, deux délicieuses cours forment un cadre idéal pour les banquets. Les hôtes peuvent se relaxer dans les salons ou sur les terrasses, dont certaines privées rejoignent les chambres spacieuses.

Das Interieur dieses hervorragend restaurierten Palais aus dem 15. Jahrhundert ist im Renaissance-Stil gehalten und passt somit zur Geschichte des Hotels. Die Eingangshalle beeindruckt mit Marmortreppe, und -säulen, schmiedeeisernen Geländern und einer Balkendecke. Das Restaurant Ripa serviert zahlreiche traditionelle Spezialitäten aus Ferrara, und zwei zauberhafte Innenhöfe sind perfekt für Bankette. Die kühlen Salons und die Terrassen – einige davon privat – laden zum Entspannen ein.

Directions: A13>Ferrara. **Price guide:** *Single L250,000; double/twin L320,000; suites L340,000–380,000.*

LA POSTA VECCHIA

PALO LAZIALE – 00055 LADISPOLI, (ROME), ITALY
TEL: +39 0699 49501 FAX: +39 0699 49507 E-MAIL: info@postavecchia.com

This superb 17th century villa, overlooking the sea and six hectares of lovely parkland, is built on 2000 year old foundations. Much of its original structure, including some stone doorways and fireplaces, has been preserved and some ancient mosaics can be viewed in the small Roman museum on the ground floor of the hotel. Guests may enjoy the private beach and other excellent leisure facilities on site or nearby.

Cette superbe villa du XVIIème siècle, surplombant la mer et 6 hectares de parc magnifique, est construite sur des fondations dâtant de plus de 2000 ans. Une bonne partie de sa structure originale, dont quelques portes en pierre et des cheminées ont été préservées. D'anciennes mosaïques peuvent être contemplées dans le petit musée romain au rez-de-chaussée de l'hôtel. Les visiteurs pourront profiter de la plage privée et d'autres équipements de loisirs mis à leur disposition sur place ou à proximité.

Diese superbe Villa aus dem 17. Jahrhundert, die auf einem 2000 Jahre alten Fundament erbaut wurde, liegt inmitten von 6 ha herrlichster Parklandschaft mit Blick zum Meer. Viel von ihrer ursprünglichen Form wurde erhalten, darunter einige Türöffnungen und Kamine aus Stein, und in dem kleinen römischen Museum im Erdgeschoss kann man ein altes Mosaik bestaunen. Ein Privatstrand lädt zum Sonnenbad ein, und weitere Freizeitmöglichkeiten können vor Ort oder in nächster Nähe genutzt werden.

Directions: A12>Torre in Pietra>SSI North>37 km. **Price guide:** *Double/twin L600,000; suites L1,600,000.*

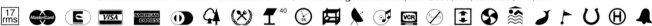

HOTEL FARNESE

VIA ALESSANDRO FARNESE, 30 (ANGOLO VIALE GIULIO CESARE), 00192 ROME, ITALY
TEL: +39 06 321 25 53/4 FAX: +39 06 321 51 29

An aristocratic 19th century villa, set in a quiet tree-lined residential area, the Hotel Farnese features graceful archways and elegant classical Italian furniture, chandeliers from Murano and decorative frescos, colourful rugs and fine antiques. A buffet breakfast is the only meal served in the subterranean dining room, but drinks will be brought to the terrace overlooking St Peters Cupola.

Villa aristocratique du XIXème siècle et située dans un quartier résidentiel paisible aux rues bordées d'arbres, l'Hôtel Farnese est remplie de superbes voûtes, de meubles italiens classiques et élégants, de lustres de Murano, de fresques décoratives, de tapis colorés et de beaux objets anciens. Seul le petit déjeuner-buffet est servi dans la salle à manger en sous-sol mais des boissons vous seront amenées à toute heure sur la terrasse dont la vue donne sur le dôme de Saint-Pierre.

Das Hotel Farnese, eine aristokratische Villa aus dem 19. Jahrhundert, ist in einer ruhigen und von Bäumen umsäumten Wohngegend gelegen und mit zierlichen Torbögen, elegantem, klassischen italienischen Mobiliar, Murano-Lüstern und dekorativen Fresken, bunten Teppichen und erlesenen Antiquitäten geschmückt. Im Untergeschoss wird ein Frühstücksbuffet serviert, und Getränke werden auf der Terrasse mit Ausblick auf die Kuppel des Petersdoms eingenommen.

Directions: *Lepanto Metro station.* **Price guide:** *Single L290,000–340,000; double/twin L420,000–500,000; junior suites L530,000.*

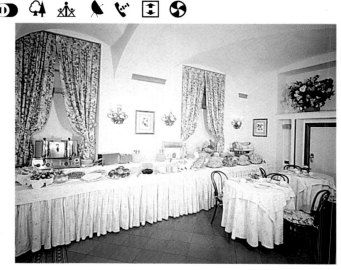

HOTEL GIULIO CESARE

VIA DEGLI SCIPIONI 287, 00192 ROME, ITALY
TEL: +39 06 321 0751 FAX: +39 06 321 1736 E-MAIL: giulioce@uni.net

The Giulio Cesare, situated close to some of the most glorious streets in Rome, is the essence of comfort. Offering its guests a unique blend of hospitality, relaxation and excellent service, this 18th century neo-classical hotel is ideal for either business or pleasure. The intimate bar is delightful with a fine collection of wines. Whilst there is no restaurant, sumptuous dishes are served at all times of the day in the bar and garden.

Le Giulio Cesare, proche des rues les plus prestigieuses de Rome, est la quintessence du confort. Offrant un degré exceptionnel d'hospitalité, de détente et de qualité de service, cet hôtel néo-classique est idéal pour les voyageurs d'affaires comme pour les touristes. Le bar intime est charmant et offre une palette de grands vins exceptionnelle. Bien qu'il n'y ait pas de restaurant, de succulents plats sont servis à toute heure de la journée dans le bar ou dans le jardin.

Das Giulio Cesare liegt in der Nähe einiger der prachtvollsten Strassen Roms und ist der Inbegriff von Komfort. Mit seiner einzigartigen Mischung aus Gastfreundschaft, Entspannung und exzellentem Service ist dieses neoklassiche Hotel aus dem 18. Jahrhundert ideal sowohl für Urlauber als auch Geschäftsreisende. Die intime Bar wartet mit einer erlesenen Auswahl an Weinen auf. Zwar besitzt das Hotel kein Restaurant, doch in der Bar oder im Garten werden rund um die Uhr verlockende Speisen serviert.

Directions: *Lepanto tube.* **Price guide:** *Single L440,000; double/twin L540,000.*

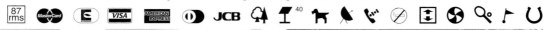

Romantik Hotel Barocco

PIAZZA BARBERINI, 9, 00187 ROME, ITALY
TEL: +39 06 48 72 001 FAX: +39 06 48 59 94 E-MAIL: hotelbarocco@hotelbarocco.it

This delightful intimate hotel is situated in the centre of Rome. Its architecture indicates that it was built during the 19th century art deco era. Lovely warm cherrywood dominates the interior décor in the fin de siècle entrance hall and in the bedrooms. The bathrooms are luxuriously furnished in marble. Guests can enjoy drinks at the small bar, and there is a breakfast room on the ground floor.

Cet hôtel de charme à l'atmosphère intime est situé dans le centre de Rome. Son architecture indique qu'il date de la période Art Déco du XIXème siècle. L'acajou chaleureux et superbe domine le hall d'entrée de décoration fin de siècle et les chambres. Les salles de bain sont luxieusement meublées et décorées en marbre. Le clients peuvent prendre un verre au petit bar, et il y a également une salle de petit déjeuner au rez de chaussée.

Dieses zauberhafte und persönliche Hotel liegt im Zentrum von Rom. Seine Architektur verrät, dass es im 19. Jahrhundert während der Art-Déco-Ära erbaut wurde. Wundervoll warmes Kirschholz prägt das Innendekor in der Fin-de-Siècle-Eingangshalle wie auch die Zimmer. Die Bäder sind luxuriös und in Marmor gehalten. In der kleinen Bar können die Gäste Drinks zu sich nehmen, oder sich im Frühstücksraum im Erdgeschoss stärken.

Directions: *Located where Via Barberini meets the Via del tritone and Via Veneto.* **Price guide:** *Single/double/twin L290,000–550,000; suites on request.*

HOTEL PUNTA EST

VIA AURELIA 1, 17024 FINALE LIGURE, ITALY
TEL: +39 019 600611 FAX: +39 019 600611

Set in a late 18th century Genovese villa, the Hotel Punta Est has enjoyed a rich and cultured past. The former summer residence of Professor Delachi, composer and musician at the Scala of Milan, was transformed into a four star hotel in 1971. The property, which offers excellent accommodation and superb facilities, is an ideal venue for family holidays as guests may relax by the outdoor pool or on the beach.

Situé dans une vieille villa génoise du début du XVIIIème siècle, l'hôtel Punta Est a un passé riche en culture. Ancienne résidence estivale du Professeur Delachi, compositeur et musicien à la Scala de Milan, la villa a été transformée en hôtel 4 étoiles en 1971. La propriété, qui offre un logement excellent et un service hors-pair, est un endroit idéal pour des vacances familiales. Les visiteurs peuvent se relaxer tant à la piscine extérieure qu'au bord de la plage.

Das Hotel Punta Est, eine Genoveser Villa aus dem späten 18. Jahrhundert, ist von einer langen und kulturreichen Geschichte geprägt. Die ehemalige Sommerresidenz des Professor Delachi, Komponist und Musiker an der Mailänder Scala, wurde 1971 in ein 4-Sterne-Hotel umgewandelt, das nun hervorragende Unterkunft und Einrichtungen bietet. Das Hotel ist ideal für Familien – Gross und Klein kann sich am Swimmingpool oder am Strand vergnügen und entspannen.

Directions: *Genoa > Autostrada A10 > San Remo > Finale Ligure.* **Price guide:** *Single L250,000; double/twin L400,000; suite L400,000–800,000.*

GRAND HOTEL VILLA BALBI

VIALE RIMEMBRANZA 1, 16039 SESTRI LEVANTE (GE), ITALY
TEL: +39 0185 42941 FAX: +39 0185 482459 E-MAIL: villabalbi@pn.inet.it

Built as a summer palace in the 17th century, this hotel overlooks the spectacular Gulf of Tigullio. The charming bedrooms are decorated in tranquil colours, all having lovely views over the water or the park. The Il Parco Restaurant specialises in Ligurian dishes and fish straight from the sea. With such peaceful surroundings, marvellous views, the pool and private beach, guests seldom leave the site, but golf and tennis are nearby.

Construit pour servir de résidence d'été au XVIIème siècle, la Villa Balbi surplombe le spectaculaire Golfe de Tigullio. Les ravissantes chambres sont décorées avec des couleurs douces et jouissent de belles vues sur la mer ou le parc. Le restaurant Il Parco propose principalement des plats liguriens et du poisson fraîchement pêché. Grâce à ce cadre merveilleux, aux vues magnifiques, à la piscine et à la plage privée, les visiteurs n'ont guère besoin de quitter l'hôtel, sauf peut-être pour jouer au golf ou au tennis à proximité.

Im 17. Jahrhundert als Sommerpalast erbaut, bietet dieses Hotel einen traumhaften Ausblick über den Golf von Tigullio. Die charmanten Zimmer sind in sanften Farben eingerichtet und haben alle eine herrliche Sicht auf das Meer oder den Park. Das Restaurant Il Parco ist auf ligurische Gerichte und fangfrischen Fisch spezialisiert. Bei einer so bezaubernden Umgebung – Pool und Privatstrand sind ebenfalls vorhanden – verlassen die Gäste das Gelände nur selten, doch Golf und Tennis sind in der Nähe möglich.

Directions: A12>Sestri Levante>Centro Città. **Price guide:** *Single L90,000–210,000; double/twin L190,000–320,000; suites L350,000–480,000.*

ALBERGO TERMINUS

LUNGO LARIO TRIESTE, 14–22100 COMO, ITALY
TEL: +39 031 329111 FAX: +39 031 302550 E-MAIL: larioterminus@galactica.it

This fine example of turn-of-the-century architecture has a spectacular view across Lake Como. The hall impresses with tall pillars and carved balustrade, and all the spacious reception rooms have beautiful ceilings, graceful period furniture and handsome paintings. The bedrooms, some designated non-smoking, have soundproof doors and windows and air conditioning. There is a gymnasium, sauna and massage facilities.

Cet exemple raffiné d'architecture de début de siècle jouit de vues spectaculaires sur le lac de Côme. Le hall est imposant avec ses grandes colonnes et sa balustrade sculptée. Les salons spacieux se distinguent par de magnifiques plafonds, des meubles d'époque élégants et de beaux tableaux. Les chambres, dont certaines sont non-fumeur, sont équipées de portes et de fenêtres insonorisées et sont climatisées. L'hôtel dispose d'un gymnase, d'un sauna et de services de massages.

Dieses hervorragende Beispiel für Architektur der Jahrhundertwende bietet eine herrliche Sicht über den Comer See. Die Eingangshalle beeindruckt mit hohen Säulen und einem geschnitzten Geländer, und jeder der grossen Empfangsräume hat zauberhaft verzierte Decken und ist mit eleganten Stilmöbeln und schönen Bildern gefüllt. Die Zimmer – einige designiert für Nichtraucher – haben schalldichte Fenster und Türen sowie Klimaanlage. Ausserdem stehen Fitnessraum, Sauna und Massage zur Verfügung.

Directions: *Switzerland>A9>Como Nord>Lungo Lario>Cattaneo Street>Lecco Bergamo.* **Price guide:** *Single L195,000–240,000; double/twin L240,000–356,000; suites L500,000–680,000.*

PrimaHotels

HOTEL VILLA FLORI

VIA CERNOBBIO, 22100 COMO, ITALY
TEL: +39 031 33820 FAX: +39 031 570379 E-MAIL: *lariovillaflori@galactica.it*

Built on the spot where General Garibaldi married his Giuseppina, this traditional hotel is in a superb position on the edge of Lake Como, set against a backdrop of its own verdant park, fragrant from orange and lemon trees. It has its own landing stage for guests arriving by yacht or motor boats. 18th century splendour is omnipresent with draped windows, decorated ceilings and chandeliers adorning the salons.

Construit à l'endroit où le Général Garibaldi épousa Giuseppina, cet hôtel traditionnel est placé de façon fantastique au bord du lac de Côme. Il se dresse sur le flanc de son parc verdoyant, qui embaume d'orangers et de citronniers. L'hôtel dispose même de son propre appontement, idéal pour les visiteurs arrivant en voilier ou en bateau à moteur! Le faste du XVIIIème siècle est omniprésent dans tout l'hôtel avec des tentures ornant les fenêtres, des plafonds décorés et des lustres dans les salons.

Dieses traditionelle Hotel wurde am Ufer des Comer Sees erbaut, an der Stelle, an der General Garibaldi seine Giuseppina ehelichte. Den Hintergrund bildet ein üppiger Park, der das Aroma von Orangen- und Zitronenbäumen versprüht. Überall ist die Pracht des 18. Jahrhunderts spürbar, und kunstvolle Vorhänge, prunkvoll verzierte Decken und Lüster zieren die Aufenthaltsräume. Diejenigen, die per Yacht oder Motorboot anreisen, können direkt an der hoteleigenen Anlegestelle an Land gehen.

Directions: A9>Como North>Como. **Price guide:** *Single L220,000–283,000; double/twin L240,000–356,000; suites L570,000.*

ALBERGO SAN LORENZO

PIAZZA CONCORDIA 14, 46100 MANTOVA, ITALY
TEL: +39 0376 220500 FAX: +39 0376 327194 E-MAIL: hotel@hotelsanlorenzo.it

The Albergo San Lorenzo is a city hotel widely reputed to be the best in Mantua. A pastel green colour scheme dominates the interior, with antique furniture and interesting period pieces adorning the spacious and comfortable lounge. The serene and stylish bedrooms feature every modern comfort. Overlooking the magnificent St Andrews cathedral, the terrace is often frequented by guests wishing to indulge in an afternoon beverage and enjoy the glorious panoramic vista.

L'Albergo San Lorenzo est un hôtel citadin réputé comme étant le meilleur de Mantoue. Le vert pastel est la couleur dominante à l'intérieur. Le salon, confortable et spacieux, est orné de meubles anciens et d'objets d'époque fascinants. Les chambres, au calme et décorées avec élégance, offrent tout le confort moderne. La terrasse, surplombant la somptueuse cathédrale de Saint André, est souvent fréquentée par les hôtes désirant boire quelque chose en cours d'après-midi et admirer le superbe panorama.

Das Albergo San Lorenzo gilt als das beste Hotel der Stadt. Das Interieur ist in einem pastellgrünen Farbton gehalten, und der geräumige und gemütliche Salon ist mit antiken Gegenständen und interessanten Stilmöbeln ausgestattet. Die freundlichen und eleganten Zimmer bieten jeglichen modernen Komfort. Die Terrasse überblickt die prachtvolle St.-Andreas-Kathedrale und ist ideal für einen Nachmittagsdrink bei herrlicher Aussicht.

Directions: *Exit 22 > Mantova Nord > central roundabout.* **Price guide:** *Single L300,000; double/twin L360,000; suites L330,000–420,000.*

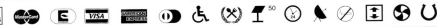

CAPITOL MILLENNIUM

VIA CIMAROSA 6, 20144 MILANO, ITALY
TEL: +39 02 438591 FAX: +39 02 4694724 E-MAIL: capitol@tin.it

Close to Leonardo Da Vinci's masterpiece, The Last Supper, and in the heart of Milan's prestigious residential area, guests will enjoy the attention to detail and elegance of this exquisite hotel. All bathrooms are held in marble and feature a Jacuzzi. The restaurant serves succulent Italian specialities and low calorie dishes, whilst the bar offers delicious cocktails. There is a fully equipped fitness centre with the option of a personal trainer, athletic massage or shiatsu massage.

Au coeur du prestigieux quartier résidentiel de Milan, à proximité de la Cène, le chef-d'oeuvre de Léonard de Vinci, les voyageurs découvrent un hôtel exquis dont l'élégance s'appuie sur un grand souci du détail. Les salles de bains sont habillées de marbre et dotées d'un jacuzzi. Le restaurant propose des spécialités italiennes irrésistibles et des plats allégés, et le bar prépare des cocktails délicieux. Massages et shiatsu vous attendent dans le centre de culture physique, qui met aussi un entraîneur personnel à votre disposition.

In der Nähe von Leonardo da Vinci's 'Abendmahl' und im Herzen von Mailands feinster Wohngegend liegt dieses elegante, prachtvolle Hotel. Liebe zum Detail zeigt sich auch in den Marmorbädern, die alle einen Jacuzzi besitzen. Im Restaurant werden verlockende italienische Spezialitäten sowie kalorienarme Küche serviert, und die Bar lädt zu einem köstlichen Cocktail ein. Ein vollausgestattetes Fitnesszentrum mit persönlichem Trainer und Sport- oder Shiatsu-massage steht ebenfalls zur Verfügung.

Directions: Follow directions to Milano Fiere > hotel is near Corso Vercelli. **Price guide**: *Single L318,000–375,000; double/twin L390,000–520,000; suites L600,000–700,000.*

HOTEL AURIGA

VIA PIRELLI 7, 20124 MILAN, ITALY
TEL: +39 02 66 98 58 51 FAX: +39 02 66 98 06 98 E-MAIL: auriga@auriga-milano.com

Built in the 1950s, the recent addition of a new marble façade has brought the Hotel Auriga into the nineties. Set in the centre of Milan, this fine property features every contemporary convenience whilst affording many luxurious nuances. The interior has been decorated in bold colours reflecting Milan's sunny climate. The comfortable bedrooms are well-apointed and the bathrooms spacious and decorated in marble.

Construit en 1950, l'ajout récent d'une façade en marbre a apporté à l'hôtel Auriga une aura des années 1990. Situé au centre de Milan, cette propriété raffinée comprend tout les équipements modernes tout en offrant nombre de gadgets luxueux. L'intérieur fût décoré en couleurs vives pour refléter le climat milanais. Les chambres confortables sont bien équipées et les salles de bain spacieuses sont décorées en marbre.

Die erst kürzlich erneuerte Marmorfassade macht das Auriga, das in den 50er Jahren erbaut wurde, ein Hotel der 90er. Im Zentrum von Mailand gelegen, bietet dieses Hotel jede moderne Annehmlichkeit und zahlreiche luxuriöse Feinheiten. Das Interieur ist in leuchtenden Farben gehalten, die Mailands sonniges Ambiente perfekt widerspiegeln. Die gemütlichen Zimmer sind gut ausgestattet, und die Badezimmer geräumig und in Marmor gehalten.

Directions: *Milano Centrale railway.* **Price guide:** *Single L290,000; double/twin L390,000; suites L450,000.*

RELAIS VILLA POMELA

VIA SERRAVALLE 69, 15067 NOVI LIGURE (AL), ITALY
TEL: +39 0143 329910 FAX: +39 0143 329912 E-MAIL: dopomela@tin.it

Set on a hill in the verdant countryside of Northern italy, the Villa Pomela with its elegant façade and high roof resembles an ancient medieval castle. Guests may dine in the two interlocking rooms of the Al Cortese restaurant which leads on to the fine jardin d'hiver. The impressive menu comprises a fusion of local Mediterranean delicacies with some international flavours.

Perchée sur une colline de la campagne verdoyante du nord de l'Italie, la Villa Pomela, avec son élégante façade et son toit pointu, ressemble à un ancien château médiéval. Les hôtes peuvent dîner dans les deux salles communicantes du restaurant Al Cortese qui donne sur un jardin d'hiver raffiné. L'impressionnant menu offre un mélange de mets méditerranéens de la région et de saveurs internationales.

Die Villa Pomela liegt auf einem Hügel inmitten grüner Landschaft im Norden Italiens und ähnelt mit ihrer eleganten Fassade und dem hohen Dach einer mittelalterlichen Burg. Die Gäste dinieren in den zwei miteinander verbundenen Räumen des Restaurants Al Cortese, das auf einen zauberhaften Wintergarten hinausführt. Die eindrucksvolle Speisekarte bietet eine köstliche Mischung aus regionaler Mittelmeerküche und internationalen Gerichten.

Directions: *A7>Serravalle>Scrivia>Novi Ligure.* **Price guide:** *Single L200,000; double/twin L295,000; suites L400,000.*

HOTEL VICTORIA

VIA NINO COSTA 4, 10123 TORINO, ITALY
TEL: +39 011 5611909 FAX: +39 011 5611806 E-MAIL: reservation@hotelvictoria–torino.com

This charming family-run town house hotel is spacious, airy and – despite its central location – quiet and peaceful. Throughout the interior, a light shade of green predominates, and an abundance of plants and flowers adds an extra personal touch to the surroundings. The public rooms are bedecked with lovely antiques which the hotel's owners have acquired during their travels throughout the world. A delightful breakfast room overlooks a colourful internal courtyard, and fine local cuisine may be sampled in numerous restaurants in the vicinity.

Ce charmant hôtel sous forme de maison de ville familiale est spacieux, aéré et, en dépit de sa localisation centrale, tranquille et paisible. A l'intérieur, une nuance douce de verts domine, et une abondance de plantes et de fleurs ajoute une touche personnelle à l'atmosphère. Les salles communes sont ornées de superbes antiquités que les propriétaires de l'hôtel ont acquis durant leurs voyages autour du monde.La salle de petit déjeuner s'ouvre sur la cour intérieure, riche en couleurs, et la cuisine locale peut être dégustée dans les nombreux restaurants aux alentours.

Dieses charmante familiengeführte Hotel ist luftig und geräumig und – trotz seiner zentralen Lage – absolut ruhig. Im ganzen Haus dominiert ein hellgrüner Farbton, und üppige Pflanzen- und Blumenarrangements sorgen für eine persönliche Note. Die Aufenthaltsräume sind voll von feinsten Antiquitäten, die die Besitzer von ihren zahlreichen Reisen um die ganze Welt mitgebracht haben. Der Frühstücksraum überblickt einen farbenfrohen Innenhof, und zahlreiche Restaurants in der Nähe locken mit feinster italienischer Küche.

Directions: *A4>Turin/Torino>Centro citta.* **Price guide:** *Single L180,000–220,000; double/twin L260,000–290,000; suites L335,000.*

HOTEL VILLA PARADISO DELL'ETNA

VIA PER VIAGRANDE 37, 95037 SAN GIOVANNI LA PUNTA, ITALY
TEL: +39 095 7512409 FAX: +39 095 7413861 E-MAIL: hotelvilla@paradisoetna.it

Built in 1927 and frequented by artists and well-known personalities, this grand hotel exudes sophistication and opulence. The façade is elegant with its pillars, wrought iron balconies and tall windows. The surrounding grounds are beautiful and the sight of the volcano from the Roof Garden is breathtaking. Fine antiques, traditional comfortable seating, art deco stained glass and cheeky cherubs add to the stylish ambience.

Construit en 1927 et fréquenté par des artistes et des personnalités célèbres, cet hôtel prestigieux dégage sophistication et opulence. Son élégante façade est ornée de colonnes, de balcons en fer forgé et de grandes fenêtres. Le parc environnant est magnifique et la vue sur le volcan depuis le jardin sur le toit, est époustouflante. De beaux objets anciens, des sièges confortables traditionnels, des vitraux Art déco et des chérubins espiègles contribuent à son atmosphère stylée.

Dieses 1927 erbaute feine Hotel wurde bereits von Künstlern und bekannten Persönlichkeiten besucht, und besitzt eine elegante und opulente Atmosphäre. Die Fassade beeindruckt mit Säulen, schmiedeeisernen Balkonen und grossen Fenstern. Die umgebende Landschaft ist einfach herrlich, und vom Dachgarten hat man eine atemberaubende Sicht auf den Ätna. Erlesene Antiquitäten, traditionelle, gemütliche Sessel, Art-Deco-Buntglas und rundliche Cherubim tragen zum stilvollen Ambiente bei.

Directions: A18>San Gregorio>San Giovanni La Punta. **Price guide:** *Single L280,000; double/twin L380,000; suites L510,000.*

HELLENIA YACHTING HOTEL

VIA JANNUZZO 41, 98035 GIARDINI NAXOS (ME) ITALY
TEL: +39 (0)942 51737 FAX: +39 (0)942 54310 E-MAIL: booking@hotel–hellenia.it

Situated on the sandy beach of Giardini Naxos, this hotel is the ideal place to relax and unwind. Many of the cool and bright rooms have a balcony or terrace. The reception is well lit and spacious, and well-equipped conference rooms are available for meetings and private celebrations. Succulent Sicilian cuisine can be enjoyed in the elegant restaurant. There is also a poolside bar and a wonderful private beach, whilst the energetic visitor may enjoy windsurfing, hire a boat or play golf.

Situé sur la plage sablonneuse de Giardini Naxos, cet hôtel est idéal pour se détendre. Bon nombre des chambres claires et fraîches s'ouvrent sur une terrasse ou un balcon privés. La réception est spacieuse et bien éclairée, et des salles de congrès bien équipées sont disponibles pour les réunions et les réceptions privées. Une cuisine sicilienne succulente est servie dans l'élégant restaurant. L'hôtel compte aussi une piscine avec bar et une belle plage privée. Les visiteurs peuvent jouer au golf, faire de la planche à voile ou louer un bateau.

Dieses am Strand von Giardini Naxos gelegene Hotel ist der ideale Ort für völlige Entspannung. Viele der kühlen, hellen Zimmer sind mit Balkon oder Terrasse ausgestattet. Die Rezeption ist hell und geräumig, und gut ausgestatte Konferenzräume stehen für Geschäftveranstaltungen und private Feiern zur Verfügung. Das elegante Restaurant bietet köstliche sizilianische Spezialitäten, daneben gibt es einen Swimmingpool mit Bar sowie einen herrlichen Privatstrand. Sportbegeisterte können zwischen Windsurfen, Bootsverleih und Golf wählen.

Directions: *A18 exit Giardini Naxos > Recanati > follow signs.* **Price guide:** *Single L180,000–264,000; double/twin L270,000–408,000; suites L370,000–500,000.*

HOTEL BAIA TAORMINA

STATALE DELLO IONIO 39, 98030 MARINA D'AGRO (ME), ITALY
TEL: +39 0942 756292 FAX: +39 0942 756603

Overlooking the beautiful Baia di Taormina, this peaceful, brand new hotel is built on a cliff that gently slopes down to the sea. With its wide arches and terraces and the use of local materials, the hotel blends perfectly with its surroundings. All bedrooms have views over the sea and are furnished according to local tradition. Excellent cuisine is accompanied by live music on the terrace. For leisure, guests enjoy the hotel's two swimming pools and a beauty centre specialising in thalassotherapy.

Cet hôtel tout neuf se dresse sur une falaise qui descend doucement vers la mer, d'où il domine la superbe baie de Taormina. Grâce à ses grandes arches, à ses terrasses et à l'usage de matériaux de la région, l'hôtel se fond harmonieusement dans le décor paisible. Les chambres offrent une vue sur la mer et sont meublées dans le style traditionnel de la région. Des repas savoureux accompagnés de musique se prennent sur la terrasse. L'hôtel comprend deux piscines et un centre de beauté spécialisé en thalassothérapie.

Dieses brandneue Hotel mit Blick auf die herrliche Bucht von Taormina liegt auf einer sanft zum Meer hinunterführenden Klippe. Mit seinen grosszügigen Torbögen und Terrassen und der Verwendung von einheimischen Materialien ist es perfekt an seine friedvolle Umgebung angepasst. Alle Zimmer bieten Meerblick und sind nach örtlicher Tradition eingerichtet. Köstliche Speisen werden zu Live-Musik auf der Terrasse serviert, und für Freizeitvergnügen sorgen zwei Swimmingpools und ein Thalassotherapie-Beautyzentrum.

Directions: Catania > A18 towards Messina, exit Taormina > Messina > Letojanni> Forza d'Agrò. **Price guide:** *Single L160,000–270,000; double/twin L250,000–450,000.*

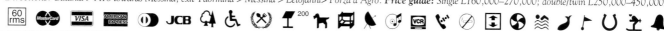

HOTEL ROMA

VIA MINERVA 10, 96100 SIRACUSA, ITALY
TEL: +39 0931 465626 FAX: +39 0931 465535 E-MAIL: info@hotelroma.sr.it

Dating back to 1880, the Hotel Roma maintains some of its original columns and vaults, but rooms are now elegantly furnished and offer all modern comforts. Located in Ortigia, in the heart of Siracusa, the hotel is the perfect base from which to explore the splendours of this historical and artistic centre close to Piazza Duomo with all its restaurants and bars. Hotel Roma has a warm family atmosphere, with a restaurant that serves both local and Italian dishes and international cuisine.

Cet hôtel qui date de 1880 a gardé certaines de ses colonnes et voûtes d'origine tout en adoptant un style élégant et les commodités du monde moderne. Situé sur Ortygie, au coeur de Syracuse, il constitue une base parfaite pour découvrir les splendeurs de ce quartier artistique historique, à deux pas de la Piazza Duomo où abondent les restaurants et les bars. L'hôtel Roma se distingue par une ambiance familiale accueillante. Son restaurant offre des plats locaux et italiens ainsi qu'une cuisine internationale.

Das auf das Jahr 1880 zurückgehende Hotel Roma hat sich einige seiner Originalsäulen und Gewölbe erhalten, doch alle Räume sind nun elegant möbliert und bieten jeden modernen Komfort. Das in Ortigia, im Herzen von Syrakus gelegene Hotel ist ideal zum Erkunden des historischen und künstlerischen Zentrums in der Nähe der Piazza Duomo mit ihrer Vielzahl von Restaurants und Bars. Das Hotel Roma besitzt eine freundliche Familienatmosphäre und ein Restaurant, das einheimische, aber auch italienische und internationale Küche bietet.

Directions: *Palermo A19 to Catania SS114 to Siracusa (about 50km)*. **Price guide:** *Single L240,000; double/twin L350,000; suite L450,000.*

HOTEL VILLA SANT' ANDREA

VIA NAZIONALE 137, 98030 TAORMINA MARE (ME), ITALY
TEL: +39 0942 23125 FAX: +39 0942 24838 E-MAIL: ricevimento.vsa@framon–hotels.com

This unique and gorgeous hotel was a private villa built in the 1830s and has retained its dignified ambience whilst being transformed into a small part of paradise on the bay of Mazzaro. Set right on the water's edge, the Sant' Andrea is protected by exotic tropical gardens. The elegant salon is peaceful, and watching the lights of the fishing fleet from the well-stocked piano bar is a pleasant way to spend an evening. Delicious cuisine is served in the two restaurants, L'Oliviero and the St Andrea.

Cet hôtel unique et magnifique fût originellement une villa privée construite dans les années 1830. Elle et a gardé son ambiance de l'époque lorsqu'elle a été transformée en petit coin de paradis sur la baie de Mazzaro. Située tout au bord de l'eau, le Sant' Andrea est entouré de jardins exotiques tropicaux. L'élégant salon est paisible et regarder les lumières des bateaux de pêcheurs depuis le sympathique piano bar est une excellente façon de passer une soirée. Une délicieuse cuisine est servie dans les deux restaurants, L'Oliviero et le St Andrea.

Dieses einzigartige, herrliche Hotel war ursprünglich eine private Villa, die in den 30er Jahren des 18. Jahrhunderts erbaut wurde. Beim Umbau in dieses paradiesische Anwesen an der Bucht von Mazzaro wurde das ursprüngliche Ambiente erhalten. Das Sant' Andrea liegt direkt am Wasser und ist durch exotische tropische Gärten von aussen abgeschirmt. Der elegante Salon ist eine Oase der Ruhe, und die gutbestückte Pianobar ein idealer Ort, um einen schönen Abend zu verbringen. Zwei Restaurants, L'Oliviero und das St Andrea sorgen für kulinarischen Genuss.

Directions: *Route 18>Taormina.* **Price guide:** *Single L220,000–345,000; double/twin L320,000–530,000; suites L120,000 supplement.*

ROMANTIK HOTEL OBERWIRT

ST FELIXWEG 2, 39020 MARLING-MERAN, ITALY
TEL: +39 0473 44 71 11 FAX: +39 0473 44 71 30 E-MAIL: oberwirt@dnet.it

An inn offering hospitality since the 15th century, this hotel has been owned by the Waldner family since 1749. Part of it has an even longer history, such as the outdoor pool in an original Roman design. The Tyrolean bar is very convivial, although on fine days guests may prefer to sip their apéritifs on the terrace, which is floodlit at night. Guests appreciate the fitness centre, with its indoor pool, sauna, Jacuzzi and massage facilities.

Cette auberge qui offre son hospitalité depuis le XVème siècle appartient à la famille Waldner depuis 1749. Une partie de l'hôtel a une histoire encore plus ancienne puisque la piscine extérieure est d'un design de l'époque romaine. Le bar tyrolien est convivial et les jours de beaux temps les clients pourront prendre un apéritif sur la terrace, illuminée la nuit. Les visiteurs apprécieront le centre de sport, avec sa piscine couverte, son sauna, son Jacuzzi et ses services de massage.

Dieses Hotel bietet seine Gastfreundschaft bereits seit dem 15. Jahrhundert an und befindet sich seit 1749 im Besitz der Familie Waldner. Teilweise hat es sogar eine längere Geschichte, wie man zum Beispiel am Freibad erkennen kann, das nach einem römischen Vorbild gebaut wurde. Die Tiroler Bar ist gemütlich und einladend, doch im Sommer nehmen die Gäste ihren Apéritif meist auf der Terrasse ein, die abends in Flutlicht getaucht ist. Für die Sportlichen gibt es einen Fitnessbereich mit Hallenbad, Sauna, Jacuzzi und Massage.

Directions: *Innsbruck Verona road>Bozen Sud>Meran>Marling.* **Price guide:** *Single L130,000–170,000; double/twin L250,000–300,000; suites L300,000–440,500.*

ROMANTIK HOTEL STAFLER

MAULS, 10, 39040 FREIENFELD NR STERZING (BZ), ITALY
TEL: +39 0 472 77 11 36 FAX: +39 0 472 77 10 94

This romantic hotel is built in the local style, against an impressive background of mountains – the perfect place to stop on a leisurely European tour. Succulent regional dishes based on local produce are prepared by the talented chef and wines from the area are recommended. This is a marvellous place for families, the big well-kept gardens providing room for the children to play while their parents relax in the sun.

Cet hôtel romantique, construit dans le style de la région, se profile sur un paysage impressionnant de montagnes. Il s'agit d'une étape idéale lorsqu'on fait tranquillement le tour de l'Europe. Des plats succulents régionaux basés sur les produits locaux sont préparés par un chef talentueux et des vins de la région vous seront recommandés. Cet endroit est merveilleux pour les familles, les enfants ont de la place pour jouer dans le grand jardin bien entretenu tandis les parents se détendent au soleil.

Dieses romantische Hotel wurde im regionstypischen Stil erbaut und bildet mit seiner Lage am Fusse eindrucksvoller Berge einen perfekten Aufenthaltsort auf einer Europareise. Der Koch verwendet einheimische Zutaten für seine köstlichen regionalen Gerichte, und empfiehlt dazu den passenden Wein. Das Hotel ist ideal für Familien; die Kinder können die weitläufigen Gärten erkunden, während sich die Eltern gemütlich ein Sonnenbad geniessen.

Directions: *A22>Brixen Bressanone>Brenner>Mauls.* **Price guide:** *Single L105,000–130,000; double/twin L170,000–220,000; suites L190,000–240,000.*

PARK HOTEL MIGNON

VIA GRABMAYR 5, 39012 MERANO, ITALY
TEL: +39 0473 230353 E-MAIL: info@hotelmignon.com

Close to the famous promenades of Merano and surrounded by its own green park, lies the family-run Park Hotel Mignon. The hotel is bright and harmoniously decorated with a relaxing and regenerating atmosphere. For those whishing to be pampered, the health and beauty centre offers personalised programmes and treatments. The excellent cuisine includes South Tyrolian and international dishes. In the evenings, guests may enjoy live music at the piano bar or in the garden by the swimming pool.

A proximité des célèbres promenades de Merano, cet hôtel familial entouré d'un parc verdoyant invite à se détendre dans un cadre lumineux et harmonieux. Qui souhaite se faire dorloter sera comblé par les programmes et les traitements personnalisés offerts par le centre de beauté et de remise en forme. Le menu savoureux est composé de spécialités du Haut-Adige et de plats internationaux. Le soir, les visiteurs se laissent bercer par la musique dans le piano-bar ou dans le jardin, au bord de la piscine.

In der Nähe der berühmten Meraner Promenaden und umgeben von seinem eigenen Park liegt das familiengeführte Park Hotel Mignon. Es ist hell und harmonisch eingerichtet und besitzt eine entspannende Atmosphäre. Wer sich verwöhnen lassen will, findet im Gesundheits- und Schönheitszentrum eine Reihe von individuellen Programmen und Behandlungen. Für kulinarischen Genuss sorgen köstliche Südtiroler und internationale Speisen, und abends erfreuen sich die Gäste an Live-Musik in der Pianobar oder im Garten am Pool.

Directions: *Brennero > exit Bolzano Sud > Merano Sud > Maia Alta*. **Price guide:** *Single L145,000–200,000; double/twin L290,000–400,000; suites L380,000–500,000.*

POSTHOTEL WEISSES RÖSSL

VIA CAREZZA 30, 39056 NOVA LEVANTE (BZ), DOLOMITES, ITALY
TEL: +39 0471 613113 FAX: +39 0471 613390 E-MAIL: posthotel@postcavallino.com

Situated at the end of the impressive Val d'Ega, at the heart of the Dolomites, lies this former staging post with its frescoed façades and flower-bedecked balconies. Since 1865, the Wiedenhofer Family has been welcoming guests, in winter for skiing and in summer for walking, climbing and golf in this alpine wonderland. Guests feast on exquisitely prepared Tyrolean and Italian dishes, accompanied by fine local wines from the cellar. Leisure facilities include outdoor and indoor swimming pool, Jacuzzi, sauna, steam bath and beauty salon.

Au bout de l'impressionnant Val d'Ega et en plein coeur des Dolomites est situé cet ancien relais avec ses façades en fresques et des balcons fleuris. Depuis 1865, la famille Wiedenhofer accueille les visiteurs dans cet environnement alpin merveilleux, pour le ski en hiver et pour la marche, l'escalade et le golf en été. Les hôtes se régalent de délicieux plats italiens et tyroliens accompagnés d'excéllents vins locaux trouvés dans la cave. Les équipements comprennent une piscine couverte et une en plein air, un Jacuzzi, sauna, hammam et salon de beauté.

Am Ende des eindrucksvollen Eggentales im Herzen der Dolomiten liegt diese ehemalige Poststation mit ihren verzierten Fassaden und blumengeschmückten Balkonen. Seit 1865 empfängt die Familie Wiedenhofer Gäste, die im Winter zum Skifahren und im Sommer zum Wandern, Bergsteigen und Golfen in diese herrliche Gegend kommen. Für kulinarischen Genuss sorgen exquisite Tiroler und italienische Gerichte und erlesene Weine aus dem Keller. Das Hotel bietet Hallen- und Freibad, Whirlpool, Sauna, Dampfbad und Schönheitssalon.

Directions: A22>Bolzano North>Val d'Ega-Lago di Carezza>Nova Levante. **Price guide:** *Single L130,000–200,000; double/twin L120,000–200,000; suites L170,000–400,000.*

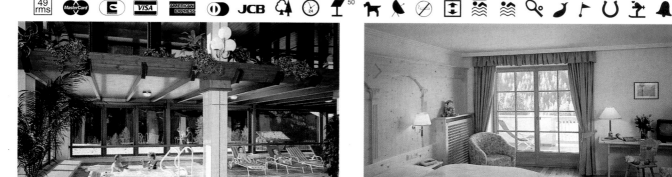

ROMANTIK HOTEL LE SILVE DI ARMENZANO

06081 LOC. ARMENZANO, ASSISI (PG), ITALY
TEL: +39 075 801 9000 FAX: +39 075 801 9005 E-MAIL: hotellesilve@tin.it

This small hotel dates back to before the birth of St Francis of Assisi, the patron saint of animals. Le Silve is 700 metres above sea level, built on a plateau at the foot of the Subasio mountains. The air is scented by olive groves, and deer and horses ramble through the beautiful countryside. Umbrian cooking is delicious and here, the bread is baked traditionally in the fireplace. A charming sense of unspoilt rural simplicity is created by touches such as alfresco dining and country furniture.

Ce petit hôtel dâte d'avant la naissance de Saint François d'Assise, le saint patron des animaux. Le Silve se situe à 700 mètres au dessus du niveau de la mer. Il a été construit sur un plateau, au pied des montagnes du Subasio. L'air y est parfumé par les oliveraies et des biches et des chevaux gambadent dans le magnifique parc. La cuisine ombrienne est délicieuse et le pain proposé est cuit de façon traditionnelle dans la cheminée. Le diner servi à l'extérieur et le mobilier de style campagnard dégagent un agréable sentiment de simplicité rurale.

Dieses kleine Hotel existierte bereits vor der Geburt von Franz von Assisi, dem Schutz-patron der Tiere. Es liegt 700 Meter über dem Meeresspiegel auf einem Plateau am Fusse der Subasio Berge und vom Duft der Olivenhaine umgeben. Wild und Pferde durchstreifen die herrliche Landschaft. Die Küche Umbriens ist einfach köstlich, und das Brot wird traditionell im Holzofen gebacken. Man spürt ein unbeschwertes Gefühl von ländlicher Schlichtheit, das durch rustikales Mobiliar und Essen unter freiem Himmel noch betont wird.

Directions: *Perugia>Assisi>s.75>Armenzo*. **Price guide:** *Single L150,000; double/twin L300.000.*

ALBERGO QUATTRO FONTANE

30126 LIDO DI VENEZIA, ITALY
TEL: +39 041 526 0227 FAX: +39 041 526 0726 E-MAIL: quafonve@tin.it

A distinctive country house set in an idyllic garden on the Lido amongst orchards and productive vineyards, away from the hustle and bustle of Venice, the Albergo is only ten minutes by water-bus from San Marco square. Signore Bevilacqua, whose family owned the property for over 40 years, has collected some very unusual antique furniture, art and artefacts from all over the world. Venetian specialities complement wine from local vineyards.

Maison de campagne raffinée dans un jardin idyllique sur le Lido, l'Albergo, avec ses vergers et ses vignobles, est à seulement 10 minutes en navette-bateau de la place Saint Marc. Le Signore Bevilacqua, dont la famille est propriétaire depuis plus de 40 ans, a collectionné des meubles, de l'art et des objets façonnés originaux provenant du monde entier. Des spécialités vénitiennes complètent la carte de vins des producteurs locaux.

Dieses herrliche Landhaus liegt in einem idyllischen Garten am Lido, umgeben von Obstplantagen und Weinbergen und fernab vom geschäftigen Treiben Venedigs, aber innerhalb von zehn Minuten per Boot vom Markusplatz zu erreichen. Signore Bevilacqua, dessen Familie das Hotel seit über 40 Jahren besitzt, hat eine Sammlung ungewöhnlicher Antiquitäten, Gemälde und Kunstgegenstände aus aller Welt. Für kulinarischen Genuss sorgen venezianische Spezialitäten und Weine aus einheimischen Weinbergen.

Directions: Lido via San Marco>Albergo. **Price guide:** Single L330,000–390,000; double/twin L450,000–575,000.

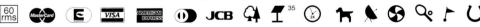

Latvia

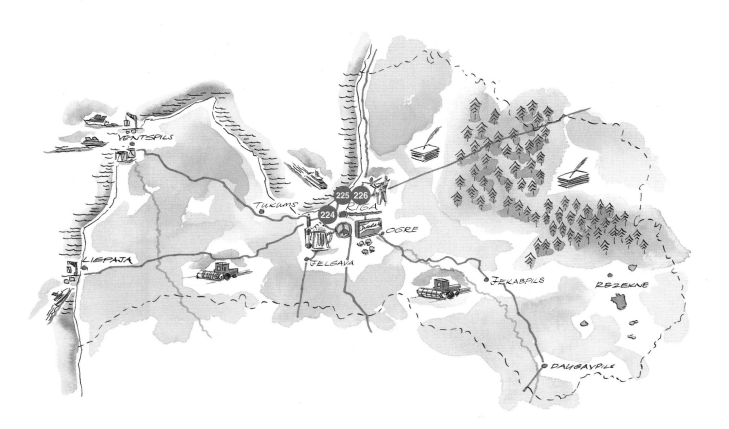

HOTEL DE ROME

KALKU STR. 28, RIGA, LV 1050, LATVIA
TEL: +371 7087600 FAX: +371 7087606 E-MAIL: reservation@derome.lv

Close to the commercial section of Riga, overlooking the city gardens and the Freedom Monument, the new Hotel de Rome has a splendid façade influenced by Latvia's art deco era. The interior is contemporary with spacious bedrooms, decorated in harmonious colours and comfortable furniture. Enjoy the legendary Otto Schwarz restaurant or indulge in opera music, played in the café Romas Operas Galerija.

Près du quartier commercial de Riga, le nouvel hôtel de Rome affiche une façade splendide influencée par l'Art déco letton. Il jouit d'une vue sur le parc de la ville et le monument de la liberté. L'intérieur est contemporain avec de grandes chambres, décorées en couleurs harmonieuses et garnies de meubles confortables. Allez découvrir le légendaire restaurant Otto Schwarz ou régalez vous des chants de l'opéra, joué dans le café Romas Operas Galerija.

Nahe des Geschäftsviertels von Riga gelegen und mit Blick über die Stadtgärten sowie das Freiheitsdenkmal, erstrahlt das neue Hotel de Rome mit seiner prächtigen, von der lettischen Art-Deco-Ära beeinflussten Fassade. Das Interieur ist zeitgenössisch, mit geräumigen Zimmern, die in harmonischen Farben gehalten und mit bequemen Möbeln eingerichtet sind. Das schon legendäre Restaurant Otto Schwarz ist ein Hochgenuss, und ebenso die Opernmusik im Café Romas Operas Galerija.

Directions: Ship/Plane/Train/Car > Riga. **Price guide:** Single LVL91; double/twin LVL100; suites LVL125.

HOTEL GRAND PALACE

PILS IELA 12, RIGA, LV 1050, LATVIA
TEL: +371 704 4000 FAX: +371 704 4001 E-MAIL: grandpalace@consul–hotels.com

This is a truly grand hotel surrounded by majestic historic buildings in the heart of the cobblestoned 15th century town of Riga. With a combined atmosphere of Old Russian and European it offers the highest standard of accommodation with many interesting touches. The 56 air-conditioned guestrooms and suites have every possible comfort and the general air of sheer elegance complements the award-winning cuisine served in the sumptuous Seasons restaurant and informal Orangerie.

Cet hôtel grandiose situé au coeur de la ville pavée du 15ème siècle de Riga est entouré de superbes bâtiments historiques. Combinant une atmosphère à la fois russe et européenne, Le Grand Palace offre un hébergement de la plus grande qualité avec de nombreux aspects originaux. Les 56 chambres et suites climatisées bénéficient de tout le confort possible. Une atmosphère d'élégance absolue règne et complète la cuisine, plusieurs fois primée, servie dans le magnifique restaurant Seasons ou à l'Orangerie, plus informelle.

Dieses prachtvolle Hotel liegt umgeben von majestätischen historischen Bauten und kopf-steingepflasterten Strassen im Herzen der über 500 Jahre alten Stadt Riga. Vom altrussischen sowie europäischen Stil beeinflusst, bietet es höchsten Standard an Unterkunft und zahlreiche interessante Details. Die 56 klimatisierten Zimmer und Suiten bieten jeglichen Komfort und das allgegenwärtige elegante Ambiente passt perfekt zu den mit Preisen ausgezeichneten Speisen, die im feinen Seasons Restaurant und in der informellen Orangerie serviert werden.

Directions: *Twenty minutes from the airport.* **Price guide:** *Single US$218.30; double/twin US$253.70.*

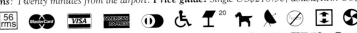

HOTEL "KONVENTA SETA"

KALEJU STR. 9/11, RIGA, LV 1050, LATVIA
TEL: +371 708 7501 FAX: +371 708 7515

The Konventa Seta is situated in the Latvian capital of Riga, an 800 year-old Hanseatic city on the banks of the Daugava. Behind the historical façade lie 80 rooms and 60 apartments, pleasantly furnished with contemporary comfort. Elements of the past mingle harmoniously with the modern whilst creating a sense of bygone days. The cosy bar features Latvian paintings and mouthwatering dishes are served in the intimate restaurant.

Le Konventa Seta se situe à Riga, capitale de la Lettonie et ville hanséatique vieille de 800 ans installée sur les berges de la Dangava. La façade historique cache 80 chambres et 60 appartements, agréablement meublés et agrémentés de tout le confort moderne. Des éléments du passé se mélangent harmonieusement avec le contemporain, tout en créant une ambiance surannée. Le confortable bar est décoré de peintures lettones et le restaurant intime offre des plats appétissants.

Das Konventa Seta liegt in Lettlands Hauptstadt Riga, einer 800 Jahre alten Hansestadt am Ufer der Daugava. Hinter der historischen Fassade befinden sich 80 Zimmer und 60 Appartements, angenehm eingerichtet und mit jedem modernen Komfort. Merkmale des alten Gebäudes mischen sich harmonisch mit modernen Annehmlichkeiten und erzeugen ein Ambiente aus vergangenen Tagen. Lettische Gemälde zieren die Wände der gemütlichen Bar, und köstliche Gerichte werden in dem intimen Restaurant serviert.

Directions: Set in the heart of the old town. **Price guide:** Single LVL46; double/twin LVL55; suites LVL60–70.

Luxembourg

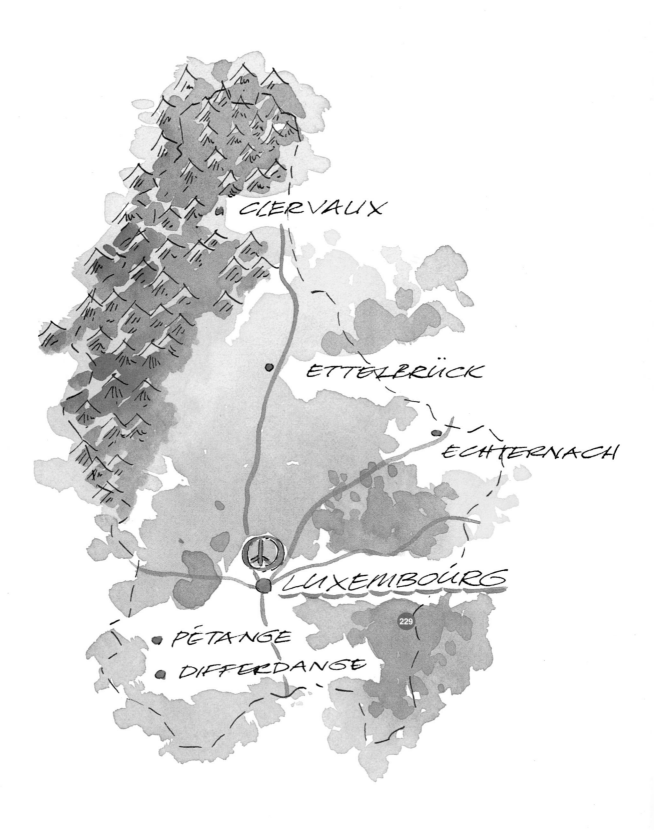

CLERVAUX

ETTELBRÜCK

ECHTERNACH

LUXEMBOURG

229

PÉTANGE

DIFFERDANGE

HOTEL SAINT NICOLAS

31 ESPLANADE, 5533 REMICH, LUXEMBOURG
TEL: +352 26 663 FAX: +352 26 6636 66 E-MAIL: hotel@pt.lu

Set in the picturesque town of Remich, this family-run hotel affords fantastic views across the esplanade and lush vineyards as it lies on the banks of the river Moselle. The eclectic hotel features unusual public rooms adorned with interesting paintings. Blue glass lights add a touch of modernism to the corridors. The hotel's Lohengrin Restaurant is a gastronomic delight comprising traditional French cuisine.

Situé dans la ville pittoresque de Remich, cet hôtel familial offre des vues fantastiques sur l'esplanade et les vignobles étant situé sur les berges de la rivière Moselle. Cet hôtel éclectique a des salles communes originales décorées de peintures uniques. Les lumières bleues des couloirs ajoutent une touche de modernisme. Le restaurant de l'hôtel, le Lohengrin est un délice gastronomique proposant une cuisine traditionnelle française.

Das familiengeführte Hotel Saint Nicolas, das an der Mosel mitten in der malerischen Stadt Remich gelegen ist, bietet spektakuläre Ausblicke auf die Uferpromenade und die üppigen Weinberge. Die Aufenthaltsräume sind originell, mit interessanten Bildern geschmückt, und blaue Glaslampen sorgen für einen modernen Touch. Das Restaurant Lohengrin mit seiner traditionellen französischen Küche ist ein gastronomischer Hochgenuss.

Directions: *Luxembourg > E29 > Remich*. **Price guide:** *Single BF2800; double/twin BF3400 –BF4600; suitesBF4900.Gastronomic offer (incl.2 nights)BF6300.*

Monaco

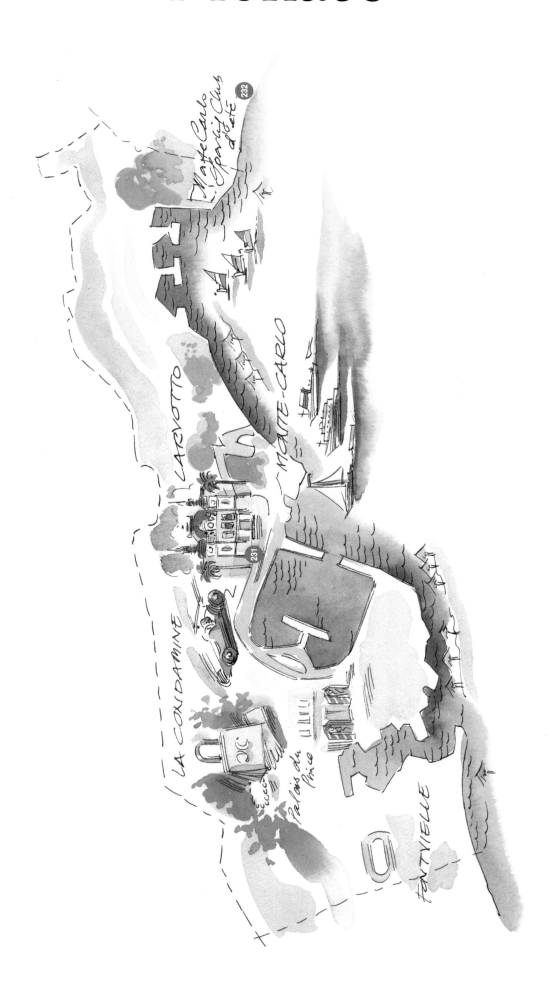

AMBASSADE HOTEL

HERENGRACHT 341, 1016 AZ AMSTERDAM, THE NETHERLANDS
TEL: +31 20 5550222 FAX: +31 20 5550277 E-MAIL: info@ambassade-hotel.nl

The Ambassade is a most attractive hotel in the heart of Amsterdam. Originally ten separate houses, each the home of a wealthy merchant on the Herengracht (the "Gentlemen's Canal"), the hotel has been converted into one building which retains all the erstwhile interior architecture and the external façades. The luxurious float and massage centre Koan Float, owned by the hotel, is situated further along the street.

L'Ambassade est un hôtel très attrayant dans le coeur d'Amsterdam. Originellement dix maisons séparées, chacune étant la maison d'un riche marchand de Herengracht (Le Canal des Gentlemen), l'hôtel a été converti en un bâtiment qui comprend toute l'architecture intérieure ancienne et les façades extérieures d'époque. Le luxieux centre de massage Koan Float, appartenant à l'hôtel, est situé à proximité.

Das Ambassade ist ein höchst attraktives Hotel im Herzen von Amsterdam. Ursprünglich waren es zehn separate Häuser, ein jedes im Besitz eines reichen Kaufmanns auf der Herengracht (Herrenkanal). Das Hotel wurde zu einem einzigen Gebäude umgebaut, wobei das ehemalige Interieur sowie die Architektur und die Aussenfassaden erhalten blieben. Das hoteleigene, luxuriöse Float- und Massagezentrum Koan Float befindet sich ein paar Häuser weiter.

Directions: *Schiphol Airport > taxi.* **Price guide:** *Single FL290–350; double/twin FL350–395; suites FL475–650.*

THE CANAL HOUSE HOTEL

KEIZERSGRACHT 148, 1015 CX AMSTERDAM, THE NETHERLANDS
TEL: +31 20 622 5182 FAX: +31 20 624 13 17 E-MAIL: canalhousehotel@compuserve.com

The Canal House is a neat, old-fashioned hotel tucked away in a quiet residential area in the heart of Amsterdam. Built as a town house in the 17th century, modern facilities have been introduced, but there is no television in the bedrooms. The furnishings comprise fine fabrics, tapestries, gilt frame mirrors and old oil paintings. Breakfast is served in an elegant room with a large chandelier and splendid views.

C'est un hôtel élégant de style ancien caché dans un quartier résidentiel calme en plein coeur d'Amsterdam. Construit comme une maison de ville au XVIIème siècle, les équipements modernes ont été installés mais il n'y a pas de télévision dans les chambres. L'ameublement comprend des tissus raffinés, des tâpisseries, des miroirs dorés et de vieilles peintures à l'huile. Le petit déjeuner est servi dans une pièce élégante avec un grand lustre et des vues splendides.

Das Canal House ist ein adrettes, den Auffassungen der früheren Zeit entsprechendes Hotel, das in einer ruhigen Wohngegend im Herzen von Amsterdam liegt. Es wurde als Stadthaus im 17. Jahrhundert erbaut und obwohl moderne Einrichtungen vorhanden sind, gibt es kein Fernsehen in den Zimmern. Die Einrichtung umfasst erlesene Stoffe, Gobelins, vergoldete Spiegel und alte Ölgemälde. Das Frühstück wird in einem eleganten Raum mit grossem Lüster serviert und bietet eine herrliche Aussicht.

Directions: A10 > exit 103 > Centrum. **Price guide:** *Double/twin FL295–395.*

SEVEN ONE SEVEN

PRINSENGRACHT 717, 1017 JW AMSTERDAM, THE NETHERLANDS
TEL: +31 20 42 70 717 FAX: +31 20 42 30 717 E-MAIL: info@717hotel.nl

This property is so exclusive that only a small brass number plaque indicates that there is a popular venue behind the shuttered façade. Built as an 18th century town house, Seven One Seven is an architectural delight. Inside is a beautiful composition of old and new created by the fashion designer Kees van der Valk. Marble floors, curiosities and oddities, canvas draped windows and leopard skin chairs blend with fine antiques.

Cette propriété est si exclusive que seule une petite plaque en cuivre indique sa présence derrière une façade à volets. Construit au XVIIIème siècle en tant que maison de ville, Seven One Seven a une architecture surprenante. Une belle harmonie entre l'ancien et le moderne règne à l'intérieur qui a été créé par le designer de mode Kees van der Valk. Des sols en marbre, des curiosités, des objets étranges, des fenêtres drapées de toiles et des chaises en peau de léopard sont combinées avec de superbes antiquités.

Nur eine winzige Kupferplakette verrät, dass sich hinter den geschlossenen Fensterläden ein erstklassiges exklusives Hotel befindet. Das Seven One Seven, ein Stadthaus aus dem 18. Jahrhundert, ist ein architektonischer Genuss. Das Innere, gestaltet von Hollands Trend-designer Kees van der Valk, zeigt eine fesselnde Verbindung von Alt und Neu: Marmorböden, aussergewöhnliche und seltsame Objekte, Fenster mit Segeltuchvorhängen und mit Leopardenfell überzogene Stühle harmonisieren perfekt mit feinsten Antiquitäten.

Directions: *In the heart of the old centre.* ***Price guide:*** *Suite FL525–975.*

LANDHUISHOTEL & RESTAURANT BLOEMENBEEK

BEUNINGERSTRAAT 6, 7587 DE LUTTE, THE NETHERLANDS
TEL: +31 541 551224 FAX: +31 541 552285 E-MAIL: bloemenbeek@silencehotel.nl

This lovely, sprawling country house hotel and restaurant offers guests the most modern and luxurious accommodation and is an ideal base from which to explore the beautiful countryside dotted with stately castles and manor houses. The en suite guest rooms are comfortable and beautifully furnished with a number of them featuring a Jacuzzi. Dining is excellent and there is a beautiful Mediterranean 'Spa' with Jacuzzi, sauna and steam bath.

Ce charmant hôtel-restaurant de campagne offre un hébergement de grand luxe des plus modernes et constitue une base idéale pour explorer une belle région parsemée de châteaux et de manoirs imposants. Les chambres avec salles de bains sont confortables et élégantes. Certaines d'entre elles disposent même d'un Jacuzzi. La cuisine est excellente, et l'hôtel possède également un magnifique centre de remise en forme méditerranéen avec Jacuzzi, sauna et hammam.

Dieses charmante, weitläufige Landhotel und Restaurant bietet modernste und luxuriöseste Unterkunft und ist ein idealer Ausgangspunkt , um die herrliche Umgebung und die zahlreichen imposanten Schlösser und Herren-häuser zu erkunden. Die Zimmer sind en suite, gemütlich und elegant eingerichtet, und einige haben einen Jacuzzi. Die Küche ist exzellent, und das Hotel verfügt über ein attraktives mediterranes 'Spa' mit Whirlpool, Sauna und Dampfbad.

Directions: Leave A1 at Exit 34. **Price guide:** *Single FL205–375; double/twin FL295–450; suites FL275–450.*

HOTEL DE DUINRAND

STEEGERF 2, 5151 RB DRUNEN, THE NETHERLANDS
TEL: +31 416 372498 FAX: +31 416 374919 EMAIL: hotel@deduinrand.nl

The Restaurant De Duinrand belongs to an exclusive club, Les Patrons Cuisiniers which comprises the top seventeen restaurants in Holland. Peace and privacy are ensured as the hotel is surrounded by extensive well-kept gardens. Before dining, guests can order cocktails in the lounge or on the terrace, while deciding which exquisite dishes to order from the menus, with wine suggestions for each course.

Le restaurant De Ruinrand appartient à un club exclusif, les "Patrons Cuisiniers" qui regroupe les 17 meilleures tables de Hollande. Paix et intimité sont assurés à l'hôtel qui est entouré d'un grand jardin parfaitement entretenu. Avant de dîner, les clients peuvent déguster un cocktail dans le salon ou sur la terrace, tout en décidant quel met délicieux commander, chaque plat ayant un vin spécialement recommandé.

Das Restaurant „De Duinrand" ist Mitglied des Clubs „Les Patrons Cuisiniers", dem die 17 besten Restaurants in Holland angehören. Ruhe und Abgeschiedenheit sind garantiert, da das Hotel von ausgedehnten und gepflegten Gärten umgeben ist. Gäste können auf der Terrasse oder im Salon Cocktails zu sich nehmen und dabei die exquisiten Gerichte der Speisekarte studieren, mit Weinvorschlägen für jeden Gang.

Directions: A2 > A59 > Drunen > restaurant. **Price guide:** *Single FL195; double/twin FL225; suites FL225–600.*

JACHTSLOT DE MOOKERHEIDE

HEUMENSEBAAN 2, 6584 CL MOLENHOEK, THE NETHERLANDS
TEL: +31 24 358 30 35 FAX: +31 24 358 43 55

The Jugendstil castle at Mookerheide is now an acclaimed restaurant serving exquisite home-grown produce from the garden and featuring a well-stocked cellar. The castle has up-to-date facilities combined with a historic fairy tale atmosphere complemented by original features such as period furniture and a stunning stained glass hunting scene above the staircase. The luxurious bedrooms are comfortable and spacious, all with Jacuzzi. The lodge also caters for meetings in 'The Hall of Knights'.

Le château de Jugendstil à Mookerheide est aujourd'hui un restaurant réputé qui propose des mets délicats préparés avec les produits du jardin et possède une excellente cave. Le château bénéficie de tous les équipements modernes mais garde une atmosphère de conte de fées grâce à des caractéristiques originelles telles que les meubles d'époque et l'impressionnant vitrail représentant une scène de chasse. Les chambres luxueuses sont confortables et spacieuses, toutes avec Jacuzzi. L'hôtel reçoit également des conférences dans le 'Salon des Chevaliers'.

Das Jugendstilschloss in Mookerheide ist heute ein beliebtes Restaurant. Für die exquisiten Gerichte werden Produkte aus dem eigenen Garten verwendet, ergänzt von Weinen aus dem eindrucksvollen Keller. Modernste Einrichtungen verbinden sich hier mit einer märchenhaften Atmosphäre, die durch ursprüngliche Details wie Stilmöbel und eine atemberaubende Jagdszene im Treppenhaus noch verstärkt wird. Die luxuriösen Zimmer sind komfortabel und geräumig, und alle haben Jacuzzi. Der 'Rittersaal' steht für Geschäftstreffen zur Verfügung.

Directions: *Leave A73 at Malden-Mook exit > Mook > turn left before railway.* **Price guide (excl. breakfast):** *Single FL160–185; double/twin FL220–255; suites FL225–470. Breakfast FL27,50.*

HOTEL DE WIEMSEL
WINHOFFLAAN 2, 7631 HX OOTMARSUM, NETHERLANDS
TEL: +31 541 292 155 FAX: +31 541 293 295 E-MAIL: info@wiemsel.nl

An enchanting medieval village and a thriving farm form the background of this excellent and attractive hotel located some 80 miles east of Amsterdam. Outdoor living is encouraged with bright garden furniture set out on the terrace round the pool – perfect for alfresco breakfast or apéritifs. Marvellous picnic hampers can be arranged for those borrowing bicycles to explore the countryside.

Un village médiéval enchanteur et une ferme prospère forment l'environnement de ce charmant hôtel situé à environ 130 km à l'est d'Amsterdam. A l'extérieur, vous pourrez profiter des confortables meubles de jardins sur la terrace de la piscine, qui est idéale pour des petits déjeuners ou des apéritifs alfresco. De superbes paniers de picnics peuvent être organisés pour ceux qui veulent emprunter des bicyclettes et explorer la campagne.

Ein zauberhaftes mittelalterliches Dorf und ein Bauernhof bilden die Kulisse dieses exzellenten Hotels, das etwa 130 km östlich von Amsterdam liegt. Die Terrasse am Pool, mit farbenfrohen Gartenmöbeln versehen, zieht selbst den grössten Stubenhocker ins Freie. Und wo könnte man besser ein Frühstück al fresco oder einen Apéritif geniessen? Für diejenigen, die mit dem Fahrrad die Umgebung erkunden wollen, werden verlockende Picknickkörbe gepackt.

Directions: A1 > Hengelo > Oldenzaal/Ootmarsum > Denekamp. **Price guide:** *Single FL335; double/twin FL455; suites FL525–750.*

RESTAURANT HOTEL SAVELBERG

OOSTEINDE 14, 2271 EH VOORBURG, THE NETHERLANDS
TEL: +31 70 3872081 FAX: +31 70 3877715

This enchanting hotel can be found in the old village of Voorburg, not far from the Hague. It has been restored with great care and is now a listed historical building. Guests are immediately aware of the grace evocative of its past combined with the luxury of today. The handsome restaurant has won many accolades for its inspired use of seasonal fare and absolutely superb wine list. It offers gourmet , à la carte and delicious set menues.

Cet hôtel enchanteur est situé dans le vieux village de Voorburg, non loin de La Hague. Il a été restauré avec grand soin et est de nos jours un bâtiment historique classé. Le visiteur sera immédiatement frappé par la grâce évocatrice de son passé combiné avec le luxe d'aujourd'hui. Le joli restaurant a gagné plusieurs accolades pour son menu saisonnier créatif et pour sa carte de vins absolument superbe. Ce dernier propose un choix de menus délicieusement traditionnels, gastronomiques ou à la carte.

Dieses zauberhafte Hotel befindet sich in dem alten Dorf Voorburg, nicht weit entfernt von Den Haag. Es wurde behutsam restauriert und ist heute ein historisches Gebäude unter Denkmalschutz. Seine elegante Atmosphäre, die vergangene Zeiten wachruft, verbindet sich perfekt mit modernstem Luxus. Das reizende Restaurant wurde bereits mehrfach für seine inspirierten Gerichte und herausragende Weinkarte ausgezeichnet, und bietet Gourmet-, à la carte und köstliche Tagesmenues.

Directions: *Amsterdam A4 > Rotterdam/Delft > A12 > Voorburg > Oosteinde 14*. **Price guide (excl. breakfast):** *Double/twin FL250–350; suites FL375–595.*

Norway

De Historiske Hotel

DALEN HOTEL

PO BOKS 123, 3880 DALEN, NORWAY
TEL: +47 35 07 70 00 FAX: +47 35 07 70 11 E-MAIL: dalenhaa@online.no

Once a favourite retreat for the crowned heads and aristocracy of Europe, the Dalen was built in 1894, its architecture inspired by Norway's historic stave churches. The imposing structure was created in the dragon style – the Norwegian version of the 'Swiss chalet' architecture popular throughout Europe at the time – with its dragon heads, turrets and cornices. Norwegian specialities and international cuisine is served in the elegant dining room.

Un des refuges préférés des têtes couronnées et de l'aristocratie européenne, le Dalen a été construit en 1894. Son architecture a été inspirée par les églises en bois historiques de Norvège. La structure imposante a été créée dans le style dragon, version norvégienne des chalets suisses. Populaire en Europe à l'époque, cette architecture est reconnaissable à ses têtes de dragons, ses tourrelles et ses corniches. Dans l'élégante salle à manger, des spécialités norvégiennes et des plats internationaux figurent sur l'excellente carte.

Das Dalen, einst eine bevorzugte Stätte der gekrönten Häupter und Adeligen aus ganz Europa, wurde 1894 erbaut. Die Architektur ist deutlich von den historischen norwegischen Stave-Kirchen inspiriert. Das eindrucksvolle Gebäude wurde im Drachenstil erschaffen – die norwegische Version der Schweizer Chalet-Architektur, die zur damaligen Zeit in Europa sehr populär war – mit typischen Drachen-köpfen, Türmchen und Gesims. Im eleganten Speisesaal werden norwegische Spezialitäten und internationale Gerichte serviert.

Directions: *Between Stavanger and Oslo; 20km south of E134.* **Price guide:** *Single NOK800; double/twin NOK1070–1300; suites NOK1600.*

HOTEL REFSNES GODS

PO BOX 236, 1501 MOSS, NORWAY
TEL: +47 69 27 83 00 FAX: +47 69 27 83 01 E-MAIL: refsnes.gods@c2i.net

Situated in the beautiful island of Jeløy overlooking Oslo Fjord, this former manor house has been renowned for its hospitality and glittering social gatherings since its construction in the 1770s. The architecture, ambience and many of the house's original features have been carefully preserved and restored over the years, offering visitors a refreshing and excellent combination of historical and modern facilities. Imaginative Scandinavian and French dishes are served in the elegant restaurant.

Situé sur la belle île de Jeløy et surplombant le Fjord Oslo, cet ancien manoir a toujours été renommé pour son hospitalité et sa douceur sociale depuis sa construction dans les années 1770. L'architecture, l'ambiance et nombres de caractéristiques originales ont été préservées avec soin et restorées à travers les années, offrant au visiteur un combinaison rafraîchissante et excellente d'installations modernes et anciennes. Une cuisine scandinave et française pleine d'imagination est servie dans l'élégant restaurant.

Auf der schönen Insel Jeløy gelegen und mit Blick auf den Fjord von Oslo ist dieses ehemalige Herrenhaus schon seit 1770 für seine Gastfreundschaft und sein reges gesellschaftliches Treiben bekannt. Bei Renovierungen im Laufe der Jahre wurden Architektur, Ambiente und zahlreiche ursprüngliche Merkmale des Hotels erhalten, und die Gäste können heute eine eindrucksvolle Mischung aus historischen und modernen Einrichtungen bewundern. Im eleganten Restaurant werden einfallsreiche skandinavische und französische Gerichte serviert.

Directions: *Oslo > E6 > Moss*. ***Price guide:*** *Single NOK895–1195; double/twin NOK1195–1425.*

FIRST HOTEL BASTION

SKIPPERGATEN 7, 0152 OSLO, NORWAY
TEL: +47 22 47 77 00 FAX: +47 22 33 11 80

The First Bastion is a modern hotel with contemporary fabrics, fireplace and lighting in the Library/Bar, yet it has lovely polished old wooden floors enhancing the ambience. The bedrooms, decorated in warm colours and with comfort, meet various needs – non-smoking, smoking, adapted for those with mobility problems or for guests with special business needs. A marvellous Oslo Breakfast is served in the attractive dining room.

Le First Bastion est un établissement moderne, dont la bibliothèque / bar est décorée de tentures, d'une cheminée et de lumières modernes mais qui comporte également un vieux parquet, ce qui accentue son charme. Les chambres, décorées en couleurs chaudes, sont confortables et conviennent à tous les goûts: non-fumeur, fumeur, équipées pour ceux qui ont des problèmes de mobilité ou adaptées à une clientèle d'affaires. Un merveilleux petit déjeuner façon Oslo est servi dans l'élégante salle à manger.

Das First Bastion ist ein modernes Hotel mit zeitgenössischen Stoffen, Kamin und entsprechender Beleuchtung in der Bibliothek/Bar, und herrlichen polierten Holzböden. Die behaglichen Zimmer sind in warmen Farben gehalten und erfüllen verschiedenste Bedürfnisse – Nichtraucher, Raucher, Gäste mit Mobilitätsproblemen oder Geschäftsreisende. Ein ausgezeichnetes Osloer Frühstück wird im attraktiven Speisesaal serviert.

Directions: *Old Oslo centre*. **Price guide:** *Single NOK690–1245; double/twin NOK990–1495.*

GLOPPEN HOTELL

6823 SANDANE, NORWAY
TEL: +47 57 86 53 33 FAX: +47 57 86 60 02 E-MAIL: glopphot@vestdata.no

A wild and captivating landscape encompasses the Gloppen Hotell, which is often frequented by angling enthusiasts. In bygone times, the salmon fishermen indulged in hearty meals and this tradition has been retained as guests feast upon four-course dinners in one of the enchanting dining rooms. The Gloppen river provides excellent salmon fishing whilst numerous other outdoor activities can be pursued nearby.

Un paysage sauvage et captivant entoure le Gloppen Hotell, qui est souvent fréquenté par les mordus de la pêche à la ligne. Jadis, les pêcheurs de saumon s'offraient de copieux repas et cette tradition a été perpétuée de nos jours. En effet, les clients peuvent déguster des dîners de quatre plats dans l'une des ravissantes salles à manger. La rivière Gloppen offre d'excellentes possibilités de pêche au saumon et de nombreuses autres activités de plein air peuvent être organisées dans les environs.

Von wilder, beeindruckender Landschaft umrahmt, wird das Gloppen Hotell besonders gerne von Anglern aufgesucht. In der Vergangenheit gönnten sich die Lachsangler stets ein herzhaftes Essen, und diese ansprechende Tradition wird heutzutage für die Gäste fortgeführt: mit einem üppigen 4-Gänge-Menue in einem der zauberhaften Restaurants. Der Fluss Gloppen bietet exzellente Möglichkeiten zum Lachsangeln, und zahlreiche andere Aktivitäten im Freien sind in der Umgebung möglich.

Directions: Sandane centre. **Price guide:** *Single NOK695–945; double/twin NOK890–1290.*

De Historiske Hotel

WALAKER HOTELL

6879 SOLVORN, SOGN, NORWAY

TEL: +47 576 82080 FAX: +47 576 82081 E-MAIL: walaker.hotel@sf.telia.no

This historic hotel started life as a farm with an inn and coach station, and its original buildings date from about 1650. The bedrooms are furnished in a simple style and retain a special appeal for guests wishing to experience the atmosphere of bygone times and sleep under an old roof. The barn, built in 1883, has been restored and turned into an art gallery, where exhibitions are held every summer. Leisure activities may include guided ice walks, available at the glacial centre in Jostedal.

Cet hôtel historique était originellement une auberge et un relais, dont la construction dâte des environs de 1650. Les chambres sont meublées dans un style simple et dégagent un attrait particulier pour les visiteurs souhaitant vivre une expérience teintée d' "autrefois". La ferme, construite en 1883, a été restaurée et transformée en gallerie d'art, où des expositions sont organisées l'été. Les activités peuvent notamment inclure des randonnées guidées sur la glace, au centre glaciaire de Jostedal.

Dieses historische Hotel war einst ein Bauernhof mit Gasthof und Kutschstation, und die alten Gebäude stammen aus der Zeit um 1650. Die Zimmer sind in einfachem Stil gehalten und besonders attraktiv für diejenigen, die die Atmosphäre vergangener Zeiten erleben und unter einem alten Dach nächtigen wollen. Die 1883 erbaute Scheune wurde restauriert und in eine Kunstgallerie umgewandelt, die nun jeden Sommer für Ausstellungen bereitsteht. Am Gletscherzentrum in Jostedal kann man geführte Eiswanderungen unternehmen.

Directions: Sognefjord >road 55. *Price guide:* Single NOK550–980; double/twin NOK880–1280.

De Historiske Hotel

FLEISCHER'S HOTEL

5700 VOSS, NORWAY

TEL: +47 56 52 05 00 FAX: +47 56 52 05 01 E-MAIL: hotel@fleischers.no

This grand hotel is set in a superb position, overlooking the lake. The façade, with its towers and pointed dormer windows, is reminiscent of Switzerland. Built in 1889 and still run by the same family, the hotel has been discreetly modernised without losing its original charm. There is a warm ambience in the foyer with its convivial and elegant salons. Delicious food including local fish and Norwegian specialities is served in the restaurant with its warm colour scheme.

Ce grand hôtel est situé idéalement au dessus du lac. La façade, avec ses tours et ses lucarnes pointues qui sont des reminiscences suisses. Construit en 1889 et toujours tenu par la même famille, l'hôtel a été modernisé intelligemment sans perdre son charme originel. Il y a une ambiance chaleureuse dans le salon avec ses salons amicaux et élégants. Le restaurant, qui se caractérise par des couleurs chaudes, propose une cuisine délicieuse, avec notamment du poisson de la région et des spécialités norvégiennes.

Dieses Grand Hotel hat eine herrliche Lage mit Aussicht über den See. Die Fassade mit ihren Türmen und spitzen Giebelfenstern erinnert an die Schweiz. 1889 erbaut und immer noch von der gleichen Familie geführt, wurde das Hotel umsichtig renoviert, ohne seinen ursprünglichen Charme zu verlieren. Das Foyer strahlt mit seinen freundlichen und eleganten Salons ein gemütliches Ambiente aus. Das Restaurant ist in warmen Farben gehalten und serviert köstliche norwegische Spezialitäten und Fisch der Region.

Directions: Bergen > E16 > Voss. **Price guide:** *Single NOK975; double/twin NOK1290.*

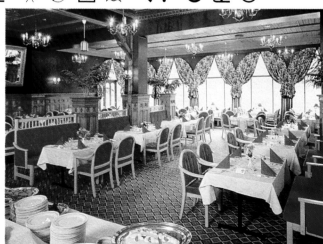

Portugal

POUSADA DE ALIJÓ - BARÃO DE FORRESTER

5070–031 ALIJÓ, PORTUGAL
TEL: +351 259 95 94 67 FAX: +351 21 844 20 85/7 E-MAIL: guest@pousadas.pt

Situated in the heart of the Douro Wine Region in a small village called Alijó, belonging to the prestigious 'Pousadas de Portugal' chain, this hotel is the perfect base from which to explore the numerous quintas in the vicinity, the vineyards of the world famous port wine. The spacious rooms are comfortable and tastefully decorated, and the restaurant offers a wide range of the finest traditional Portuguese cuisine. Guests can enjoy a cruise on the river Douro or go for a country walk in one of Portugal's most beautiful landscapes.

Situé au coeur de la région viticole du Douro, dans le petit village d'Alijó, cet hôtel, appartenant à la prestigieuse chaîne des Pousadas de Portugal, est idéal pour explorer les nombreuses quintas des environs et les vignobles produisant le célèbre porto. Les chambres sont spacieuses et décorées avec goût, et le restaurant offre un éventail de plats portugais traditionnels d'une qualité remarquable. Les visiteurs peuvent faire un tour en bateau sur le Douro ou se promener dans l'une des plus belles régions du Portugal.

Das im Herzen des Weingebiets Douro in einem kleinen Dörfchen namens Alijó gelegene Hotel gehört zu der renommierten Hotelkette 'Pousadas de Portugal'. Es ist ideal zur Erkundung der vielen Quintas dieser Gegend, der Weinberge des weltberühmten Portweins. Die geräumigen Zimmer sind bequem und geschmackvoll eingerichtet, und das Restaurant bietet eine grosse Auswahl erlesenster traditioneller Gerichte. Die Gäste können eine Schiffsreise auf dem Fluss Douro machen oder Spaziergänge in einer der reizvollsten Gegenden Portugals unternehmen.

Directions: *Near Vila Real.* **Price guide:** *Double/twin Esc16,300–25,100.*

CASA DOMILU

ESTRADA DE BENAGIL, APARTADO 1250, PRAIA DO CARVOEIRO, 8400 LAGOA, PORTUGAL
TEL: +351 282 350 610 FAX: +351 282 358 410 E-MAIL: casa.domilu@mail.telepac.pt

Designed and built by its owner, Mr D'Almeida, this hotel was originally a private villa set in subtropical gardens but is now a family-run residence. The eclectic bedrooms are a fusion of the past and present – filled with antiques whilst offering every modern amenity. Specialising in traditional Portuguese dishes and complemented by a selection of international cuisine, the restaurant offers a light luncheon menu à la carte. The hotel's comprehensive new health and fitness centre features an indoor pool, Jacuzzi, sauna and steamroom.

Dessinée et construite par son proprietaire, M. D'Almeida, cet hôtel était à l'origine une maison particulière plantée dans un jardin subtropical et est à présent une résidence familiale. Les chambres éclectiques combinent passé et présent, sont truffées d'antiquités et offrent tout confort moderne. Spécialisé en plats traditionnels portugais et complété par une sélection internationale, le restaurant propose un déjeuner léger à la carte. Le nouveau centre de santé et de remise en forme vous offre piscine couverte, Jacuzzi, sauna et bain turc.

Dieses von subtropischen Gärten umgebene Hotel wurde von seinem Besitzer, Herrn D'Almeida, entworfen und erbaut, und war ursprünglich eine private Villa. In den Zimmern verbinden sich Vergangenheit und Gegenwart, Antikes harmonisiert mit modernsten Annehmlichkeiten. Das Restaurant ist auf traditionell portugiesische Gerichte spezialisiert, die durch eine Auswahl internationaler Speisen ergänzt werden. Ausserdem wird ein leichtes à la carte Lunch angeboten. Das umfangreiche neue Fitnesszentrum bietet Hallenbad, Jacuzzi, Sauna und Dampfbad.

Directions: *Faro > IP1 > Portimao > Lagoa > Carvoeiro*. **Price guide:** *Single Esc10,800–18,000; double/twin Esc14,500–24,000; suites Esc22,000–40,000.*

FORTE DE S. FRANCISCO

5400 CHAVES, PORTUGAL

TEL: +351 276 333 700 FAX: +351 276 333 701 E-MAIL: webmaster@forte–s–francisco–hoteis.pt

The historic Forte de S. Francisco is situated in the ancient town of Chaves, famous for its thermal spa discovered 2000 years ago. The hotel was built by the Franciscan order in the 16th century and is surrounded by imposing walls. This National monument has been stunningly restored, creating a relaxing and authentic atmosphere. The rooms and public places feature original and exquisite furniture, and the excellent restaurant serves mouth-watering local specialities.

Cet hôtel historique se situe dans la vieille ville de Chaves, célèbre pour ses thermes découverts il y a 2 000 ans. Construit par les Franciscains au XVIe siècle, le Forte de S. Francisco est entouré de murailles imposantes. Remarquablement bien restauré, ce Monument National jouit d'une atmosphère authentique propice à la détente. Les chambres et les salons sont pourvus de beaux meubles d'origine. L'excellent restaurant sert des spécialités locales irresistibles.

Das historische Forte de S. Francisco liegt in der traditionsreichen Stadt Chaves mit ihren berühmten, vor 2000 Jahren entdeckten Thermalquellen. Das Hotel wurde im 16. Jahrhundert vom Franziskanerorden errichtet und ist von beeindruckenden Mauern umgeben. Das geschmackvoll renovierte und unter Denkmalschutz stehende Gebäude bietet eine authentische, entspannende Atmosphäre. Alle Räume sind mit erlesenem Mobiliar ausgestattet, und das hervorragende Restaurant bietet köstliche einheimische Spezialitäten.

Directions: Chaves is approximately 60 km from Vila Real on EN2. **Price guide:** Single Esc15,000–20,000; double/twin Esc18,000–23,000; suites Esc21,000–29,000.

POUSADA DE CONDEIXA - SANTA CRISTINA

3150–142 CONDEIXA-A-NOVA, PORTUGAL
TEL: +351 239 94 40 25 FAX: +351 21 844 20 85/7 E-MAIL: guest@pousadas.pt

Belonging to the prestigious Pousadas de Portugal chain, just 2 km away from the Roman ruins at Conimbriga and 15 km from the ancient university town of Coimbra, this Pousada is steeped in local history. Its cool, elegant interior and surrounding countryside make it the ideal place to relax and unwind. Guests can take day trips to the beaches of Figuera de Foz, which are just a short drive away, before returning to sample delightful regional cuisine that includes fresh fish and rich Portuguese desserts.

Appartenant à la prestigieuse chaîne des Pousadas de Portugal, cette pousada empreinte d'histoire se trouve à 2 km seulement des ruines romaines de Conimbriga et à 15 km de la vieille ville universitaire de Coimbra. Ses pièces élégantes et fraîches et le paysage environnant sont une invitation à la douceur de vivre et au repos. Les visiteurs vont passer la journée sur les plages de Figueira de Foz, à peu de distance en voiture, avant de retourner à l'hôtel pour un festin de plats régionaux à base de poisson frais, suivi de succulents desserts portugais.

Nur 2 km von den Ruinen des römischen Conimbriga und 15 km von der alten Universitätsstadt Coimbra entfernt befindet sich diese geschichtsreiche Pousada, die zu der renommierten Hotelkette 'Pousadas de Portugal' gehört. Das kühle, elegante Interieur und die Umgebung machen das Hotel zu einem Ort der totalen Entspannung. Gäste können Tagesexkursionen zu den nahegelegenen Stränden von Figuera de Foz unternehmen, bevor sie für ein Abendessen bestehend aus regionalen Spezialitäten wie frischem Fisch und üppigen Desserts zurückkehren.

Directions: *Near Coimbra.* **Price guide**: *Double/twin Esc17,900–25,100.*

MONTE DO CASAL

CERRO DO LOBO ESTOI, 8000 FARO, ALGARVE, PORTUGAL
TEL: +351 289 990140/289 991503 FAX: +351 289 991341

This elegant Algarve country house, built in the 18th century, is peaceful with many personal touches, surrounded by almond, olive and fruit trees, with bougainvillaea climbing up the terraces and a view across the countryside to the coast. Breakfasts of squeezed orange juice and bread from the village bakery are the perfect start to the day! Dinners comprise Portuguese specialities, including the regional smoked swordfish and fine wines from the extensive cellar.

Cette élégante maison de campagne de l'Algarve, dâtant du XVIIIème siècle, est un havre de paix avec des notes personnelles et entouré d'amandiers, d'oliviers et d'arbres fruitiers. Des bougainvilliers grimpent sur les terraces et la vue donne sur les paysages et la côte. Les petits déjeuners avec oranges pressées et pain de la boulangerie du village sont un merveilleux départ pour la journée! Les dîners combinent les spécialités portugaises, l'espadon régional fumé et les vins fins de l'étonnant cave.

Dieses elegante, im 18. Jahrhundert erbaute Algarve-Landhaus ist ruhig und persönlich, umgeben von Mandel-, Oliven- und Obstbäumen. Bougainvillea rankt über die Terrassen und der Blick erstreckt sich bis zur Küste. Ein Frühstück mit frisch gepresstem Orangensaft und gebackenem Brot aus der Dorfbäckerei ist der perfekte Start in den Tag! Abends werden portugiesische Spezialitäten wie z.B. einheimischer geräucherter Schwertfisch serviert und mit erlesenen Weinen aus dem umfassenden Keller ergänzt.

Directions: *IP1 blue signs > motorway > exit % > Faro > Estoi > yellow signs > Moncarapacho.* **Price guide:** *Single Esc15,750–24,380; double/twin Esc21,000–36,500; suites Esc23,000–50,000.*

ROMANTIK HOTEL VIVENDA MIRANDA

PORTO DE MOS, 8600 LAGOS, ALGARVE, PORTUGAL
TEL: +351 282 763 222 FAX: +351 282 760 342 E-MAIL: romantik-hotel-viv.miranda@ip.pt

Vivenda Miranda is a delightful small hotel, with Moorish influence evident in its architecture. It is nestled on a bluff above the sea, surrounded by a subtropical garden, and with truly captivating views from the terrace. Hearty breakfasts and light lunches anticipate the fantastic gourmet meal served in the evening, accompanied by fine wines. For the active, tennis facilities are nearby, mountain bikes are available and sailing and windsurfing can be practised at the Marina. Golf is possible with an instructor.

Vivenda Miranda est un délicieux petit hôtel avec une influence maure dans son architecture. Il est niché sur une falaise au dessus de la mer, est entouré d'un jardin subtropical et offre des vues incroyables depuis sa terrasse. De copieux petits déjeuners et des déjeuners légers devancent le fantastique dîner gastronomique servi le soir et accompagné de vins délicats. Les plus actifs ont accès aux courts de tennis avoisinants, à des VTT et voile et windsurf peuvent être organisés à la marina. Des cours de golf peuvent être organisés.

Die Vivenda Miranda ist ein herrlich kleines Hotel, das maurische Züge in seiner Architektur trägt. Auf einer Klippe über dem Meer inmitten eines subtropischen Gartens gelegen bietet das Hotel atemberaubende Blicke von der Terrasse. Ein herzhaftes Frühstück und ein leichtes Mittagessen werden nur noch von einem Gourmetdinner am Abend übertroffen und von erlesenen Weinen vervollständigt. Aktive Gäste können in der Nähe Tennis spielen, sich ein Mountainbike leihen oder am Hafen segeln und windsurfen. Für Golf steht ein Lehrer zur Verfügung.

Directions: *Faro > EN125 > Lagos > Praia de Porto de Mos.* **Price guide:** *Single £52–£75; double/twin £47–£75; suites £52–£80.*

QUINTA DA BELA VISTA

CAMINHO DO AVISTA NAVIOS 4, 9000 FUNCHAL, MADEIRA, PORTUGAL
TEL: +351 291 706400 FAX: +351 291 706411

It is a joy to stay in this traditional house, with its tall windows and green shutters, overlooking Funchal Bay and surrounded by exotic gardens. The interiors are a blend of sophistication and rich, classical furnishings. Guests enjoy their apéritifs in the cheerful bar or on the sunny terraces before choosing between the elegant restaurant serving fine food and the best wines or the more informal dining room.

Surplombant la baie de Funchal et entourée de jardins exotiques, c'est un vrai plaisir de séjourner dans cette maison traditionnelle, avec ses grandes fenêtres et ses volets verts. L'intérieur est un mélange de sophistication et de richesse, avec des meubles classiques. Les visiteurs dégusteront leur apéritif dans le bar animé ou sur les terrasses ensoleillées avant de se décider entre le restaurant élégant servant des plats fins et les meilleurs vins ou la salle à manger plus informelle.

Ein Aufenthalt in diesem traditionellen Haus mit seinen grossen Fenstern und grünen Fensterläden, das auf die Bucht von Funchal blickt und von exotischen Gärten umgeben ist, bleibt unvergessen. Die Räume sind höchst elegant, üppig und klassisch eingerichtet. Die Gäste können in der gemütlichen Bar oder auf der sonnigen Terrasse einen Apéritif nehmen, bevor sie sich im informellen Speisesaal oder dem eleganten Restaurant von feinen Speisen und edlen Weinen verwöhnen lassen.

Directions: Main road > Rua do Dr Pita. **Price guide:** Single Esc20,250–34,000; double/twin Esc27,000–55,000; suites Esc55,300–65,000.

REID'S PALACE

9000-098 FUNCHAL, MADEIRA, PORTUGAL
TEL: +351 291 71 7171 FAX: +351 291 71 7177 E-MAIL: reidshtl@mail.telepac.pt

High on a clifftop overlooking the Bay of Funchal, this elegant fin de siècle hotel has long enjoyed its reputation as Madeira's crowning glory. A partial refurbishment complements the original Anglo-Portugese features, combining old-fashioned luxury with modern facilities. Excellent golf, water sports and wine tastings are available nearby, and there are two heated swimming pools and a sea level pool. In the evenings guests can choose between three restaurants, each with its very own distinctive ambience.

Perché sur une falaise dominant la baie de Funchal, cet élégant hôtel est depuis longtemps considéré comme le joyau de Madère. Rénové partiellement, le bâtiment original, un mélange de styles anglais et portugais, marie harmonieusement luxe classique et confort moderne. Un excellent golf, des sports nautiques et des dégustations de vins sont disponibles à proximité. Il y a deux piscines chauffées et une au niveau de la mer. Le soir, les visiteurs ont le choix entre trois restaurants, chacun avec son atmosphère particulière.

Das auf einer Klippe hoch über der Bucht von Funchal gelegene Fin-de-siècle Hotel gilt seit langem als Madeiras glorreiche Krönung. Das teilweise renovierte Hotel hat sich viele seiner ursprünglichen, angloportugiesischen Merkmale erhalten und kombiniert altmodischen Luxus mit modernen Einrichtungen. In der Nähe sind Golf, Wassersport und Weinproben möglich, und es gibt zwei beheizte Pools und einen Pool auf Meeresebene. Am Abend hat man die Wahl zwischen drei Restaurants, von denen jedes sein ganz eigenes Ambiente besitzt.

Directions: By Air to Funchal Airport. **Price guide:** Single Esc38,000–75,000; double/twin Esc49,500–98,000; suite Esc120,000–510,000.

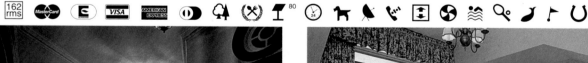

CASA D'AZURARA

RUA NOVA 78, 3530 MANGUALDE, PORTUGAL
TEL: +351 232 612010 FAX: +351 232 612010

Situated in the Dão wine district, this family-run 18th century townhouse hotel offers a friendly and personal service. Its cosy atmosphere is enhanced by open fireplaces and beautiful wooden floors, while each of the traditionally furnished bedrooms retains character and individuality. In summer, dining is al fresco, and guests can discover fine Portugese cuisine and enjoy the beautifully kept lawns and century-aged Camellia Garden.

Situé dans la région viticole du Dão, cet hôtel particulier du XVIIIe siècle offre un service cordial et personnalisé. Les cheminées et le magnifique parquet accentuent l'atmosphère intime et confortable qui règne à l'intérieur. Décorée dans un style traditionnel, chaque chambre a un cachet bien à elle. L'été, les visiteurs dégustent des spécialités portugaises sous les étoiles et se promènent sur les pelouses impeccables du jardin parfumé par les camélias centenaires.

Dieses im Weingebiet Dão gelegene und familiengeführte Hotel aus dem 18. Jahrhundert wurde im Stil eines Stadthauses errichtet und bietet freundlichen, persönlichen Service. Die gemütliche Atmosphäre wird durch offene Kamine und prächtige Holzfussböden unterstrichen, während jedes der traditionell eingerichteten Schlafzimmer über einen einzigartigen Charakter verfügt. Während des Sommers erfreuen sich die Gäste an erlesener portugiesischer Küche 'al fresco' und den gepflegten Rasenanlagen und den alten Kameliengarten.

Directions: A1 > IP5 or IP3 to Viseu > follow signs to Mangualde. **Price guide:** *Single Esc16,000–20,500; double/twin Esc17,500–22,000; suites Esc23,000–26,000.*

CONVENTO DE SÃO PAULO

ALDEIA DA SERRA, 7170 REDONDO, PORTUGAL
TEL: +351 266 98 91 60 FAX: +351 266 99 91 04 E-MAIL: hotelconvspaulo@mail.telepac.pt

Situated between Estremoz and Redondo in the Alentejo, Convento de São Paulo, or the Monastery of Saint Paul was constructed in 1182 by monks seeking a tranquil location to pray. Many vestiges of the 12th century have remained; the original chapel and church are popular venues for weddings and special events, whilst the bedrooms are the old chambers of the monks. Guests dine beneath the splendour of 18th century fresco paintings in the stylish restaurant.

Situé dans l'Alentejo, entre Estremoz et Redondo, le Convento de São Paulo fût construit en 1182 par des moines en quête d'endroit tranquille pour prier. De nombreux vestiges du XIIème siècle ont été conservés; la chapelle et l'église originales sont des endroits populaires pour les mariages ou les occasions spéciales, et les anciennes cellules des moines servent aujourd'hui de chambres. Les hôtes dînent sous de somptueuses fresques du 18ème siècle, dans l'élégante salle à manger.

Convento de São Paulo, "das Kloster des Heiligen Paulus", liegt zwischen Estremoz und Redondo und wurde 1182 von Mönchen erbaut – sie suchten einen ruhigen Platz, um zu beten. Viele Spuren aus dem 12. Jahrhundert sind hier erhalten geblieben: Die ursprüngliche Kapelle und die Kirche sind bei Hochzeiten und feierlichen Anlässen sehr begehrt, und die alten Kammern der Mönche sind die heutigen Gästezimmer. Im eleganten Restaurant diniert man unter herrlichen Fresken aus dem 18. Jahrhundert.

Directions: Lisbon > A6 > Evora/Estremoz > Redondo. **Price guide**: Single Esc16,00–30,00 ; double/twinEsc21,500–35,000; suites Esc29,000–42,000.

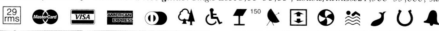

Pousada De São Brás De Alportel

8150–054 SÃO BRÁS DE ALPORTEL, PORTUGAL
TEL: +351 289 84 23 05 FAX: +351 21 844 20 85/7 E-MAIL: guest@pousadas.pt

Nestled in the mountains near some of the most beautiful beaches of the Algarve, yet just 15 minutes from Faro airport, this gem of a hotel, which belongs to the prestigious Pousadas de Portugal chain, is not only unique and full of character, but away from the crowded tourist tracks. Fine Portuguese wines, fresh local fish and tempting, rich desserts typify the delicious local gastronomy, and the stunning views from the hotel combine to make this an enchanting holiday destination. The Pousada has its own swimming pool and tennis court.

Situé à deux pas de certaines des plus belles plages de l'Algarve, hors des sentiers battus mais à 15 minutes seulement de l'aéroport de Faro, cet hôtel montagnard unique et plein de charme, appartenant à la prestigieuse chaîne des Pousadas de Portugal, est un vrai petit bijou. Les vins portugais de choix, le poisson frais de la région et les desserts exquis vous jouent une symphonie gastronomique irrésistible. Des vues spectaculaires complètent le tableau et font de cet hôtel doté d'une piscine et d'un terrain de tennis un lieu de vacances idyllique.

In den Bergen nahe einiger der schönsten Algarvestrände, fernab vom Touristenrummel und nur 15 Minuten vom Flughafen von Faro entfernt, liegt dieses charaktervolle Juwel von einem Hotel, das zu der renommierten Hotelkette 'Pousadas de Portugal' gehört. Erlesene portugiesische Weine, fangfrischer Fisch und üppige Desserts sind typisch für die örtliche Küche, und machen das Hotel zusammen mit seinen atemberaubenden Aussichten zu einem traumhaften Ferienziel. Ein Swimmingpool und Tennisplatz stehen ebenfalls zur Verfügung.

Directions: 15 minutes north of Faro airport. **Price guide:** *Double/twin Esc16,900–25,100; suites Esc21,300–32,200.*

POUSADA DE VILA VIÇOSA - D. JOÃO IV

7160 VILA VIÇOSA, PORTUGAL

TEL: +351 268 98 07 42 FAX: +351 21 844 20 85/7 E-MAIL: guest@pousadas.pt

Belonging to the prestigious Pousadas de Portugal chain, this fascinating luxury hotel is set in the former convent of Chagas de Cristo, close to the Royal Palace in Vila Viçosa. Guests can marvel at the history in the restored convent cells, retreats and oratories. The beautifully decorated rooms add to the charm and character of this unique setting. Guests may enjoy exquisite regional dishes as well as closely guarded and delicious Pousada recipes, after a day of exploring the fascinating surroundings.

Appartenant à la prestigieuse chaîne des Pousadas de Portugal, cet hôtel fascinant est aménagé dans l'ancien couvent de Chagas de Cristo, près du Palais Royal à Vila Viçosa. Les visiteurs découvrent son histoire à travers les cellules et les oratoires restaurés. Superbement décorées, les chambres accentuent le charme et le caractère de ce cadre exceptionnel. Après avoir passé la journée à explorer une région fascinante, les visiteurs se régalent de plats régionaux et de délicieuses spécialités maison dont les recettes sont un secret bien gardé.

Dieses faszinierende, von Legenden umwobene Hotel gehört zu der renommierten Hotelkette 'Pousadas de Portugal' und liegt im ehemaligen Kloster Chagas de Cristo, nahe des königlichen Palastes in Vila Viçosa. Die Gäste können die Geschichte des Klosters an den Kammern und Gebetsräumen bewundern, und wunderschöne Zimmer unterstreichen den Charme dieses einzigartigen Ortes. Besucher können die faszinierende Landschaft erkunden und sich anschliessend zu regionalen Speisen und streng gehüteten Pousada-Rezepten niederlassen.

Directions: *Near Estremoz.* **Price guide:** *Double/twin Esc20,900–31,900; deluxe rooms Esc24,700–39,500 suites Esc40,300–53,100.*

Spain

HOTEL SUITES ALBAYZIN DEL MAR

AVENIDA COSTA DEL SOL, 23, 18690 ALMUNECAR (GRANADA), SPAIN
TEL: +34 958 63 21 61 FAX: +34 958 63 12 37 E-MAIL: jmegias@moebius.es

Albayzin del Mar is a striking mixture of traditional Moorish and Andalusian architecture and is ideally situated only ten minutes from Nerja, in the historical resort town of Almuñecar. The long wide beach with its watersports and popular bar is just 800 metres away. There is a diving school, windsurfing, water and jet skiing. In the summer, guests can cook their own fresh fish or meat in the outside Grill restaurant. A comprehensive new beauty farm is due to open on 1st December 2000.

Cet hôtel est un mélange étonnant d'architecture traditionnelle maure et andalouse situé dans la ville balnéaire historique d'Almuñecar, à dix minutes de Nerja. Une vaste plage à tout juste 800 mètres de l'hôtel, permet des activités nautiques et dispose d'un bar populaire. Une école de plongée, des équipements de planche à voile, de ski nautique ou de jet-ski sont également disponibles. L'été, les hôtes peuvent cuisiner eux-mêmes leur poisson ou leur viande sur le grill extérieur du restaurant. Un centre de beauté complet doit ouvrir le 1er décembre 2000.

Dieses Hotel ist eine eindrucksvolle Mischung aus traditioneller maurischer und andalusischer Architektur und liegt im historischen Resort Almuñecar, nur 10 Minuten von Nerja entfernt. Der ausgedehnte Strand mit seiner einladenden Bar ist nur 800 Meter entfernt. Wassersportler können einen Tauchkurs machen, windsurfen, oder sich mit Wasserski und Jetski fithalten. Im Sommer bereiten die Gäste am Grill im Freien ihr eigenes Abendessen mit frischem Fisch oder Fleisch zu. Das Hotel eröffnet am 1. Dezember 2000 eine umfassende neue Schönheitsfarm.

Directions: Coast road>Malaga>Motril>Almunecar. *Price guide:* Rooms from £100.

HACIENDA EL SANTISCAL

**AVDA. EL SANTISCAL 129 (LAGO DE ARCOS), 11630 ARCOS DE LA FRONTERA, SPAIN
TEL: +34 956 70 83 13 FAX: +34 956 70 82 68 E-MAIL: santiscal@gadesinfo.com**

Surrounded by fields of sunflowers, this 15th century manor house, exquisitely restored, offers glorious views of the lake and historic town of Arcos. A welcoming atmosphere envelopes the property as Señora Gallardo invites guests into her home to enjoy the ambience of a traditional Andalusian Hacienda. Traditional home-cooked dishes feature vegetables, olives and oranges grown in the Hacienda's own groves and gardens. A mobile phone is provided for the guests in each room.

Entouré de champs de tournesols, ce manoir du XVème siècle, restauré de façon exquise, offre des vues imprenables sur le lac et la ville historique d'Arcos. Une accueillante atmosphère caractérise la propriété, et Madame Gallardo invite les hôtes dans sa demeure afin de leur faire profiter de l'ambiance traditionnelle d'une Hacienda andalouse. Des plats traditionnels faits-maison sont composés des légumes, olives et oranges qui ont poussé dans le verger et le potager de la Hacienda. Un téléphone portable est mis à la disposition des clients dans chaque chambre.

Umgeben von Sonnenblumenfeldern bietet dieses perfekt restaurierte Herrenhaus aus dem 15. Jahrhundert herrliche Ausblicke auf den See und die historische Stadt Arcos. Eine herzliche Atmosphäre liegt über der Hazienda und Señora Gallardo lädt ihre Gäste ein, das Ambiente einer typisch andalusischen Hazienda zu geniessen. Für die traditionellen selbstgemachten Gerichte werden Gemüse, Oliven und Orangen aus den eigenen Hainen und Gärten verwendet. Die Zimmer sind mit Mobiltelefonen für die Gäste ausgestattet.

Directions: *N342>Antequera>Arcos de la Frontera>1st right to 'El Bosque'*. **Price guide:** *Single Pts9,000–13,200; double/twin Pts13,000–16,000; suitesPts18,000–20,000.*

LA POSADA DEL TORCAL

29230 VILLANUEVA DE LA CONCEPCION, MALAGA, SPAIN
TEL: +34 95 203 11 77 FAX: +34 95 203 10 06 E-MAIL: laposada@mercuryin.es

This idyllic Andalusian Cortijo is situated on a hilltop estate overlooking the magnificent El Torcal National Park – a perfect base from which to explore this region. The ten spacious and individually decorated rooms are filled with fine antiques and ceramics. Leisure activities include tennis, horse riding and spa facilities. There is an elegant salon, and innovative Spanish and international cuisine is served in the intimate winter dining room or the spectacular terrace restaurant. Córdoba, Ronda, Granada and Seville are all within easy driving distance.

Ce charmant cortijo andalou se dresse dans un domaine situé au sommet d'une colline dominant le magnifique parc national El Torca – base idéale pour explorer la région. Les dix chambres spacieuses joliment décorées sont parées de beaux meubles anciens et de céramiques. La Posada compte un élégant salon et une cuisine espagnole et internationale innovatrice est servie dans la salle à manger intime ou sur la fabuleuse terrasse. Les activités incluent tennis, équitation et l'utilisation du spa. Cordoue, Ronda, Grenade et Séville ne sont pas loin en voiture.

Dieses idyllische andalusische Cortijo liegt auf einer Anhöhe mit Blick auf den El Torcal Nationalpark – ein perfekter Standort, um die Region zu erkunden. Die zehn geräumigen, individuell gestalteten Zimmer sind mit feinen Antiquitäten und Keramikarbeiten geschmückt. Freizeitaktivitäten schliessen Tennis, Reiten und Kurbäder ein. Innovative spanische und internationale Küche wird im Winterspeisesaal oder im sensationellen Terrassenrestaurant serviert. Córdoba, Ronda, Granada und Sevilla sind bequem mit dem Auto zu erreichen.

Directions: N331>Antequera>exit 148>Casabermeja>Villanueva de la Concepción. **Price guide:** *Single Pts12,840; double/twin Pts19,260; suites Pts32,100.*

EUROPE   AMERICA

AT&T Direct® Service

The easy way to call home

FOR EASY CALLING WORLDWIDE:
1. Just dial the AT&T Access Number for the country you are calling from.
2. Dial the phone number you're calling.
3. Dial your AT&T Calling Card, AT&T Corporate, AT&T Universal, MasterCard,® Diners Club,®
American Express,® or Discover® card number.

Global
connection
with the AT&T
Network

AT&T
direct
service

MARBELLA CLUB HOTEL GOLF RESORT & SPA

BULEVAR PRINCIPE ALFONSO VON HOHENLOHE, S/N, 29600 MARBELLA, SPAIN
TEL: +34 95 282 22 11 FAX: +34 95 282 98 84 E-MAIL: hotel@marbellaclub.com

Located on the Costa del Sol, only five minutes from Marbella, this sophisticated Andalusian residence stands in a lush, subtropical garden reaching down to the sea. Exquisite Spanish and international cuisine is served on the romantic terrace of the Grill restaurant, while the famous Beach Club restaurant and a poolside snack bar offer light meals during the day. Guests enjoy special rates at the new 18-hole Marbella Club Golf Resort, and the fully equipped luxury Thalasso Spa provides an extensive range of programmes and treatments.

Cette élégante résidence andalouse se dresse sur la Costa del Sol, à 5 minutes de Marbella, dans un parc subtropical luxuriant qui descend jusqu'à la mer. Des plats espagnols et internationaux raffinés sont servis sur la terrasse romantique de la rôtisserie. Dans la journée, le célèbre restaurant du Beach Club et le snack-bar aménagé au bord de la piscine offrent des repas légers. Les visiteurs bénéficient de tarifs spéciaux au nouveau Marbella Club Golf Resort à 18 trous et profitent du luxueux centre de thalassothérapie, qui offre toutes sortes de programmes et de soins.

An der Costa del Sol, nur fünf Minuten von Marbella entfernt, liegt diese elegante andalusische Residenz inmitten eines üppigen subtropischen Gartens. Auf der romantischen Terrasse des Grill Restaurants werden exquisite spanische und internationale Gerichte serviert und der berühmte Beach Club und die Snackbar am Pool sorgen für leichte Köstlichkeiten untertags. Die Gäste haben Sonderkonditionen im neuen 18-Loch Marbella Club Golf Resort, und das luxuriöse Thalassotherapie-Spa bietet weitere Programme und Anwendungen.

Directions: *Marbella>Golden Mile*. **Price guide:** *Double/twin FF790–1940; suites FF1670–3320. Breakfast FF80 per person.*

LAS DUNAS SUITES

CRTA. DE CADIZ KM163.5, 29689 MARBELLA/ESTEPONA (MALAGA)
TEL: +34 95 279 4345 FAX: +34 95 279 4825 E-MAIL: sales@las–dunas.com

This exciting complex is an annex to the luxurious Las Dunas Beach Hotel & Spa as residents in the suites have the benefit of the many fine facilities at the five star hotel yet can enjoy the freedom of an apartment. The stylish residences feature fully equipped modern kitchens, bathrooms and a private terrace or balcony. The Spa has a Jacuzzi, sauna, gym, therapist and beautician.

Cet extraordianire complexe hôtelier est une annexe du luxueux Las Dunas Beach Hotel & Spa. Les visiteurs séjournant dans les suites peuvent bénéficier des excellentes facilités de l'hôtel cinq étoiles tout en préservant leur indépendance dans les appartements. Ceux-ci sont décorés avec style et comportent tous des cuisines modernes entièrement équipées, des salles de bain et une terrasse ou un balcon privé. Le Spa met à votre disposition un Jacuzzi, un sauna, un gymnase, un thérapeute et une esthéticienne.

Dieses aussergewöhnliche Anwesen ist ein Anbau des Las Dunas Beach Hotel & Spa, und Gäste der Suiten können die zahlreichen Einrichtungen des 5 Sterne Hotels benutzen und gleichzeitig die Privatsphäre der eleganten Appartements geniessen. Diese verfügen über eine vollausgestattete moderne Küche, Bad und private Terrasse oder Balkon. Das Spa bietet Jacuzzi, Sauna, Fitnessraum; ausserdem werden therapeutische Behandlungen und Kosmetikanwendungen angeboten.

Directions: *Marbella>Crta. de Cadiz.* **Price guide (excl. VAT):** *Garden level suites Pts29,250–130,000.*

HOTEL BYBLOS ANDALUZ

MIJAS GOLF APT. 138, 29640 FUENGIROLA, (MALAGA), SPAIN
TEL: +34 95 247 30 50 FAX: +34 95 258 6327 E-MAIL: commerical@byblos-andaluz-com

This luxurious property offers glorious views over the surrounding mountains, gardens and golf courses. The comfortable, sybaritic bedrooms have excellent en suite facilities. There are 2 delightful restaurants, El Andaluz, with its Sevillian courtyard, and the sophisticated Le Nailhac. The Louison Bobet Institute of Thalassotherapy is the largest in Europe and offers many health facilities including subaquatic massages.

Cette propriété luxueuse offre des vues imprenables sur les montagnes environnantes, les jardins et le terrain de golf. Les chambres confortables et sybarites ont de magnifiques salles de bains. L'hôtel a deux délicieux restaurants, El Andaluz, avec sa cour sévillane et Le Nailhac plus sophistiqué. L'Institut Louison Bobet de thalassothérapie est le plus grand d'Europe et propose nombre de services de santé incluant des massages subaquatiques.

Dieses luxuriöse Anwesen trumpft mit traumhaften Blicken auf die umliegenden Berge, Parks und Golfplätze. Die gemütlichen Zimmer haben hervorragende En-suite-Annehmlichkeiten. Es gibt zwei exzellente Restaurants: El Andaluz mit seiner Sevillianer Innenhof, und das erlesene Le Nailhac. Das Louison Bobet Institut für Thalassotherapie is das grösste seiner Art in Europa und bietet zahlreiche Fitness- und Gesundheits-anwendungen, wie z.B. Unterwassermassagen.

Directions: *Fuengirola>Malaga>Cadiz.* **Price guide:** *Single Pts30,000–40,900; double/twin Pts38,000–50,000; suitesPts66,000–195,000.*

HOTEL MONASTERIO SAN MIGUEL

CALLE LARGA 27, 11500 PUERTO DE SANTA MARIA (CADIZ), SPAIN
TEL: +34 956 540 440 FAX: +34 956 542 604 E-MAIL: monasterio@jale.com

Monasterio San Miguel is a fine baroque building with all the original features carefully conserved during its transformation from the monastery to a hotel. It is set in a magnificent garden complete with tropical plants and swimming pool. A generous buffet breakfast is provided and the à la carte restaurant serves exquisite dishes based on fresh produce from the region and a variety of fish from the Bay of Cádiz.

Le Monasterio San Miguel est un bâtiment baroque raffiné dont toutes les caractéristiques originales ont été conservées lors de sa transformation en hôtel. Il se dresse dans un magnifique jardin garni de plantes tropicales et agrémenté d'une piscine. Un généreux petit déjeuner-buffet est proposé et le restaurant à la carte sert de succulents repas composés à partir de produits frais régionaux et d'une variété de poissons pêchés dans la baie de Cadiz.

Das barocke Gebäude des Monasterio San Miguel wurde umsichtig von einem Kloster in ein Hotel umgebaut, wobei grösste Sorgfalt auf den Erhalt der ursprünglichen Merkmale gelegt wurde. Es ist umgeben von einem herrlichen Garten mit tropischen Pflanzen und Swimmingpool. Ein üppiges Buffet steht zum Frühstück bereit, und das à la carte Restaurant serviert exquisite Speisen, für die frische Zutaten der Region und Fisch aus der Bucht von Cádiz verwendet werden.

Directions: *Puerto de Santa Maria centre.* **Price guide:** *Single Pts16,200–24,700; double/twin Pts20,200–29,600; suite Pts46,700–62,600.*

CORTIJO AGUILA REAL

CRTA. GUILLENA–BURGUILLOS KM 4, 41210 GUILLENA, SEVILLE, SPAIN
TEL: +34 95 578 50 06 FAX: +34 95 578 43 30 E-MAIL: hotel@aguilareal.com

This charming Andalusian country house was perfectly restored as a hotel in 1991 and features well-appointed bedrooms and junior suites. Each room has been given its own individual décor and name. Hand-painted furniture and extravagant tapestries adorn the walls. The homemade dishes comprise fresh local produce as well as food grown on the hotel farm. The beautiful surrounding gardens create a peaceful, relaxing environment.

Cet élégant manoir andalou a été superbement restauré en hôtel en 1991 et propose des chambres et des junior suites impeccables. Chaque chambre se distingue par son propre nom et sa décoration spécifique. Des meubles peints à la main et de somptueuses tapisseries ornent les murs. Les plats faits-maison sont élaborés à partir de produits régionaux frais ou de la ferme de l'hôtel. Les superbes jardins environnants forment un cadre paisible et relaxant.

Dieses zauberhafte andalusische Landhaus wurde 1991 perfekt in ein Hotel umgewandelt und bietet nun gutausgestattete Zimmer und Suiten. Jeder Raum hat einen anderen Namen, ist individuell gestaltet und mit handbemalten Möbeln und extravaganten Wandbehängen geschmückt. Für die hauseigene Küche werden Produkte aus der Gegend oder aus eigenem Anbau verwendet. Die herrlichen umliegenden Gärten schaffen eine friedliche und erholsame Atmosphäre.

Directions: *SE-30>N630>Merida>A460.* **Price guide (Excl. VAT):** *Double/twin Pts16,000–19,000; suites Pts22,000–27,000.*

The Leading Hotels of the World®

HACIENDA BENAZUZA

41800 SANLÚCAR LA MAYOR, SEVILLE, SPAIN
TEL: +34 95 570 33 44 FAX: +34 95 570 34 10 E-MAIL: hbenazuza@anakis.es

Hacienda Benazuza stands on a hill overlooking the Guadimar river valley. The spirit of Benazuza is enhanced by the lavish decoration of its public rooms and opulent bedrooms with magnificent works of art and valuable antiques. There are two restaurants, La Alquería, specialising in international and mediterranean dishes, and the Alberca, next to the pool, cultivating the art of traditional Andalusian cooking.

L'Hacienda Benazuza se dresse sur une colline surplombant la vallée de la rivière Guadiamar. Le charme de Benazuza réside dans la décoration luxueuse de ses salons et de ses chambres opulentes, agrémentées de superbes oeuvres d'art et d'antiquités inestimables. L'hôtel dispose de deux restaurants: La Alquería, spécialisé en plats internationaux et méditerranéens et le Alberca, au bord de la piscine, qui propose de l'art culinaire traditionnel andalou.

Die Hacienda Benazuza liegt auf einem Hügel mit Blick auf den Fluss Guadimar. Das Dekor der Aufenthaltsräume und die opulenten Zimmer mit ihren herrlichen Kunstgegenständen und wertvollen Antiquitäten unterstreicht das üppige Ambiente des Hotels. Zwei Restaurants laden zu Gaumenfreuden ein: La Alquería, das auf internationale und Mittelmeerküche spezialisiert ist, und das am Pool gelegene Alberca mit seinen traditionellen andalusischen Speisen.

Directions: Seville>A49>Huelva>Sanlucar. **Price guide:** Single Pts31,000–47,000; double/twin Pts39,000–57,000; suites Pts52,000–170,000.

ALMENARA HOTEL - GOLF

11310 AVENIDA ALMENARA, SOTOGRANDE, SPAIN
TEL: + 34 956 582 000 FAX: + 34 956 582 001 E-MAIL: almenara.hotel@sotogrande.com

This is a new hotel with stunning views over the countryside to the distant Mediterranean and surrounded by four of Europe's finest golf courses. There is modern design throughout, and the bedrooms are cool, tastefully furnished and fitted to the highest standard. Dining is a delight: there are three restaurants including the Gaia with its fusion of Spanish and Asian cuisine and the more casual Veinteeocho, a café for golfers and guests. Guests can tone-up in the impressive health club with heated pool, or laze around a spectacular outdoor pool.

Il s'agît là d'un nouvel hôtel àvec des vues splendides sur le paysage éloigné de la Méditerranée et entouré par quatre des plus prestigieux parcours de golf d'Europe. Ce nouvel hôtel, avec de superbes vues sur la campagne et au loin la Méditerranée, est entouré par quatre des plus prestigieux parcours de golf d'Europe. Les visiteurs peuvent faire de l'exercice dans l'impressionnant centre de remise en forme ou lézarder autour de la superbe piscine en plein air qui est entourée de sable.

Dieses neue Hotel bietet herrliche Aussichten auf die Umgebung und das Mittelmeer und ist von vier der besten Golfplätze Europas umgeben. Das Interieur ist modern, die kühlenden Zimmer sind geschmackvoll und nach höchstem Standard eingerichtet. Drei Restaurants sorgen für kulinarischen Genuss, darunter das spanisch-asiatische Gaia und das weniger formelle Café Veinteeocho. Ein eindrucksvolles Fitnesszentrum mit beheiztem Pool und ein Freibad mit Strandumgebung stehen ebenfalls zur Verfügung.

Directions: Málaga to Cádiz coast road E15 to Exit 130. **Price guide:** Single Pts23,500–29,500; double/twin Pts 24,000–32,000; suites Pts59,000–74,000.

SA PEDRISSA

CARRETERA VALLDEMOSSA-DEIA, 07179 DEIA, MALLORCA, BALEARIC ISLANDS, SPAIN
TEL: +34 971 63 91 11 FAX: +34 971 63 94 56 E-MAIL: sapedrissa@stl.logiccontrol.es

Situated on a hill below the Tramuntana Mountains, this small luxury hotel is surrounded by olive trees and affords breathtaking views over the Mediterranean. Sa Pedrissa has been carefully converted and fits perfectly into the natural beauty of its surroundings. Guests may try honey, eggs and olive oil still produced on the 'Finca', while relaxing on a terrace or in the gardens, and feast on local Mediterranean cuisine by candlelight. Service is attentive and personal. Massages and beauty treatments are also available.

Perché sur une colline dominée par la Sierra de Tramuntana, ce petit hôtel de luxe entouré d'oliviers jouit d'une vue superbe sur la Méditerranée. Soigneusement transformée en hôtel, Sa Pedrissa est en parfaite harmonie avec la beauté naturelle du paysage. Les visiteurs goûtent les oeufs, le miel et l'huile d'olive produits sur place, se détendent sur la terrasse ou dans le jardin, et dégustent à la chandelle des plats locaux aux saveurs méditerranéennes. Le service est attentionné et personnalisé. L'hôtel propose aussi des massages et des soins de beauté.

Auf einem Hügel unterhalb des Tramuntana Gebirges gelegen und von Olivenbäumen umgeben bietet dieses kleine Luxushotel atemberaubende Blicke auf das Mittelmeer. Sa Pedrissa wurde geschickt renoviert und in die natürliche Schön-heit seiner Umgebung eingefügt. Die Gäste können Eier, selbstprodu-zierten Honig und Olivenöl kosten, während sie auf einer der Terrassen oder im Garten entspannen. Abends wird bei Kerzenschein mediterrane Kost serviert. Auch Massagen und Schönheitsbehandlungen werden angeboten.

Directions: Entrance marked off Deía-Valldemosa. **Price guide:** Single Pts15,000–20,000; double/twin Pts25,000–30,000; suites Pts35,000–55,000.

GRAN HOTEL BAHIA DEL DUQUE

38660 ADEJE, COSTA ADEJE, TENERIFE SOUTH, CANARY ISLANDS
TEL: +34 922 74 69 00 FAX: +34 922 74 69 25 E-MAIL: comercial@bahia-duque.com

This hotel is a private romantic village created on a gentle hill sloping down to the sea. 19 houses in turn-of-the-century Canarian architecture form this prestigious complex in a large estate with sculptured terraces and pools. The furniture has been specially designed, the floors are cool Spanish tiles and the bathrooms are luxurious. Descending towards the coast, guests will find a patio surrounded by eight restaurants.

Cet hôtel est un village romantique privé créé sur une pente douce descendant sur la mer. 19 maisons qui reflètent l'architecture canarienne du début du siècle forment un complexe prestigieux au milieu d'une grande propriété agrémentée de terrasses richement ornées et de piscines. Les meubles ont été spécialement conçus, les sols sont de belles céramiques espagnoles et les salles de bain sont luxueuses. En descendant vers la côte, les visiteurs trouveront un patio et huit restaurants.

Dieses Hotel ist ein romantisches, privates Dorf, das auf einem leicht zum Meer abfallenden Hügel gelegen ist. Die renommierte Anlage besteht aus 19 Häusern im Stil kanarischer Architektur um die Jahrhundertwende, und liegt inmitten eines ausgedehnten Grundstücks mit gepflegten Terrassen und Pools. Das Mobiliar wurde eigens für das Hotel entworfen, die Böden sind mit kühlenden spanischen Fliesen versehen und die Badezimmer sind reiner Luxus. In Richtung Meeresufer liegt ein von acht Restaurants umrahmter Innenhof.

Directions: *Reina Sofia Airport*. **Price guide**: *Single Pts36,600–65,700; double/twin Pts39,700–70,400; suites Pts71,100–231,000.*

HOTEL BOTÁNICO

AVDA. RICHARD J. YEOWARD, URB. BOTANICO, 38400 PUERTO DE LA CRUZ, TENERIFE, CANARY ISLANDS
TEL: +34 922 38 14 00 FAX: +34 922 38 39 93 E-MAIL: hotelbotanico@hotelbotanico.com

The Botánico stands in extensive gardens filled with tropical plants, bridges over lakes with fountains playing and shady places for those wishing to escape the sun. The lavish rooms provide every possible extra and glamorous bathrooms. Choose between three delightful restaurants offering grills, Thai or Italian dishes. There are special rates at all the local golf courses. Guests will be met at the airport upon request.

Le Botánico est situé dans un immense jardin orné de plantes tropicales, de ponts traversant les lacs, de fontaines et d'endroits ombragés pour ceux souhaitant échapper au soleil. Les chambres somptueuses fournissent tous les agréments possibles et ont des salles de bain séduisantes. Vous pourrez choisir entre trois délicieux restaurants proposant des barbecues, des plats thaïlandais ou italiens. Il y a des tarifs préférentiels dans tous les golfs environnants. Les visiteurs seront acheminés depuis l'aéroport sur simple demande.

Das Botánico liegt inmitten von ausgedehnten Gärten voller tropischer Pflanzen, Brücken über kleine Teiche, Springbrunnen und schattigen Plätzen zum Schutz vor der Sonne. Die grosszügigen Zimmer bieten jedes erdenkliche Extra und haben prunkvolle Bäder. Gäste haben die Wahl zwischen drei zauberhaften Restaurants, die auf Grill-, thailändische oder italienische Gerichte spezialisiert sind. Alle Golfplätze am Ort bieten Sondertarife. Gäste werden auf Wunsch am Flugplazt abgeholt.

Directions: Guests can be met at the airport. **Price guide:** Single Pts20,000–39,000; double/twin Pts26,000–59,000; suites Pts42,000–500,000.

HOTEL JARDIN TROPICAL

CALLE GRAN BRETAÑA, 38670 COSTA ADEJE, TENERIFE, CANARY ISLANDS
TEL: +34 922 74 60 00 FAX: +34 922 74 60 60 E-MAIL: hotel@jardin-tropical.com

Built just 10 years ago, this magnificent Moorish palace with its brilliant white walls is enveloped by the exotic green foliage of its subtropical garden interspersed with blue pools and colourful flowers. The interior rooms display cool luxury, and the exclusive Las Adelfas Suites are phenomenal. Guests are spoilt for choice with the cuisine and may enjoy everything from poolside snacks to a gourmet feast.

Construit il y a tout juste 10 ans, ce magnifique palais mauresque a été embelli par des tours surmontées de dômes. L'hôtel se dresse au milieu d'un jardin exotique parsemé de bassins azur et de fleurs colorées. A l'intérieur, les chambres affichent un luxe sobre et les prestigieuses suites Las Adelfas sont remarquables. Les hôtes sont gâtés au niveau culinaire et pourront se régaler du simple snack au bord de la piscine jusqu'au véritable festin gastronomique.

Dieser herrliche, erst vor 10 Jahren erbaute maurische Palast mit seinen strahlend weissen Wänden ist umgeben von dem exotischem Grün eines subtropischen Gartens, leuchtendblauen Pools und bunten Blumen. Die Innenräume spiegeln kühlen Luxus wider, und die exclusiven Las Adelfas Suiten sind einfach prächtig. Was das Essen angeht, haben die Gäste die Qual der Wahl – vom Snack am Pool bis zum Gourmetdinner ist alles geboten.

Directions: *San Eugenio.* **Price guide:** *Single Pts18,000–55,000 ; double/twin Pts25,00–80,000; suites Pts60,000–160,000.*

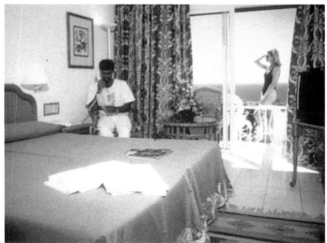

HOTEL SAN ROQUE

C/. ESTEBAN DE PONTE 32, 38450 GARACHICO, TENERIFE, CANARY ISLANDS
TEL: +34 922 13 34 35 FAX: +34 922 13 34 06 E-MAIL: info@hotelsanroque.com

This 17th century town house has been carefully restored and converted into a unique small hotel, combining the original construction with the contemporary Bauhaus style. Stone archways guide guests into the generously sized rooms that are decorated in sumptuous colours, featuring dark wooden ceilings and modern furniture. All rooms have Jacuzzi bath tubs. Fine dishes incorporating fresh fish and locally sourced produce are served.

Cet hôtel particulier du XVIIème siècle a été restauré avec soin et transformé en un petit hôtel remarquable dans lequel l'architecture d'origine se marie au style contemporain de Bauhaus. Des voûtes en pierre s'ouvrent sur des chambres spacieuses, ornées de plafonds en bois foncé et de meubles modernes. Toutes les chambres possèdent une baignoire Jacuzzi. De succulents plats sont offerts et combinent du poisson frais et des produits régionaux.

Dieses Stadthaus aus dem 17. Jahrhundert wurde umsichtig restauriert und in ein einzigartiges kleines Hotel umgewandelt. Dabei verbindet sich der Originalbau perfekt mit dem zeitgenössischen Bauhausstil. Steinerne Bögen führen in grosszügige Räume, die in üppigen Farben gehalten und mit dunklen Holzdecken und modernem Mobiliar ausgestattet sind. Alle Zimmer haben Jacuzzi-Badewannen. Gäste erfreuen sich an köstlichen Gerichten, die mit frischem Fisch und einheimischen Zutaten zubereitet werden.

Directions: Centre of Garachico. **Price guide:** *Single Pts18,000–24,000; double/twin Pts26,000–36,000; suites Pts38,000–48,000.*

HOTEL RECTOR

RECTOR ESPERABÉ 10–APARTADO 399, 37008 SALAMANCA, SPAIN
TEL: +34 923 21 84 82 FAX: +34 923 21 40 08 E-MAIL: hotelrector@teleline.es

This exclusive hotel with its elegant façade stands by the walls of the citadel looking up to the cathedral, a magnificent golden vision at night when floodlit. The interior looks cool and elegant with archways between the spacious reception hall and the welcoming bar. Unique features in the main salon are two exquisite modern stained glass windows. There are 13 bedrooms, delightfully furnished with marble bathrooms. Breakfast is served in the hotel, and for dinner, there are numerous restaurants in the vicinity.

Cet hôtel exclusif orné d'une superbe façade se dresse à côté des remparts de la citadelle; elle même dominée par la cathédrale, qui devient une vision magique lorsqu'illuminée la nuit. L'intérieur est frais et élégant, avec de belles voûtes qui séparent le spacieux hall de réception et le bar accueillant. Le salon principal est orné de deux ravissants vitraux modernes. L'hôtel compte treize chambres, délicieusement meublées avec salles de bain en marbre. Le petit déjeuner est servi à l'hôtel et de nombreux restaurants sont situés à proximité.

Dieses exklusive Hotel mit seiner eleganten Fassade liegt an einer Zitadelle neben der Kathedrale, die nachts beleuchtet wird und ein herrlich goldenes Spektakel bietet. Das Interieur ist kühl und elegant, mit Bogengängen zwischen der grossen Empfangshalle und der einladenden Bar. Hauptanziehungspunkte des Salons sind zweifellos zwei exquisite moderne Buntglasfenster. Die 13 Zimmer sind zauberhaft gestaltet und haben Marmorbäder. Frühstück wird im Hotel serviert, und am Abend locken zahlreiche Restaurants in der Umgebung.

Directions: *Madrid>Avenide de los Reyes Espana>Pa de Rector Esperabe.* **Price guide:** *Single Pts12,500; double/twin Pts17,000; suites Pts22,000.*

HOTEL CLARIS

PAU CLARIS 150, 08009 BARCELONA, SPAIN
TEL: +34 93 487 62 62 FAX: +34 93 215 79 70 E-MAIL: claris@derbyhotels.es

The former Palace of the Vedruna family still retains its graceful Renaissance façade whilst the interior is an extravagant example of avant garde design with metres of marble, glass, rare timbers and cast stone. Art pieces and 5th century Roman mosaics abound, and there is a collection of pre-Columbian art. The bedrooms are exciting, eclectic in style with antique objets d'art. Ampurdan cuisine can be sampled in the gourmet restaurant, matched by local wines.

Ancien palais de la famille Vedruna, cet hôtel a conservé son élégante façade Renaissance. A l'intérieur, les pièces offrent des exemples extravagants de décoration avant-gardiste avec du marbre, du verre, du bois rare et des pierres sculptées. Des oeuvres d'art et des mosaïques romaines du Vème siècle abondent. Il y a également une collection d'art pré-colombien. Les chambres sont originales et éclectiques avec des objets d'art anciens. La cuisine de l'Ampurdan pourra être dégustée au restaurant gourmet, avec des vins locaux appropriés.

Der ehemalige Palast der Familie Vedruna besitzt immer noch seine anmutige Renaissance-Fassade, während das Interieur ein extravagantes Beispiel für avantgardistisches Design darstellt und üppig mit Marmor, Glas, seltenem Holz und Stein, Kunstgegenständen und römischen Mosaiken aus dem 5. Jahrhundert ausgestattet ist. Auch eine Sammlung präkolumbianischer Kunst ist vorhanden. Die eklektischen Schlafzimmer sind dramatisch mit antiken Objets d'Art eingerichtet. Das Gourmetrestaurant serviert Gerichte des Ampurdan und Weine der Region.

Directions: Pau Claris>Paseo de Gracia>Calle de Valencia. **Price guide:** Single Pts49,500; double/twin Pts55,000; suites Pts65,000–140,000 (+7% IVA).

HOTEL COLON

AVENIDA DE LA CATEDRAL 7, 08002 BARCELONA, SPAIN
TEL: +34 93 301 14 04 FAX: +34 93 317 29 15 E-MAIL: colon@ncsa.es

Situated in the old Gothic quarter, this hotel offers a combination of fine accommodation, excellent service and friendly staff resulting in a most inviting ambience. The front rooms afford glorious views of the square and the 13th century cathedral whilst the suites at the rear feature picturesque terraces. Seafood is speciality with salmon, clams, squid and hake all used to create international and typical Catalan dishes.

Situé dans le vieux quartier gothique, cet hôtel offre une combinaison de logement raffiné, d'excellent service et de personnel amical qui donne une ambiance des plus sympathiques. Les chambres de devant offrent des vues superbes sur la place de la cathédrale du XIIIème siècle alors que les suites de l'arrière de l'hôtel ont des terraces pittoresques. Les fruits de mer sont la spécialité avec saumon, praires, poulpe et colin, tous cuisinés pour créer des plats internationaux et typiques catalans.

Dieses einladende Hotel liegt im Gotischen Viertel und bietet eine Kombination aus gediegener Unterkunft, exzellentem Service und freundlichem Personal. Die Zimmer an der Frontseite bieten einen herrlichen Ausblick auf den Platz und die Kathedrale aus dem 13. Jahrhundert, während die Suiten an der Rückseite auf malerische Terrassen führen. Auf der Speisekarte stehen internationale und katalanische Gerichte, die vor allem auf Fisch und Meeresfrüchten, wie Lachs, Muscheln, Tintenfisch und Seehecht, basieren.

Directions: Located in the Gothic quarter. **Price guide (excl. 7% VAT):** Single Pts17,500–22,500; double/twin Pts26,000–31,900; suites Pts46,500–51,500.

THE GALLERY

ROSSELLO 249, 08008 BARCELONA, SPAIN
TEL: +34 93 415 99 11 FAX: +34 93 415 91 84 E-MAIL: email@galleryhotel.com

Visitors to the Gallery are enveloped by the warm ambience and are treated to a personal and individual service whilst enjoying the fine standards of accommodation. Featuring a stylish blend of modern and classical decor, the bedrooms offer every possible comfort. The Scotch Bar is ideal for a preprandial drink after which fine cuisine may be enjoyed in the atmospheric Café Del Gallery. A fitness centre and separate saunas offer revitalisation to visitors returning from a day exploring vibrant Barcelona.

Les visiteurs du Gallery découvrent une atmosphère chaleureuse et un service à la fois personalisé et unique, tout en profitant de cet établissement de grand standing. Les chambres, savant mélange d'éléments modernes et classiques, offrent tout le confort possible. Le Scotch Bar est idéal pour prendre l'apéritif à la suite de quoi une excellente cuisine vous est proposée au Café Del Gallery. Saunas et club de remise en forme attendent les visiteurs en quête de revitalisation après une journée de visite dans l'excitante ville qu'est Barcelone.

Die Gallery versprüht eine herzliche Atmosphäre, die von freundlichem und persönlichem Service noch verstärkt wird. Die Unterkunft ist erstklassig, und die Zimmer, sowohl modern als auch klassisch gestaltet, bieten jeden erdenklichen Komfort. Die Scotch Bar ist ideal für einen Apéritif, und danach lässt man sich im charaktervollen Café Del Gallery von erlesenen Speisen verführen. Ein Fitnesszentrum und separate Saunen sorgen nach einem langen Tag im lebhaften Barcelona für Entspannung.

Directions: Between Rambla de Catalunya and Paseo de Gracia. **Price guide:** Single Pts32,000; double/twin Pts37,000; suites Pts48,500.

HOTEL GREVOL

CARRETERA CAMPRODON A SETCASES, 17869 LLANARS, SPAIN
TEL: +34 972 74 10 13 FAX: +34 972 74 10 87 E-MAIL: info@hotelgrevol.com

Nestling in the town of Llanars in the heart of the Spanish Pyrenees, the Hotel Grèvol is a Shangri-La for those who enjoy spending their time outdoors. This chalet-style hotel is an idyllic hideaway from the cacophony of city life. There is a fine swimming pool and a Jacuzzi, both leading out into a beautiful garden. Specialist Catalan cuisine is served in the restaurant along with a well-chosen range of Spanish and international dishes. The Grèvol is an ideal base for exploring the magnificent Pyrenees.

Niché dans la ville de Llanars, au coeur des Pyrénées espagnoles, l'hôtel Grèvol est un refuge idyllique pour ceux qui cherchent à fuir le maelstrom de la ville. Ce chalet-hôtel est un véritable paradis pour les visiteurs qui aiment les activités de plein air. Il comporte une superbe piscine et un Jacuzzi, tous deux conduisant à de magnifiques jardins. Le restaurant propose aussi bien des spécialités catalanes que de la cuisine traditionnelle espagnole ou internationale. Le Grèvol est une base idéale pour explorer les Pyrénées.

In der Stadt Llanars mitten in den spanischen Pyrenäen liegt das Hotel Grèvol, ein Mekka für jeden, der sich gern im Freien aufhält. Dieses Hotel im Chalet-Stil ist ein idyllisches Versteck, um dem hektischen Stadtleben zu entkommen. Ein herrlicher Pool und ein Jacuzzi führen in einen herrlichen Garten. Im Restaurant werden neben katalonischen Spezialitäten auch internationale und spanische Gerichte serviert. Das Grèvol ist ein perfekter Ausgangspunkt für Exkursionen in die Pyrenäen.

Directions: *A7>Girnoa>Granollers>Vic>Camprodon>Set Cases>Llanars.* **Price guide:** *Double/twin Pts18,000–21,000.*

HOTEL RIGAT PARK

PLAYA DE FENALS, 17310 LLORET DE MAR, COSTA BRAVA, SPAIN
TEL: +34 972 36 52 00 FAX: +34 972 37 04 11 E-MAIL: rigat@ctv.es

A huge park of pines, exuding the distinctive aroma common to these trees, surrounds the Rigat Park Hotel. This is an ideal base for exploring the beaches of Costa Brava and the many small Catalan towns which lie within easy reach. The bedrooms are decorated and furnished in Mediterranean style with tiled floors and marble bathrooms. Guests may play billiards or swim in the pool with its underwater music.

Une immense pinède, dégageant son arôme distinctif, entoure le Rigat Park Hotel. Il s'agît là d'une base idéale pour explorer les plages de la Costa Brava et les nombreuses petites villes catalanes qui abondent aux alentours. Les chambres sont décorées et meublées dans un style méditerranéen avec des sols carrelés et des salles de bain en marbre. Les hôtes jouent au billard ou nagent dans la piscine où l'on peut écouter de la musique sous l'eau.

Ein riesiger duftender Pinienwald umgibt das Rigat Park Hotel, das einen idealen Ausgangspunkt für Ausflüge an die Strände der Costa Brava und zu den vielen kleinen katalonischen Städten in der Nähe darstellt. Die Zimmer sind im mediterranen Stil gestaltet und möbliert und bieten Fliesenböden und Marmorbäder. Zur Entspannung oder sportlichen Betätigung können die Gäste eine Runde Billiard spielen oder im Pool zu Unterwassermusik schwimmen.

Directions: A7>exit 9>Lloret de Mar>Fenals beach. **Price guide:** Double/twin Pts21,000–35,000; suites Pts40,000–55,000.

HOTEL LA COSTA

AVENIDA ARENALES DE MAR 3, 17256 PLATJA DE PALS, (COSTA BRAVA) SPAIN
TEL: +34 972 66 77 40 FAX: +34 972 66 77 36 E-MAIL: info@lacostahotel.com

This comfortable and friendly hotel is a golfer's paradise with its own new golf course 'Golf Serres de Pals' and special green fees for playing at all 9 courses in the area, including Pals, one of the leading courses on the Spanish circuit. All 120 bedrooms are comfortable and well-equipped and there are also 57 apartments overlooking the sea. Featured among the excellent leisure facilities are an exotic multi-dimensional swimming pool, saunas, gymnasium, Jacuzzi and tennis courts.

Cet hôtel confortable et accueillant est un véritable paradis pour golfeurs. Il offre son propre parcours 'Golf Serres de Pals' et des tarifs préférentiels sur les 9 parcours voisins, notamment celui de Pals, l'un des meilleurs sur le circuit espagnol. Chacune des 120 chambres est confortable et bien équipée et l'hôtel compte également 57 appartements surplombant la mer. On remarquera en outre les superbes installations de loisir qui comportent une piscine exotique multidimentionnelle, des saunas, un gymnase, un jacuzzi et des courts de tennis.

Dieses komfortable und freundliche Hotel ist ein Paradies für Golfer: Ein eigener Golfplatz, 'Golf Serres de Pals' steht zur Verfügung, und Gäste bekommen Sonderkonditionen für alle 9 Plätze in der Umgebung, darunter Pals, eines der führenden Wettkampfgebiete Spaniens. Alle 120 Zimmer sind komfortabel und gut ausgestattet, und es stehen 57 Appartements mit Meeresblick zur Verfügung. Zu den exzellenten Freizeitmöglichkeiten gehören ein exotischer, mehrdimensionaler Pool, Sauna, Fitnessraum, Jacuzzi und Tennisplätze.

Directions: *A7>Girona Nord>La Bisbal>Pals.* **Price guide (per person):** *Single Pts14,750–25,050; double/twin Pts9,950–17,970; suites Pts11,650–20,250.*

HOTEL ESTELA BARCELONA

**AVDA. PORT D'AIGUADOLÇ S/N, 08870 SITGES (BARCELONA), SPAIN
TEL: +34 938 11 45 45 FAX: +34 938 11 45 46 E-MAIL: info@hotelestela.com**

Upon entering the hotel reception, guests are greeted by steps, waterfalls, sculptured balls and a vintage open-top car full of mirrors comprising what art critics claim to be 'a peculiar vision of the coming together of two dimensions'. Art abounds in the spacious, cool restaurant where Mediterranean cuisine is served. There is a wide terrace overlooking the gardens with two pools and sculptures 'growing' among the greenery.

En pénétrant dans le hall de l'hôtel, les visiteurs découvrent des marches, des cascades, des boules sculptées et une voiture de collection décapotable remplie de miroirs offrant ce que les critiques d'art qualifient "d'étrange vision de la rencontre de deux dimensions". L'art est à l'honneur dans le restaurant spacieux et détendu où l'on vous propose de la cuisine méditerranéenne. L'hôtel comporte également une vaste terrasse surplombant le jardin agrémenté de deux bassins et de sculptures qui "poussent" littéralement au milieu de la verdure.

Das erste, was beim Betreten dieses Hotels auffällt, sind die Treppen, Wasserfälle, gemeisselten Kugeln und ein mit Spiegeln gefülltes Oldtimer-Cabrio – von Kunstkritikern als "eine eigentümliche Vision der Vereinigung zweier Dimensionen" beschrieben. Auch in dem geräumigen, kühlen Restaurant ist Kunst allgegenwärtig, und serviert wird hier mediterrane Küche. Eine grosse Terrasse gibt den Blick auf die Gärten frei, in denen sich zwei Pools und zahlreiche Skulpturen befinden.

Directions: Barcelona>A16>C246>Sitges. **Price guide:** Single Pts15,500–20,000; double/twin Pts20,500–25,000; suites Pts23,000–34,000.

HOTEL TERMES MONTBRIO RESORT, SPA & PARK

CARRER NOU 38, 43340 MONTBRIO DEL CAMP (TARRAGONA), SPAIN
TEL: +34 977 81 40 00 FAX: +34 977 82 62 51 E-MAIL: Termes@ctv.es

The Hotel Termes Montbrio Resorts, Spa and Park is a unique example of modern architecture. The 214 beautiful en suite bedrooms are situated in a spacious annexe, all well-equipped and decorated in a colourful, modernist style. Two restaurants serve international and Mediterranean cuisine, whilst the Thermal centre features a hot spring pool, giant Jacuzzi, panoramic gymnasium and offers many beauty treatments.

L'Hotel Termes Montbrio Resort, Spa & Park est un exemple unique d'architecture moderne. Les 214 superbes chambres, situées dans une annexe spacieuse, sont toutes bien équipées et décorées dans un style moderniste et coloré. Les deux restaurants proposent une cuisine méditerranéenne et internationale. Le centre thermal, quant à lui, met à votre disposition une piscine d'eau de source chaude, un Jacuzzi géant, un gymnase panoramique et un choix de traitements de beauté.

Das Hotel Termes Montbrio Resort, Spa & Park ist ein einzigartiges Beispiel moderner Architektur. Die 214 exquisiten Zimmer, die in einem geräumigen Anbau liegen, sind hervorragend ausgestattet und in modernem, farbenfrohen Stil gehalten. Die zwei Restaurants servieren köstliche internationale und Mittelmeerküche. Das Thermalzentrum bietet einen von heissen Quellen beheizten Pool, einen riesigen Jacuzzi, einen Fitnessraum mit Panoramablick und zahlreiche Schönheitsanwendungen.

Directions: A7>direction of Tarragona>exit 37 Cambrils>follow signs to Montbrio. **Price guide:** Single Pts19,300; double/twin Pts25,000; suites Pts50,000.

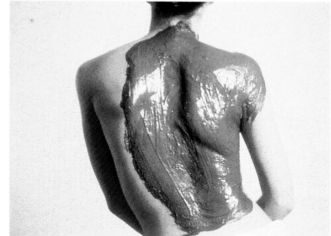

GRAND HOTEL ZERMATTERHOF

3920 ZERMATT, SWITZERLAND

TEL: +41 27 966 66 00 FAX: +41 27 966 66 99 E-MAIL: zermatterhof@zermatt.ch

The pace of life in this magnet for resolute climbers and winter sports enthusiasts is slow and of another age. No cars are allowed in the resort, so only the hum of electric trolleys and the sound of horses' hooves resound through the streets. The five-star hotel is one of a diminishing few that belong to a bygone age of grandeur. It is truly opulent with sumptuous suites, gourmet cuisine and impeccable service.

Il s'agît là d'un paradis pour les alpinistes et les fanatiques de sport d'hiver. Dans le village, le rythme de vie est ralenti à celui d'un temps suranné. Aucune voiture n'est autorisée et seuls le bourdonnement des remontées mécaniques et le bruit des sabots des chevaux résonnent dans les rues. L'hôtel 5 étoiles est un des derniers à avoir conservé une splendeur des temps passés. Il est vraiment luxueux avec de sompteueses suites, une table de gourmets et un service impeccable.

Der Lebensrhythmus dieses Ortes, der perfekt für Bergsteiger und Wintersportler geeignet ist, ist beschaulich und erinnert an vergangene Zeiten. Das Dorf ist autofrei, und so sind in den Strassen nur die Geräusche der Pferdehufe und das Surren der Elektroautos zu vernehmen. Das 5-Sterne-Hotel gehört zu den wenigen Grand Hotels vergangener Epochen, und ist wahrhaft opulent mit luxuriösen Suiten, einer Gourmetküche und makellosem Service.

Directions: *Täsch > train or helicopter > Zermatt.* **Price guide:** *Single SF260–380; double/twin SF370–800; suites SF650–1790.*

POSTHOTEL ENGIADINA

VIA MAISTRA, 7524 ZUOZ, SWITZERLAND
TEL +41 81 85 41 021 FAX: +41 81 85 43 303 E-MAIL: mail@hotelengiadina.ch

This traditional Swiss manor house is set in Zuoz, a village which has retained much of its 16th century architectural charm. In winter, the snow-covered Engadine provides superb skiing and in summer it offers wonderful walks among the flower-filled meadows, lakes and forests of the Swiss National Park. Haute cuisine and marvellous Swiss, French and Italian wines, served in the two handsome restaurants, add to the appeal.

Ce manoir suisse traditionnel est situé à Zuoz, village ayant conservé une grande partie de son charme architectural du XVIème siècle. En hiver, l'Engadine couvert de neige permet de skier et en été il permet de faire de merveilleuses promenades dans les prés fleuris, autour des lacs et à travers les forêts du parc national suisse. La haute cuisine accompagnée de merveilleux vins suisses, français et italiens ajoute à son charme.

Dieses typische Schweizer Herrenhaus liegt in Zuoz, einem Ort, der seinen architektonischen Charme des 16. Jahrhunderts bewahrt hat. Im Winter bietet das schneereiche Engadin beste Skimöglichkeiten und im Sommer laden die blumengefüllten Wiesen und die Seen und Wälder des Schweizer Nationalparks zu Wanderungen ein. Haute Cuisine und erlesene Weine der Schweiz, Frankreichs und Italiens laden zum Schlemmen und Geniessen ein.

Directions: *Chur > St. Moritz > Zuoz.* **Price guide:** *Single SF128–160; double/twin SF176–300.*

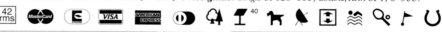

SAVILE RESIDENCE

CUKURBAG YARIMADASI, KAS/ANTALYA, TURKEY
TEL: +90 242 836 2300 UK TEL (FOR RESERVATIONS): +44 20 7625 3001

This charming country house hotel enjoys a superb location on the Kas peninsula. Reflecting the exotic character of Turkey, while matching the standards of accommodation and hospitality found in the best English country house, it boasts wonderful views. There is a private pool, spacious lounge and choice of bars. A delicious Mediterranean breakfast is included in the price, and other delights are served in the restaurant.

Ce charmant hôtel bénéficie d'un excellent positionnement sur la péninsule de Kas. Reflétant le caractère exotique de la Turquie, tout en égalant les standards de logement et d'hôtellerie des meilleurs établissements britanniques, l'hôtel bénéficie de splendides vues. Il y a une piscine privée, des salons spacieux et un choix de plusieurs bars. Un délicieux petit-déjeuner méditerranéen est inclus dans le prix, et d'autres plaisirs vous seront réservées au restaurant.

Dieses charmante Landhaushotel liegt auf der Halbinsel Kas und bietet traumhafte Aussichten. Es spiegelt perfekt das exotische Flair der Türkei wider und bietet dabei einen Standard an Unterkunft und Gastfreundschaft, wie man ihn in einem der besten englischen Landhäuser erwarten würde. Zur Entspannung stehen ein privater Pool, eine geräumige Lounge und eine Reihe an Bars zur Verfügung. Das verlockende Mittelmeerfrühstück ist inklusive, weitere Köstlichkeiten werden im Restaurant serviert.

Directions: *Dalaman > Kas > Peninsula > Savile Residence.* **Price guide:** *Suite £140–£280.*

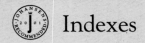

Indexes

Johansens Recommended Hotels – Europe & The Mediterranean 2001

SCOTLAND

Aberdeen	Ardoe House Hotel & Restaurant	01224 860600
Aberdeen	Thainstone House Hotel & Country Club	01467 621643
Aberfoyle	Forest Hills	01877 387277
Auchencairn	Balcary Bay Hotel	01556 640311
Auchterarder	Auchterarder House	01764 663646
Ballantrae	Glenapp Castle	01465 831212
Ballater	Darroch Learg Hotel	013397 55443
Banchory	Raemoir House Hotel	01330 824884
Beasdale By Arisaig	Arisaig House	01687 450622
Biggar	Shieldhill Castle	01899 220035
Blairgowrie	Kinloch House Hotel	01250 884237
Craigellachie	Craigellachie Hotel	01340 881204
Dunkeld	Kinnaird	01796 482 440
Dunoon	Enmore Hotel	01369 702230
East Kilbride	Macdonald Crutherland House Hotel	01355 577000
Edinburgh	The Bonham	0131 226 6050
Edinburgh	Borthwick Castle	01875 820514
Edinburgh	Channings	0131 315 2226
Edinburgh	Dalhousie Castle & Spa	01875 820153
Edinburgh	The Howard	0131 557 3500
Edinburgh	The Norton House Hotel	0131 333 1275
Edinburgh	Prestonfield House	0131 668 3346
Edinburgh	The Roxburgh	0131 240 5500
Edinburgh	The Scotsman	0131 556 5565
Elgin	Mansion House Hotel	01343 548811
Gatehouse Of Fleet	Cally Palace Hotel	01557 814341
Glasgow	Carlton George Hotel	0141 353 6373
Glasgow	Gleddoch House	01475 540711
Glenshee	Dalmunzie House	01250 885224
Grantown-On-Spey	Muckrach Lodge Hotel & Restaurant	01479 851257
Inverness	Bunchrew House Hotel	01463 234917
Inverness	Culloden House Hotel	01463 790461
Kelso	Ednam House Hotel	01573 224168
Kelso	The Roxburghe Hotel & Golf Course	01573 450331
Kilchrenan by Oban	Ardanaiseig	01866 833333
Kildrummy	Kildrummy Castle Hotel	019755 71288
Kinbuck	Cromlix House	01786 822125
Lochinver	Inver Lodge Hotel	01571 844496
Lockerbie	The Dryfesdale Country House Hotel	01576 202427
Newton Stewart	Kirroughtree House	01671 402141
Oban	Knipoch Hotel	01852 316251
Peebles	Cringletie House Hotel	01721 730233
Perth	Ballathie House Hotel	01250 883268
Perth	Huntingtower Hotel	01738 583771
Perth	Kinfauns Castle	01738 620777
Pitlochry	Pine Trees Hotel	01796 472121
Portpatrick	Fernhill Hotel	01776 810220
St Andrews	The Inn at Lathones	01334 840 494
St Boswells	Dryburgh Abbey Hotel	01835 822261
Stirling	Stirling Highland Hotel	01786 272727
Stranraer	Corsewall Lighthouse Hotel	01776 853220
Torridon	Loch Torridon Hotel	01445 791242
Troon	Lochgreen House	01292 313343
Troon	Piersland House Hotel	01292 314747
Uphall	Houstoun House	01506 853831

WALES

Aberdare	Ty Newydd Country Hotel	01685 813433
Abergavenny	Allt-Yr-Ynys Hotel	01873 890307
Abergavenny	Llansantffraed Court Hotel	01873 840678
Abersoch	Porth Tocyn Country House Hotel	01758 713303
Aberystwyth	Conrah Country House Hotel	01970 617941
Anglesey	Trearddur Bay Hotel	01407 860301
Bala	Palé Hall	01678 530285
Barmouth	Bontddu Hall	01341 430661
Beaumaris	Ye Olde Bull's Head	01248 810329
Brecon	Llangoed Hall	01874 754525
Brecon	Peterstone Court	01874 665387
Brecon Beacons	Nant Ddu Lodge Hotel	01685 379111
Cardiff	Miskin Manor Country House Hotel	01443 224204
Corwen	Tyddyn Llan Country House Hotel	01490 440264
Crickhowell	Gliffaes Country House Hotel	01874 730371
Dolgellau	Penmaenuchaf Hall	01341 422129
Harlech	Hotel Maes-Y-Neuadd	01766 780200
Lake Vyrnwy	Lake Vyrnwy Hotel	01691 870 692
Llandudno	Bodysgallen Hall	01492 584466
Llandudno	St Tudno Hotel	01492 874411
Llangammarch Wells	The Lake Country House	01591 620202
Machynlleth	Ynyshir Hall	01654 781209
Pembroke	The Court Hotel & Restaurant	01646 672273
Portmeirion Village	The Portmeirion and Castell Deudraeth	01766 770000
St David's	Warpool Court Hotel	01437 720300
Tenby	Penally Abbey	01834 843033
Usk	The Cwrt Bleddyn Hotel	01633 450521
Wrexham	Llyndir Hall Hotel	01244 571648

CHANNEL ISLANDS

Guernsey	Old Government House Hotel	01481 724921
Guernsey	St Pierre Park Hotel	01481 728282
Jersey	The Atlantic Hotel	01534 744101
Jersey	Château La Chaire	01534 863354
Jersey	Hotel L'Horizon	01534 743101
Jersey	Longueville Manor	01534 725501

Johansens Recommended Traditional Inns, Hotels & Restaurants 2001

ENGLAND

Ashbourne	Red Lion Inn	01335 370396
Ashbourne/Uttoxeter	Beeches Restaurant	01889 590288
Bakewell	The Peacock Hotel at Rowsley	01629 733518
Belford	The Blue Bell Hotel	01668 213543
Brancaster Staithe	The White Horse	01485 210262
Bridport	The Manor Hotel	01308 897616
Brighton	The Old Tollgate Restaurant And Hotel	01903 879494
Burford	The Lamb Inn	01993 823155
Burnsall	The Red Lion	01756 720204
Burton Upon Trent	Boar's Head Hotel	01283 820344
Burton upon Trent	Ye Olde Dog & Partridge	01283 813030
Calver	The Chequers Inn	01433 630231
Camborne	Tyacks Hotel	01209 612424
Cambridge	The White Horse Inn	01440 706081
Carlisle	The Tarn End House Hotel	016977 2340
Chesterfield / Sheffield	Manor House Hotel & Restaurant	01246 413971
Christchurch	The Lord Bute	01425 278884
Cirencester	The New Inn at Coln	01285 750651
Clare	The Plough Inn	01440 786789
Clavering	The Cricketers	01799 550442
Coleford	The New Inn	01363 84242
Compton Bassett	White Horse Inn	01249 813118
Coningsby	The Lea Gate Inn	01526 342370
Cranbrook	The George Hotel	01580 713348
Ditcheat	The Manor House Inn	01749 860276
Dorchester-On-Thames	The George Hotel	01865 340404
East Witton	The Blue Lion	01969 624273
Egton	The Wheatsheaf Inn	01947 895271
Eton	The Christopher Hotel	01753 811677
Evershot	Acorn Inn	01935 83228
Evesham	Riverside Restaurant And Hotel	01386 446200
Exmoor	The Royal Oak Inn	01643 851455
Falmouth	Trengilly Wartha Country Inn	01326 340332
Fordingbridge	The Three Lions Restaurant	01425 652489
Goring-On-Thames	The Leatherne Bottel Riverside Inn	01491 872667
Grimsthorpe	The Black Horse Inn	01778 591247
Grindleford	The Maynard Arms	01433 630321
Halifax/Huddersfield	The Rock Inn Hotel	01422 379721
Handcross	The Chequers At Slaugham	01444 400239
Harrogate	The Boar's Head Hotel	01423 771888
Harrogate	The George	01765 677214
Hathersage	The Plough Inn	01433 650319
Hayfield	The Waltzing Weasel	01663 743402
Helmsley	The Feathers Hotel	01439 770275
Helmsley	The Feversham Arms Hotel	01439 770766
Hindon	The Grosvenor Arms	01747 820696
Holt	The Roman Camp Inn	01263 838291
Honiton	Home Farm Hotel	01404 831278
Huddersfield	The Weavers Shed Restaurant with Rooms	01484 654284
Kenilworth	Clarendon House Bar Brasserie Hotel	01926 857668
Knutsford	Longview Hotel And Restaurant	01565 632119
Leek	The Three Horseshoes Inn & Kirk's	01538 300296
Longleat	The Bath Arms	01985 844308
Lymington	Gordleton Mill Inn	01590 682219
Lynmouth	The Rising Sun	01598 753223
Maidstone	Ringlestone Inn and Farmhouse Hotel	01622 859900
Malmesbury	The Horse And Groom Inn	01666 823904
Mells	The Talbot Inn at Mells	01373 812254
Mildenhall	The Bell Hotel	01638 717272
Newby Bridge	The Swan Hotel	015395 31681
Nottingham	Hotel Des Clos	01159 866566
Oxford	Holcombe Hotel	01869 338274
Oxford	The Jersey Arms	01869 343234
Padstow	The Old Custom House Hotel	01841 532359
Pangbourne	The George Hotel	01189 842237
Pelynt	Jubilee Inn	01503 220312
Penzance	The Summer House	01736 363744
Pickering	The White Swan	01751 472288
Port Gaverne	The Port Gaverne Inn	01208 880244
Preston	Ye Horn's Inn	01772 865230
Rugby	The Golden Lion Inn of Easenhall	01788 832265
Saddleworth	The Old Bell Inn Hotel	01457 870130
Shipton Under Wychwood	The Shaven Crown Hotel	01993 830330
Snettisham	The Rose & Crown	01485 541382
Stamford	Black Bull Inn	01476 860086
Stamford	The Crown Hotel	01780 763136
Stanton Wick	The Carpenters Arms	01761 490202
Stow-On-The-Wold	The Kings Head Inn & Restaurant	01608 658365
Telford	The Hundred House Hotel	01952 730353
Thaxted	Recorders House Restaurant	01371 830438
Thirsk	Crab & Lobster	01845 577286
Thornham	The Lifeboat Inn	01485 512236
Thorpe Market	Green Farm Restaurant And Hotel	01263 833602
Tintagel	The Port William	01840 770230
Totnes	The Sea Trout Inn	01803 762274
Upton-Upon-Severn	The White Lion Hotel	01684 592551
West Auckland	The Manor House Hotel & Country Club	01388 834834
Whitewell	The Inn At Whitewell	01200 448222
Wisbech	Crown Lodge Hotel	01945 773391
Wooler	The Tankerville Arms Hotel	01668 281581

SCOTLAND

Annan	The Powfoot Hotel	01461 700254
Edinburgh	Bank Hotel	0131 556 9940
Isle Of Skye	Hotel Eilean Iarmain	01471 833332
Kylesku	Kylesku Hotel	01971 502231
Loch Earn	Achray House on Loch Earn	01764 685231
Moffat	Annandale Arms Hotel	01683 220013
Oldmeldrum	The Redgarth	01651 872 353
Plockton	The Plockton Hotel & Garden Restaurant	01599 544274
Poolewe	Pool House Hotel	01445 781272
Stirling	Sheriffmuir Inn	01786 823285
Tighnabruaich	Royal Hotel	01700 811239

WALES

Bridgend	The Great House	01656 657644
Llanarmon Dyffryn Ceiriog	The West Arms Hotel	01691 600665
Presteigne	The Radnorshire Arms	01544 267406

CHANNEL ISLANDS

Guernsey	Les Rocquettes Hotel	01481 722176

ENGLAND

Albrighton	The Grange Hotel	01902 701711
Alcester	Arrow Mill Hotel And Restaurant	01789 762419
Alcester	The Old Windmill	01386 792801
Ambleside	Nanny Brow Country House Hotel	015394 32036
Ampleforth	Shallowdale House	01439 788325
Appleton-Le-Moors	Appleton Hall	01751 417227
Arundel	Burpham Country House Hotel	01903 882160
Ashington	The Mill House Hotel	01903 892426
Atherstone	Chapel House	01827 718949
Bamburgh	Waren House Hotel	01668 214581
Barnstaple	Downrew House Hotel	01271 342497
Bath	Apsley House	01225 336966
Bath	Bath Lodge Hotel	01225 723040
Bath	The County Hotel	01225 425003
Bath	The Old Priory Hotel	01761 416784
Bath	Paradise House	01225 317723
Bath	Villa Magdala	01225 466329
Bath	Widbrook Grange	01225 864750
Bath	Woolverton House	01373 830415
Beccles	The Elms	01502 677380
Bibury	Bibury Court	01285 740337
Biggin-By-Hartington	Biggin Hall	01298 84451
Billericay	The Pump House Apartment	01277 656579
Blockley	Lower Brook House	01386 700286
Bourton-On-The-Water	Dial House Hotel	01451 822244
Brighton	The Granville	01273 326302
Brockenhurst	Thatched Cottage Hotel & Restaurant	01590 623090
Brockenhurst	Whitley Ridge & Country House Hotel	01590 622354
Bromsgrove	Grafton Manor Country House Hotel	01527 579007
Cambridge	Melbourn Bury	01763 261151
Carlisle	Crosby Lodge Country House Hotel	01228 573618
Cartmel	Aynsome Manor Hotel	015395 36653
Cheddar	Daneswood House Hotel	01934 843145
Cheltenham	Charlton Kings Hotel	01242 231061
Chester	Green Bough Hotel	01244 326241
Chichester	Crouchers Bottom Country Hotel	01243 784995
Chippenham	Stanton Manor	01666 837552
Chipping Campden	The Malt House	01386 840295
Clearwell	Tudor Farmhouse Hotel & Restaurant	01594 833046
Coalville	Abbots Oak	01530 832 328
Combe Martin	Ashelford	01271 850469
Crediton	Coombe House Country Hotel	01363 84487
Dartmoor	Bel Alp House	01364 661217
Derby	The Homestead	01332 544300
Diss	Chippenhall Hall	01379 588180
Dorchester	Yalbury Cottage Hotel	01305 262382
Dorchester-On-Thames	The George Hotel	01865 340404
Dover	Wallett's Court	01304 852424
Dulverton	Ashwick Country House Hotel	01398 323868
Enfield	Oak Lodge Hotel	020 8360 7082
Epsom	Chalk Lane Hotel	01372 721179
Falmouth	Trelawne Hotel-The Hutches Restaurant	01326 250226
Folkestone	Sandgate Hotel at Restaurant La Terrasse	01303 220444
Gatwick	Stanhill Court Hotel	01293 862166
Glossop	The Wind In The Willows	01457 868001
Golant by Fowey	The Cormorant Hotel	01726 833426
Grasmere	White Moss House	015394 35295
Great Snoring	The Old Rectory	01328 820597
Hadleigh	'Edge Hall' Hotel	01473 822458
Hampton Court	Chase Lodge	020 8943 1862
Hamsterley Forest	Grove House	01388 488203
Harrogate	The White House	01423 501388
Hawes	Rookhurst Country House Hotel	01969 667454
Hawkshead	Sawrey House Country Hotel	015394 36387
Helmsley	The Pheasant	01439 771241
Helston	Nansloe Manor	01326 574691
Hereford	The Steppes	01432 820424
Higham	Santo's Higham Farm	01773 833812
Holt	Felbrigg Lodge	01263 837588
Ilminster	The Old Rectory	01460 54364
Ilsington	Ilsington Country Hotel	01364 661452
Isle of Wight	Rylstone Manor	01983 862806
Keswick	Dale Head Hall Lakeside Hotel	017687 72478
Keswick	Swinside Lodge Hotel	017687 72948
Kingsbridge	The White House	01548 580580
Kirkby Lonsdale	Hipping Hall	015242 71187
Launceston	Penhallow Manor Country House Hotel	01566 86206
Leominster	Lower Bache House	01568 750304
Lincoln	Washingborough Hall	01522 790340
Lorton	Winder Hall	01900 85107
Loughborough	The Old Manor Hotel	01509 211228
Ludlow	Overton Grange Hotel	01584 873500
Luton	Little Offley	01462 768243
Lydford	Moor View House	01822 820220
Lymington	The Nurse's Cottage	01590 683402
Manchester	Eleven Didsbury Park	0161 448 7711
Membury	Oxenways	01404 881785
Middlecombe	Periton Park Hotel	01643 706885
Middleham	Waterford House	01969 622090
Minchinhampton	Burleigh Court	01453 883804
Morchard Bishop	Wigham	01363 877350
New Romney	Romney Bay House	01797 364747
Newent	Three Choirs	01531 890223
North Bovey	Blackaller	01647 440322
North Norfolk Coast	The Great Escape Holiday Company	01485 518717
North Walsham	Beechwood Hotel	01692 403231
North Walsham	Elderton Lodge	01263 833547
Norwich	The Beeches Hotel & Victorian Gardens	01603 621167
Norwich	Catton Old Hall	01603 419379
Norwich	Norfolk Mead Hotel	01603 737531
Norwich	The Old Rectory	01603 700772
Norwich	The Stower Grange	01603 860210
Nottingham	Cockliffe Country House Hotel	01159 680179
Nottingham	The Cottage Country House Hotel	01159 846882
Nottingham	Langar Hall	01949 860559
Nottingham	Sutton Bonnington Hall	01509 672355
Ockham	The Hautboy	01483 225355
Oswestry	Pen-y-Dyffryn Country Hotel	01691 653700
Otterburn	The Otterburn Tower	01830 520620
Overstrand	Sea Marge Hotel	01263 579579
Owlpen	Owlpen Manor	01453 860261
Oxford	Fallowfields	01865 820416
Oxford	Westwood Country House	01865 735408
Padstow	Cross House Hotel	01841 532391
Penrith	Temple Sowerby House Hotel	017683 61578
Petersfield	Langrish House	01730 266941
Porlock Weir	Andrew's On The Weir	01643 863300
Porthleven	Tye Rock Country House & Apartments	01326 572695
Portsmouth	The Beaufort Hotel	023 92823707
Pulborough	Chequers Hotel	01798 872486
Ringwood	Moortown Lodge	01425 471404
Ross-On-Wye	Glewstone Court	01989 770367
Ross-On-Wye	Wilton Court Hotel	01989 562569
Rye	White Vine House	01797 224748
St Ives	The Countryman At Trink Hotel	01736 797571
St Keyne	The Old Rectory Country House Hotel	01579 342617
St Mawes	The Hundred House Hotel	01872 501336
Saunton	Preston House Hotel	01271 890472
Sherborne	The Grange Hotel & Restaurant	01935 813463
Shipton Under Wychwood	The Shaven Crown Hotel	01993 830330
Shrewsbury	Rowton Castle Hotel	01743 884044
Shrewsbury	Upper Brompton Farm	01743 761629
Southport	Tree Tops Country House Restaurant	01704 572430
Stanhope	Horsley Hall	01388 517239
Staverton	Kingston House	01803 762 235
Stevenage	Redcoats Farmhouse Hotel & Restaurant	01438 729500
Stow-On-The-Wold	The Tollgate Inn	01608 658389
Stratford-upon-Avon	Glebe Farm House	01789 842501
Tarporley	Willington Hall Hotel	01829 752321
Tavistock	Browns Hotel Wine bar & Brasserie	01822 618686
Thetford	Broom Hall Country Hotel	01953 882125
Tintagel	Trebrea Lodge	01840 770410
Uckfield	Hooke Hall	01825 761578
Wadebridge	Tredethy House	01208 841262
Wadebridge	Trehellas House & Memories of Malaya Restaurant	01208 72700
Warwick	The Ardencote Manor Hotel	01926 843111
Wells	Beryl	01749 678738
Wells	Glencot House	01749 677160
Wem	Soulton Hall	01939 232786
Wimborne Minster	Beechleas	01202 841684
Windermere	Broadoaks Country House	01539 445566
Windermere	Fayrer Garden House Hotel	015394 88195
Windermere	Lakeshore House	015394 33202
Witherslack	The Old Vicarage Country House Hotel	015395 52381
York	The Parsonage Country House Hotel	01904 728111

IRELAND

Caragh Lake Co Kerry	Caragh Lodge	00 353 66 9769115
Cashel Co Tipperary	Cashel Palace Hotel	00 353 62 62707
Connemara	Ross Lake House Hotel	00 353 91 550109
Craughwell	St. Clerans	00 353 91 846 555
Killarney	Killarney Royal Hotel	00 353 64 31853
Killarney Co Kerry	Earls Court House	00 353 64 34009
Kilmeaden	The Old Rectory - Kilmeaden House	00 353 51 384254
Letterkenny	Castle Grove Country House Hotel	00 353 745 1118
Riverstown, Co Sligo	Coopershill House	00 353 71 65108
Sligo, Co Sligo	Markree Castle	00 353 71 67800

SCOTLAND

Ballater, Royal Deeside	Balgonie Country House	013397 55482
Banchory	Banchory Lodge Hotel	01330 822625
Cornhill	Castle of Park	01466 751111
Dunfries	Trigony House Hotel	01848 331211
Dunkeld	The Pend	01350 727586
Edinburgh	Garvock House Hotel	01383 621067
Fintry	Culcreuch Castle Hotel & Country Park	01360 860555
Glen Cannich	Mullardoch House Hotel	01456 415460
Inverness	Culduthel Lodge	01463 240089
Isle Of Harris	Ardvourlie Castle	01859 502307
Kentallen Of Appin	Ardsheal House	01631 740227
Killiecrankie, By Pitlochry	The Killiecrankie Hotel	01796 473220
Leslie	Balgeddie House Hotel	01592 742511
Maybole	Culzean Castle	01655 884455
Nairn	Boath House	01667 454896
Oban	Dungallan House Hotel	01631 563799
Pitlochry	Knockendarroch House	01796 473473
Port Of Menteith	The Lake Hotel	01877 385258
Rothiemurchus	Corrour House	01479 810220
St. Andrews	The Inn on North Street	01334 473387
St Fillans	The Four Seasons Hotel	01764 685333
Tain	Glenmorangie House at Cadbol	01862 871671

WALES

Aberdovey	Plas Penhelig Country House Hotel	01654 767676
Betws-y-Coed	Tan-y-Foel	01690 710507
Caernarfon	Ty'n Rhos Country Hotel	01248 670489
Cardiff	Llechwen Hall	01443 742050
Conwy	The Old Rectory Country House	01492 580611
Criccieth	Tyddyn Iolyn	01766 522509
Dolgellau	Abergwynant Hall	01341 422160
Dolgellau	Plas Dolmelynllyn	01341 440273
Llandeilo	The Cawdor Arms Hotel	01558 823500
Monmouth	The Crown At Whitebrook	01600 860254
Swansea	Norton House Hotel & Restaurant	01792 404891
Tenby	Waterwynch House Hotel	01834 842464
Tintern	Parva Farmhouse and Restaurant	01291 689411

CHANNEL ISLANDS

Guernsey	Bella Luce Hotel & Restaurant	01481 238764
Guernsey	La Favorita Hotel	01481 35666
Herm Island	The White House	01481 722159
Sark Island	La Sablonnerie	01481 832061

the preferred
champagne
of johansens

MINI LISTINGS

Johansens Recommended Hotels & Inns – North America, Bermuda, The Caribbean 2001

Here in brief are the entries that appear in full in Johansens Recommended Hotels & Inns – North America, Bermuda, The Caribbean 2001. To order Johansens guides turn to the order forms at the back of this book.

BERMUDA (HAMILTON)

Rosedon Hotel

PO Box HM 290, Hamilton HMAX,
Bermuda
Tel: 1 441 295 1640
Fax: 1 441 295 5904

BERMUDA (PAGET)

Fourways Inn

PO Box PG 294, Paget PG BX, Bermuda
Tel: 1 441 236 6517
Fax: 1 441 236 5528

BERMUDA (PAGET)

Harmony Club All Inclusive

PO Box 299, South Shore Road, Paget,
Bermuda
Tel: 1 441 236 3500
Fax: 1 441 236 2624

BERMUDA (PAGET)

The Newstead Hotel

27 Harbour Road, Paget PG02, Bermuda
Tel: 1 9 441 236 6060
Fax: 1 9 441 236 7454

BERMUDA (WARWICK)

Surf Side Beach Club

90 South Shore Rd, Warwick, Bermuda
Tel: 1 441 236 7100
Fax: 1 441 236 9765

CANADA (SIDNEY)

Seaside Luxury Resort Bed & Breakfast

8355 Lockside Drive, Sidney, British
Columbia, Canada
Tel: 1 250 544 1000
Fax: 1 250 544 1001

CARIBBEAN (ANGUILLA)

Frangipani Beach Club

Po Box 1378, Meads Bay, Anguilla, West
Indies
Tel: 1 264 497 6442
Fax: 1 264 497 6440

CARIBBEAN (CURACAO)

Avila Beach Hotel

Penstraat 130, Willemstad, Curacao,
Antilles, West Indies
Tel: 599 9 461 4377
Fax: 599 9 461 1493

CARIBBEAN (DOMINICA)

Hummingbird Inn

Morne Daniel, Box 1901, Roseau, Dominica
Tel: 1 767 449 1042
Fax: 1 767 449 1042

CARIBBEAN (MARTINIQUE)

Fregate Bleu

Quartier Fregate Vauclin Rd, 97240 Le
Francois, Martinique
Tel: 596 54 54 66
Fax: 596 54 78 48

CARIBBEAN (ST LUCIA)

Mago Estate Hotel

PO Box 247, Soufriere, St Lucia
Tel: 1 758 459 5880
Fax: 1 758 459 7352

CARIBBEAN (ST LUCIA)

Windjammer Landing Villa Beach Resort

Labrelotte Bay Box 1504, Castries, St Lucia
Tel: 1 758 452 0913
Fax: 1 758 452 9454

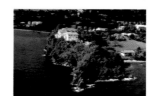

CARIBBEAN (ST VINCENT)

Camelot Inn

PO Box 787, Kingstown, St Vincent
Tel: 1 784 456 2100
Fax: 1 784 456 2233

CARIBBEAN (ST VINCENT)

Grand View Beach Hotel

Villa Point, Box 173, St Vincent, West
Indies
Tel: 1 784 458 4811
Fax: 1 784 457 4174

CARIBBEAN (TOBAGO)

Coco Reef Resort

Box 434, Scarborough, Tobago, West Indies
Tel: 1 868 639 8571
Fax: 1 868 639 8574

CARIBBEAN (TOBAGO)

Mount Irvine Bay Hotel

Box222 Mount Irvine Bay, Tobago
Tel: 1 868 639 8871
Fax: 1868 639 8800

MEXICO (IXTAPA/ZIHUATANEJO)

Hotel Villa Del Sol

Playa La Ropa s/n, PO Box 84, Zihuatanejo,
Mexico
Tel: 52 755 4 2239
Fax: 52 755 4 2758

ARIZONA (GREER)

Red Setter Inn and Cottage

8 Main Street, PO Box 133, Greer, Arizona
85927, USA
Tel: 1 888 994 7337
Fax: 1 520 735 7425

ARIZONA (PHOENIX)

Maricopa Manor

Box 7186, 15 West Pasadena Avenue,
Phoenix, Arizona 85013-2001, USA
Tel: 1 602 274 6302
Fax: 1 602 266 3904

ARIZONA (SEDONA)

Canyon Villa Inn

125 Canyon Circle Drive, Sedona, Arizona
86351, USA
Tel: 1 520 284 1226
Fax: 1 520 284 2114

ARIZONA (TUCSON)

White Stallion Ranch

9251 West Twin Peaks Road, Tucson,
Arizona 85743, USA
Tel: 1 520 297 0252
Fax: 1 520 744 2786

CALIFORNIA (CALISTOGA)

Cottage Grove Inn

1711 Lincoln Avenue, Calistoga, Californa
94515, USA
Tel: 707 942 8400 or 800 799 2284
Fax: 1 702 942 2653

CALIFORNIA (FERNDALE)

Gingerbread Mansion Inn

400 Berding Street, (PO Box 40), Ferndale,
California 95536-0040, USA
Tel: 1 707 786 4000
Fax: 1 707 786 4381

CALIFORNIA (LA JOLLA)

The Bed & Breakfast Inn at La Jolla

7753 Draper Avenue, La Jolla, California
92037, USA
Tel: 1 858 456 2066
Fax: 1 858 456 1510

CALIFORNIA (MENDOCINO)

Joshua Grindle Inn

44800 Little Lake Road, PO Box 647,
Mendocino, California 95460, USA
Tel: 1 707 937 4143

CALIFORNIA (MUIR BEACH)

Pelican Inn

Highway 1, Muir Beach, California 94965,
USA
Tel: 1 415 383 6000
Fax: 1 415 383 3424

CALIFORNIA (NAPA VALLEY)

The Ink House

1575 Helena Highway at Whitehall Lane, St
Helena, California 94574-9775, USA
Tel: 1 707 963 3890
Fax: 1 707 968 0739

CALIFORNIA (NEVADA CITY)

Red Castle Inn Historic Lodging

109 Prospect Street, Nevada City, California
95959, USA
Tel: 1 530 265 5135
Fax: 1 530 265 3560

CALIFORNIA (PALM SPRINGS)

The Willows

412 West Tahquitz Canyon Way, Palm
Springs, California 92262, USA
Tel: 1 760 320 0771
Fax: 1 760 320 0780

CALIFORNIA (SAN FRANCISCO)

Nob Hill Lambourne

725 Pine Street, San Francisco, California
94108, USA
Tel: 1 415 433 2287
Fax: 1 415 433 0975

CALIFORNIA (SANTA ANA)

Woolley's Petite Suites

2721 Hotel Terrace Road, Santa Ana,
California 92705, USA
Tel: 1 714 540 1111
Fax: 1 714 662 1643

CALIFORNIA (SOLVANG)

The Alisal Guest Ranch & Resort

1054 Alisal Road, Solvang, California
93463, USA
Tel: 1 805 688 6411
Fax: 1 805 688 2510

COLORADO (DENVER)

Historic Castle Marne

1572 Race Street, Denver , Colorado 80206,
USA
Tel: 1 303 331 0621
Fax: 1 303 331 0623

COLORADO (STEAMBOAT SPRINGS)

Vista Verde Guest Ranch

Po Box 465, Steamboat Springs, Colorado
80477, USA
Tel: 1 970 879 3858
Fax: 1 970 879 1413

CONNECTICUT (GREENWICH)

The Homestead Inn

420 Fieldpoint Road, Greenwich,
Connecticut 06830, USA
Tel: 1 203 869 7500
Fax: 1 203 869 7502

CONNECTICUT (MYSTIC)

Stonecroft Country Inn

515 Pumpkin Hill Rd, Ledyard 06339, USA
Tel: 860 572 0771
Fax: 860 572 9161

DELAWARE (REHOBOTH BEACH)

Boardwalk Plaza Hotel

Olive Avenue & The Boardwalk, Rehoboth
Beach, Delaware 19971, USA
Tel: 1 302 227 7169
Fax: 1 302 227 0561

FLORIDA (HOLMES BEACH)

Harrington House

5626 Gulf Drive, Holmes Beach, Florida
34217, USA
Tel: 1 947 778 5444
Fax: 1 941 778 0527

FLORIDA (KEY WEST)

Island City House

411 William Street, Key West, Florida
33040, USA
Tel: 1 305 294 5702
Fax: 1 305 294 1289

FLORIDA (KEY WEST)

Simonton Court Historic Inn & Cottages

320 Simonton Street, Key West, Florida
33040, USA
Tel: 1 305 294 6386
Fax: 1 305 293 8446

FLORIDA (KEY WEST)

The Paradise Inn

819 Simonton Street, Key West, Florida
33040, USA
Tel: 305 293 8007
Fax: 305 293 0807

FLORIDA (MIAMI BEACH)

Hotel Ocean

1230-1238 Ocean Drive, Miami Beach,
Florida 33139, USA
Tel: 1 305 672 2579
Fax: 1 305 672 7665

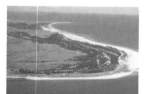

GEORGIA (LITTLE ST SIMONS ISLAND)

The Lodge on Little St. Simons Island

PO Box 21078, St Simons Island, Georgia
31522-0578, USA
Tel: 1 912 638 7472
Fax: 1 912 634 1811

GEORGIA (PERRY)

Henderson Village

125 South Langston Circle, Perry, Georgia
31069, USA
Tel: 1 912 988 8696
Fax: 1 912 988 9009

GEORGIA (SAVANNAH)

The Eliza Thompson House

5 West Jones Street, Savannah, Georgia
31401, USA
Tel: 1 912 236 3620
Fax: 1 912 238 1920

GEORGIA (SAVANNAH)

Granite Steps

126 East Gaston Street, Savannah, Georgia
31401, USA
Tel: +1 912 233 5380
Fax: +1 912 236 3116

GEORGIA (SAVANNAH)

Magnolia Place Inn

503 Whittaker Street, Savannah, Georgia
31401, USA
Tel: 1 912 236 7674
Fax: 1 912 236 1145

GEORGIA (SAVANNAH)

Presidents Quarters

225 East President Street, Savannah,
Georgia 31401, USA
Tel: 1 912 233 1600
Fax: 1 912 238 0849

HAWAII (KAILUA-KONA)

Kailua Plantation House

75-5948 Alii Drive, Kailua-Kona, Hawaii
96740, USA
Tel: 1 808 329 3727
Fax: 1 808 326 7323

LOUISIANA (NEW ORLEANS)

Windsor Court

300 Gravier Street, New Orleans, Louisiana
70130, USA
Tel: 1 504 523 6000
Fax: 1 504 596 4513

MAINE (GREENVILLE)

The Lodge at Moosehead Lake

Upon Lily Bay Road, Box 1167, Greenville,
Maine 04441, USA
Tel: 1 207 695 4400
Fax: 1 207 695 2281

MAINE (LINCOLNSVILLE)

Inn at Oceans Edge

Route 1, Lincolnville, Maine 04843, USA
Tel: +1 207 236 0945
Fax: +1 207 236 0609

MARYLAND (TANEYTOWN)

Antrim 1844

30 Trevanion Road, Taneytown, Maryland
21787, USA
Tel: 1 410 756 6812
Fax: 1 410 756 2744

MASSACHUSETTS (BOSTON)

A Cambridge House

2218 Massachusetts Avenue, Cambridge,
Massachusetts 02140-1836, USA
Tel: 1 617 491 6300
Fax: 1 617 868 2848

MASSACHUSETTS (BOSTON)

Charles Street Inn

94 Charles Street, Boston, Massachusetts
02114 4643, USA
Tel: +1 617 371 0008
Fax: +1 617 371 0009

MASSACHUSETTS (CAPE COD)

Wedgewood Inn

83 Main Street, Route 6A, Yarmouth Port,
Massachusetts 02675, USA
Tel: 1 508 362 5157
Fax: 1 508 362 5851

MASSACHUSETTS (CHATHAM)

The Captain's House Inn

369-377 Old Harbor Road, Chatham, Cape
Cod, Massachusetts 02633, USA
Tel: 1 508 945 0127
Fax: 1 508 945 0866

MASSACHUSETTS (CHATHAM)

Chatham Town House Inn

11 Library Lane, Chatham, Massachusetts
02633, USA
Tel: 508 945-2180
Fax: 508 945-3990

GAUTENG (SANDTON)

Saxon

36 Saxon Rd, Sandhurst, Gauteng 2132,
South Africa
Tel: 27 11 292 6000
Fax: 27 11 292 6001

KWAZULU - NATAL (BATTLEFIELDS)

Isandlwana Lodge

Po Box 30, Isandlwana, Kwazulu-Natal
3005, South Africa
Tel: 27 34 271 8301
Fax: 27 34 271 8306

KWAZULU -NATAL (CURRYS POST)

Old Halliwell Country Inn

PO Box 201, Howick 3290, Kwazulu, South
Africa
Tel: 27 33 330 2602
Fax: 27 33 330 3430

KWAZULU -NATAL (DRAKENSBERG)

Orchid Valley

Po Box 123, Underburg, Kwazulu-Natal
3257, South Africa
Tel: 27 33 701 1700
Fax: 27 33 701 1465

KWAZULU-NATAL (HLUHLUWE)

Falaza Game Park

PO Box 13, Hluhluwe, Kwazulu-Natal 3960,
South Africa
Tel: 27 35 562 0319
Fax: 27 35 562 0739

KWAZULU -NATAL (LAKE ST LUCIA)

Nibela Lake Lodge

Po Box 10305, Marine Parade, Kwazulu
Napal 4056, South Africa
Tel: +27 31 33 74 222
Fax: +27 31 368 2322

KWAZULU-NATAL (LIDGETTON)

Lythwood Lodge

PO Box 17, Lidgetton 3270, Kwazulu-Natal,
South Africa
Tel: 27 33 234 4666
Fax: 27 33 234 4668

KWAZULU-NATAL (MAPUTALAND)

Makakatana Bay Lodge

PO Box 65, Mtubatuba, Kwazulu-Natal
3935, South Africa
Tel: 27 35 550 4189
Fax: 27 35 550 4198

KWAZULU-NATAL (MAPUTALAND)

Mkuze Falls Game Lodge

PO Box 248, Pongola, Kwazulu-Natal 3170,
South Africa
Tel: 27 34 414 1018
Fax: 27 34 414 1021

KWAZULU-NATAL (MAPUTALAND)

Ndumo Wilderness Camp

P.O Box 78573, Sandton, Gauteng 2146,
South Africa
Tel: 27 11 883 0747
Fax: 27 11 883 0911

KWAZULU-NATAL (MAPUTALAND)

Shayamoya Game Lodge

PO Box 784, Pongola 3170, Kwazulu-Natal,
South Africa
Tel: 27 34 435 1110
Fax: 27 34 435 1008

KWAZULU- NATAL (MAPUTALAND)

White Elephant Lodge

Po Box 792, Pongola, Kwazulu- Natal 3170,
South Africa
Tel: 27 86 110 0517
Fax: 27 34 435 1117

KWAZULU-NATAL (MOOI RIVER NR GIANTS
CASTLE)

Hartford House

PO Box 31, Mooi River 3300, Kwazulu-
Natal, South Africa
Tel: 27 33 263 2713
Fax: 27 33 263 2818

KWAZULU-NATAL (PONGOLA)

Pakamisa Paradise

PO Box 1097, Pongola, Kwazulu-Natal
3170, South Africa
Tel: 27 34 413 3559
Fax: 27 34 413 1817

KWAZULU-NATAL (RORKE'S DRIFT)

Isibindi Zulu Lodge

PO Box 1593, Eshowe 3815, South Africa
Tel: 27 35 474 1504
Fax: 27 35 474 1490

MPUMALANGA (HAZYVIEW)

Casa Do Sol

PO Box 57, Hazyview 1242, Mpumalanga,
South Africa
Tel: 27 13 737 8111
Fax: 27 13 737 8166

MPUMALANGA (SABI SAND)

Idube Game Reserve

PO Box 2617, Northcliff 2115, Gauteng,
South Africa
Tel: 27 11 888 3713
Fax: 27 11 888 2181

MPUMALANGA (SABI SAND)

Leopard Hills Private Game Reserve

PO Box 612, Hazyview,1242, Mpumalanga,
South Africa
Tel: 27 13 737 6626
Fax: 27 13 737 6628

MPUMALANGA (SABI SAND)

Ulusaba Private Game Reserve

PO Box 71, Skukuza, Mpumalanga 1350,
South Africa
Tel: 27 13 735 5460
Fax: 27 13 735 5171

MPUMALANGA (WHITE RIVER)

Savanna Private Game Reserve

PO Box 3619, White River 1240,
Mpumalanga, South Africa
Tel: 27 13 737 7902
Fax: 27 13 737 7919

NORTHERN PROVINCE (HOEDSPRUIT)

Tshukudu Game Lodge

PO Box 289, Hoedspruit 1380,
Mpumalanga, South Africa
Tel: 27 15 793 2476
Fax: 27 15 793 2078

NORTHERN PROVINCE (TIMBAVATI)

Kings Camp

PO Box 427, Nelspruit 1200, Mpumalanga,
South Africa
Tel: 27 15 793 3633
Fax: 27 15 793 3634

NORTHERN PROVINCE (TZANEEN)

Coach House

PO Box 544, Tzaneen 0850, Northern
Province, South Africa
Tel: 27 15 307 3641
Fax: 27 15 307 1466

NORTHERN PROVINCE (WELGEVONDEN)

Makweti Safari Lodge

PO Box 310, Vaalwater 0530, Northern
Province, South Africa
Tel: 27 83 458 6122
Fax: 27 83 459 1153

WESTERN CAPE (CAPE TOWN)

Cape Grace Hotel

West Quay, Victoria & Alfred Waterfront,
Cape Town, Western Cape, South Africa
Tel: 27 21 410 7100
Fax: 27 21 419 7622

WESTERN CAPE (CAPE TOWN - CLAREMONT)

The Vineyard Hotel

Colinton Road, Newlands 7700, Cape
Town, Western Cape, South Africa
Tel: 27 21 683 3044
Fax: 27 21 683 3365

WESTERN CAPE (CAPE TOWN - CONSTANTIA)

Sérénité Wellness Centre

16 Debaren Close
Constantia, Cape Town, South Africa
Tel: 27 21 713 1760
Fax: 27 21 713 0049

WESTERN CAPE (CAPE TOWN - FALSE BAY)

Colona Castle

PO Box 273, Muizenberg 7950, South Africa
Tel: 27 21 788 8235
Fax: 27 21 788 6577

WESTERN CAPE (CAPE TOWN - HOUT BAY)

Tarragona Lodge

Cnr of Disa River Road & Valley Road, PO
Box 26887, Hout Bay 7872, Western Cape ,
South Africa
Tel: 27 21 790 5080
Fax: 27 21 790 5095

WESTERN CAPE (CAPE TOWN - ORANJEZICHT)

Villa Belmonte Manor House

33 Belmont Avenue,Oranjezicht, Cape
Town, Western Cape, South Africa
Tel: 27 21 462 1576
Fax: 27 21 462 1579

WESTERN CAPE (CAPE TOWN - SEAPOINT)

The Clarendon

67 Kloof Road,PO Box 224, Seapoint,Cape
Town, Western Cape, South Africa
Tel: 27 21 439 3224
Fax: 27 21 434 6855

WESTERN CAPE (CAPE TOWN - SEAPOINT)

Huijs Haerlem

25 Main Drive,Sea Point, PO Box
493,Green Point, Cape Town, Western
Cape, South Africa
Tel: 27 21 434 6434
Fax: 27 21 439 2506

WESTERN CAPE (CAPE TOWN - SEAPOINT)

Winchester Mansions

221 Beach Road, Sea Point, Western Cape,
South Africa
Tel: 27 21 434 2351
Fax: 27 21 434 0215

WESTERN CAPE (CAPE TOWN - WINELANDS)

Steenberg Country Hotel

PO Box 10802, Steenberg Estate, Cape
Town, Western Cape 7945, South Africa
Tel: 27 21 713 2222
Fax: 27 21 713 2221

WESTERN CAPE/GARDEN ROUTE (KNYSNA)

Belvidere Manor

PO Box 1195, Knynsa, Western Cape, South
Africa
Tel: 27 44 387 1055
Fax: 27 44 387 1059

WESTERN CAPE/GARDEN ROUTE (KNYSNA)

Falcons View Manor

PO Box 3083, Knysna, Western Cape 6570,
South Africa
Tel: 27 44 382 6767
Fax: 27 44 382 6430

WESTERN CAPE/GARDEN ROUTE (KNYSNA)

Milkwood Bay Guest House

PO Box 179, Knysna, Western Cape 6570,
South Africa
Tel: 27 44 384 0092
Fax: 27 44 384 1120

WESTERN CAPE/GARDEN ROUTE (MOSSEL BAY)

Reins Coastal Nature Reserve

PO Box 298, Albertinia, Western Cape,
South Africa
Tel: 27 28 735 3322
Fax: 27 28 735 3324

WESTERN CAPE/GARDEN ROUTE (OUDTSHOORN)

Rosenhof Hotel

264 Baron Van Reede Street, Oudtshoorn,
Western Cape 6620, South Africa
Tel: +27 44 279 1791
Fax: +27 44 279 1793

WESTERN CAPE/GARDEN ROUTE (PLETTENBERG BAY)

Hog Hollow Country Lodge

PO Box 503, Plettenberg Bay, Western Cape
6600, South Africa
Tel: 27 44 53 48879
Fax: 27 4453 48879

WESTERN CAPE/GARDEN ROUTE (PLETTENBERG BAY)

Kurland

PO Box 209, The Crags, Western Cape 6602, South Africa
Tel: +27 44 53 480 82
Fax: +27 44 53 486 99

WESTERN CAPE/GARDEN ROUTE (PLETTENBERG BAY)

Laird's Lodge

P.O Box 657, Plettenberg Bay, Western Cape 6600, South Africa
Tel: 27 4453 27721
Fax: 27 4453 27671

WESTERN CAPE/GARDEN ROUTE (PLETTENBERG BAY)

The Lodge On The Bay

77 Beachy Head Drive, Po Box 206, Plettenberg Bay, Western Cape 6600, SA
Tel: 27 44 533 4724
Fax: 27 44 533 2681

WESTERN CAPE/GARDEN ROUTE (PLETTENBERG BAY)

Mallard River Lodge

PO Box 532, Plettenberg Bay, Western Cape 6600, South Africa
Tel: 27 44 533 2982
Fax: 27 44 535 9336

WESTERN CAPE/GARDEN ROUTE (PLETTENBERG BAY)

Milkwood Manor

Lookout Beach, Plettenberg Bay, Western Cape 6600, South Africa
Tel: 27 44 533 0420
Fax: 27 44 533 0921

WESTERN CAPE/GARDEN ROUTE (PLETTENBERG BAY)

Plettenberg Park

Po Box 167, Plettenberg Bay, Western Cape 6600, South Africa
Tel: 27 (44) 533 9067
Fax: 27 (44) 533 9092

WESTERN CAPE/GARDEN ROUTE (WILDERNESS)

Palms Wilderness

Owen Grant Street No 1, Wilderness, Western Cape 6560, South Africa
Tel: 27 44 877 1420
Fax: 27 44 877 1422

WESTERN CAPE/WINELANDS(FRANSCHOEK)

La Couronne

Robertsvlei Road, Franschhoek 7690, Western Cape, South Africa
Tel: 27 21 876 2770
Fax: 27 21 876 3788

WESTERN CAPE/WINELANDS (FRANSCHOEK)

Résidence Klein Oliphants Hoek

14 Akademie Street, Franschhoek, Western Cape 7690, South Africa
Tel: 27 21 876 2566
Fax: 27 21 876 2566

WESTERN CAPE/WINELANDS (GREYTON)

Greyton Lodge

46 Main Street, Greyton 7233, Western Cape, South Africa
Tel: 27 28 254 9876
Fax: 27 28 254 9672

WESTERN CAPE/WINELANDS (HERMON)

Bartholomeus Klip Farmhouse

PO Box 36, Hermon, Western Cape, South Africa
Tel: 27 22 448 1820
Fax: 27 22 448 1829

WESTERN CAPE/WINELANDS (LITTLE KAROO)

Mimosa Lodge

Church Street, Montague, Western Cape, South Africa
Tel: 27 23 614 23 51
Fax: 27 23 614 24 18

WESTERN CAPE/WINELANDS (PAARL)

Palmiet Valley Estate

PO Box 9085, Klein Drakenstein,Paarl, Western Cape 7628, South Africa
Tel: 27 21 862 7741
Fax: 27 21 862 6891

WESTERN CAPE/WINELANDS (PAARL)

Pontac Manor Hotel and Restaurant

16 Zion Street, Paarl 7646, Western Cape, South Africa
Tel: 27 21 872 0445
Fax: 27 21 872 0460

WESTERN CAPE/WINELANDS (STELLENBOSCH)

d'Ouwe Werf

302 Church Street, Stellenbosch, Western Cape, South Africa
Tel: 27 21 887 4608
Fax: 27 21 887 4626

WESTERN CAPE/WINELANDS (STELLENBOSCH)

Lanzerac Manor & Winery

PO Box 4, Stellenbosch, Western Cape 7599, South Africa
Tel: 27 21 887 1132
Fax: 27 21 887 2310

WESTERN CAPE/WINELANDS (STELLENBOSCH)

Lyngrove Country House

PO Box 7275, Stellenbosch 7599, Western Cape, South Africa
Tel: 27 21 842 2116
Fax: 27 21 842 2118

WESTERN CAPE/WINELANDS (STELLENBOSCH)

River Manor

No.6 The Avenue, Stellenbosch, Western Cape, South Africa
Tel: 27 21 887 9944
Fax: 27 21 887 9940

WESTERN CAPE/WINELANDS (STELLENBOSCH)

Zandberg Farm

PO Box 5337, Somerset West, Stellenbosch Wine Route, Western Cape 7135, South Africa
Tel: 27 21 842 2945

WESTERN CAPE/WINELANDS (TULBAGH)

Rijk's Ridge Country House

PO Box 340, Tulbagh, Western Cape, South Africa
Tel: 27 23 230 1006
Fax: 27 23 230 1125

ZAMBIA (SOUTH LUANGWA)

Chibembe Camp

Private Bag 286x Ridgeway, Lusaka, Zambia
Tel: 260 1265814
Fax: 260 1 262291

ZIMBABWE (VICTORIA FALLS)

The Victoria Falls Hotel

P.O Box 10, Victoria Falls, Zimbabwe
Tel: 263 13 4751/61
Fax: 263 13 2354/4443

ZAMBIA (SOUTH LUANGWA)

Kafunta River Lodge

Po Box 83, Mfuwe, Zambia
Tel: 260 62 45026
Fax: 260 62 45026

ZAMBIA (SOUTH LUANGWA)

NSEFU Lodge

Po Box 80, Mfuwe, Zambia, Zambia
Tel: 260 62 45090
Fax: 260 62 45051

ZIMBABWE (CHIREDZI-SOUTH EAST LOWVELD)

Nduna Safari Lodge

Malilangwe Private Wildlife Reserve,
Reservations P.O Box MP845 Mount
Pleasant, Harare, Zimbabwe
Tel: 263 4 722 983
Fax: 263 4 735 530

ZIMBABWE (CHIREDZI-SOUTH EAST LOWVELD)

Pamushana

Malilangwe Private Wildlife Reserve,
Reservations P.O Box MP845 Mount
Pleasant, Harare, Zimbabwe
Tel: 263 4 722 983
Fax: 263 4 735 530

ZIMBABWE (HARARE)

Meikles Hotel

Jason Moyo Avenue, PO Box 594, Harare,
Zimbabwe
Tel: 263 4 707721
Fax: 263 4 707754

ZIMBABWE (HWANGE)

The Hide Safari Camp

PO Box ST274, Southerton, Harare,
Zimbabwe
Tel: 263 4 660554
Fax: 263 4 621216

ZIMBABWE (LAKE KARIBA)

Sanyati Lodge

PO Box Cy3371, Causeway, Harare
Tel: 263 4 701732
Fax: 263 4 72 1737

ZIMBABWE(MATOBO HILS)

Royal Kingdom Lodge

Po Box AC891, Ascot Bulawayo, Zimbabwe
Tel: 263 11 401 446
Fax: 263 9 60662

ZIMBABWE (VICTORIA FALLS)

The Stanley and Livingstone

PO Box 106, Victoria Falls, Zimbabwe,
Zimbabwe
Tel: 263 13 4557
Fax: 263 4 13 4421

MINI LISTINGS

Johansens Recommended Hotels & Lodges – Australia, New Zealand, The Pacific 2001

Here in brief are the entries that appear in full in Johansens Recommended Hotel & Lodges – Australia, New Zealand, The Pacific 2001.
To order Johansens guides turn to the order forms at the back of this book.

NEW SOUTH WALES (BRAIDWOOD)

The Doncaster Inn

Wilson Street, Braidwood, New South
Wales 2622, Australia
Tel: +61 2 4842 2356
Fax: +61 2 4842 2521

NEW SOUTH WALES (BUNDANOON)

Oaks Court Country House

Ross Street, Bundanoon, New South Wales
2578, Australia
Tel: +61 2 4883 6858
Fax: +61 2 4883 6196

NEW SOUTH WALES (HARDY'S BAY)

Headlands, Broken Bay

Po Box 10, Hardy's Bay, New South Wales
2257, Australia
Tel: +61 2 4360 1933
Fax: +61 2 4360 2013

NEW SOUTH WALES (SYDNEY)

The Harbour Rocks Hotel

34-52 Harrington Street, Sydney, New
South Wales 2000, Australia
Tel: +61 2 9251 8944
Fax: +61 2 9251 8900

NEW SOUTH WALES (TOOWOON BAY)

Kims Beachside Retreat

16 Charlton Street, Toowoon Bay, New
SouthWales 2261, Australia
Tel: +61 2 4332 1566
Fax: +61 2 4333 1544

NEW SOUTH WALES (ULLADULLA)

Ulladulla Guest House

39 Burrill Street, Ulladulla, New South
Wales 2539, Australia
Tel: +61 2 4455 1796
Fax: +61 2 4454 4660

NEW SOUTH WALES (WENTWORTH FALLS)

Whispering Pines

178-186 Falls Rd, Wentworth Falls, New
South Wales 2782, Australia
Tel: +61 2 4757 1449
Fax: +61 2 4757 1219

AUSTRALIAN CAPITAL TERITTORY (CANBERRA)

The York Canberra

31 Giles Street, Kingston, Canberra,
Austalian Capital Territory 2604, Australia
Tel: +61 2 6295 2333
Fax: +61 2 6295 9559

QUEENSLAND (BLOOMFIELD)

Bloomfield Rainforest Lodge

PO Box 966, Cairns, Queensland 4870,
Australia
Tel: +61 7 4035 9166
Fax: +61 7 4035 9180

QUEENSLAND (ATHERTON TABLELANDS)

Bracken Ridge Lodge

65 Vance Close, Yungaburra, Atherton
Tablelands, Queensland 4872, Australia
Tel: +61 7 4095 3421
Fax: +61 7 4095 3461

QUEENSLAND (DAINTREE)

Daintree Eco Lodge and Spa

20 Daintree Rd, Daintree, Queensland 4873,
Australia
Tel: +61 7 4098 6100
Fax: +61 7 4098 6200

QUEENSLAND (FRASER ISLAND)

Kingfisher Bay Resort and Village

Fraser Island, Urangan, Queensland 4655,
Australia
Tel: +61 7 4120 3333
Fax: +61 7 4127 9333

QUEENSLAND (GREEN ISLAND)

Green Island Resort

Po Box 898, Cairns, Queensland 4870,
Australia
Tel: +61 7 4031 3300
Fax: +61 7 4052 1511

QUEENSLAND (MONTVILLE)

The Falls B&B & Rainforest Cottages

20 Kondalilla Falls Road, Montville,
Queensland 4560, Australia
Tel: +61 7 5445 7000
Fax: +61 7 5445 7001

QUEENSLAND (PLANET DOWNS)

Planet Downs

Outback, Queensland, Australia
Tel: +61 7 3265 5022
Fax: +61 7 3265 3978

QUEENSLAND (SPRINGBROOK)

Springbrook Mountain Manor

2814 Springbrook Rd, Springbrook,
Queensland 4213, Australia
Tel: +61 7 5533 5344
Fax: +61 7 5533 5344

QUEENSLAND (WHITSUNDAY)

Laguna Quays

Kunapipi Springs Road, Whitsunday,
Queensland 4800, Australia
Tel: +61 7 4947 7777
Fax: +61 7 4949 7770

SOUTH AUSTRALIA (ADELAIDE-THORNGATE)

Myoora Heritage Accommodation

4 Carter Street, Thorngate, Adelaide, South
Australia 5082, Australia
Tel: +61 8 8344 2599
Fax: +61 8 8344 9575

SOUTH AUSTRALIA (ADELAIDE-STIRLING)

Thorngrove Manor

2 Glenside Lane, Stirling, Adelaide, South
Australia 5152, Australia
Tel: +61 8 8339 6748
Fax: +61 8 8370 9950

SOUTH AUSTRALIA (SEVENHILL-CLARE VALLEY)

Thorn Park Country House

College Road, Sevenhill, Clare Valley,
South Australia 5453, Australia
Tel: +61 8 8843 4304
Fax: +61 8 8843 4296

VICTORIA (BEECHWORTH)

Beechworth House

5 Dingle Road, Beechworth, Victoria 3747,
Australia
Tel: +61 3 5728 2817
Fax: +61 3 5728 2737

VICTORIA (EILDON)

Eucalypt Ridge

564 Skyline Road, Eildon, Victoria 3713,
Australia
Tel: +61 3 5774 2033
Fax: +61 3 5774 2610

VICTORIA (HALLS GAP-GRAMPIANS)

Marwood

Mount Zero Rd, Halls Gap, Victoria 3381,
Australia
Tel: +61 3 5356 4231
Fax: +61 3 5356 4513

VICTORIA (KALORAMA - MT DANDENONG)

Grey Gables

3 Grange Rd, Kalorama, Victoria 3766,
Australia
Tel: +61 3 9761 8609
Fax: +61 3 9728 8033

VICTORIA (LAKES ENTRANCE)

Deja Vu

17 Clara Street, Lakes Entrance, Victoria
3909, Australia
Tel: +61 3 5155 4330
Fax: +61 3 5155 3718

VICTORIA (MELBOURNE)

Hotel Lindrum

26 Flinders Street, Melbourne, Victoria
3000, Australia
Tel: +61 3 9668 1111
Fax: +61 3 9668 1199

VICTORIA (MOOROODUC)

Woodman Estate

136 Graydens Road, Moorooduc, Victoria
3933, Australia
Tel: +61 3 5978 8455
Fax: +61 3 5978 8522

VICTORIA (MOUNT BEAUTY)

Dreamers Mountain Accommodation

Kiewa Valley Highway, Tawonga South,
Mount Beauty, Victoria 3699, Australia
Tel: +61 3 5754 1222
Fax: +61 3 5754 1333

VICTORIA (PHILLIP ISLAND)

The Castle-Villa by the Sea

7-9 Steele Street, Cowes, Phillip Island,
Victoria 3922, Australia
Tel: +61 3 5952 1228
Fax: +61 3 5952 3926

VICTORIA (RED HILL)

Lindenderry at Red Hill

142 Arthurs Seat Rd, Red Hill, Victoria
3937, Australia
Tel: +61 3 5989 2933
Fax: +61 3 5989 2936

VICTORIA (ROMSEY)

Cope-Williams Winery

Glenfern Rd, Romsey, Victoria 3434,
Australia
Tel: +61 3 5429 5428
Fax: +61 3 5429 5655

VICTORIA (TORQUAY)

Freshwater Green Country House

3 Jetti Lane, Torquay, Victoria 3228,
Australia
Tel: +61 3 5261 3366
Fax: +61 3 5261 9266

VICTORIA (YARRA VALLEY)

Chateau Yering

Melba Highway, Yering, Yarra Valley,
Victoria 3770, Australia
Tel: +61 3 9237 3333
Fax: +61 3 9237 3300

WESTERN AUSTRALIA (BROOME)

McAlpine House

84 Herbert Street, Broome, Western
Australia 6725, Australia
Tel: +61 8 9192 3886
Fax: +61 8 9192 3887

WESTERN AUSTRALIA (BROOME)

North Star Charters

PO Box 654, Shop 2, 25 Carnarvon Street,
Broome, Western Australia 6725, Australia
Tel: +61 8 9192 1829
Fax: +61 8 9192 1830

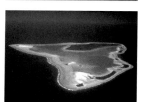

WESTERN AUSTRALIA (PERTH)

Joondalup Resort

Country Club Boulevard, Joondalup, Perth,
Western Australia 6027, Australia
Tel: +61 8 9400 8888
Fax: +61 8 9400 8889

COOK ISLANDS (AITUTAKI)

Aitutaki Pearl Beach Resort

PO Box 99, Aitutaki, Cook Islands
Tel: +682 31 201
Fax: +682 31 202

COOK ISLANDS (RAROTONGA)

Crown Beach Resort

PO Box 47, Rarotonga, Cook Islands
Tel: +682 23 953
Fax: +682 23 951

COOK ISLANDS (RAROTONGA)

Rarotongan Beach Resort

Po Box 103, Rarotonga, Cook Islands
Tel: +682 25 800
Fax: +682 25 799

FIJI ISLANDS (LAUTOKA)

Blue Lagoon Cruises

183 Vitogo Parade, Lautoka, Fiji Islands
Tel: +679 661 622
Fax: +679 664 098

FIJI ISLANDS (MAMANUCA ISLANDS)

Tokoriki Island Resort

PO Box 10547, Nadi Airport, Nadi, Fiji
Islands
Tel: +679 725 474
Fax: +679 725 928

FIJI ISLANDS (MATANGI ISLAND)

Matangi Island Resort

Matangi Island, Fiji Islands
Tel: +679 880 260
Fax: +679 880 274

FIJI ISLANDS (SAVUSAVU)

Namale Resort

PO Box 244, Savusavu, Fiji Islands
Tel: +679 850 435
Fax: +679 850 400

FIJI ISLANDS (TAVEUNI ISLAND)

Taveuni Island Resort

Taveuni Island, Fiji Islands
Tel: +679 880 441
Fax: +679 880 466

FIJI ISLANDS (TOBERUA ISLAND)

Toberua Island Resort

GPO Box 567, Suva, Fiji Islands
Tel: +679 302 356
Fax: +679 302 215

FIJI ISLANDS (YASAWA ISLANDS)

Turtle Island, Fiji

Yasawa Islands, PO Box 9371 Nadi Airport,
Nadi, Fiji Islands
Tel: +61 3 9618 1100
Fax: +61 3 9618 1199

FIJI ISLANDS (YASAWA ISLANDS)

Yasawa Island Resort

PO Box 10128, Nadi Airport, Nadi, Fiji
Islands
Tel: +679 722 266
Fax: +679 724 456

NORTH ISLAND (AUCKLAND)

Aachen House Boutique Hotel

39 Market Rd, Remuera, Auckland, New
Zealand
Tel: +64 9 520 2329
Fax: +64 9 524 2898

NORTH ISLAND (GISBORNE)

Acton Estate

577 Back Ormond Road, Gisborne, New
Zealand
Tel: +64 6 867 9999
Fax: +64 6 867 1116

NORTH ISLAND (HAWKES BAY - HAVELOCK NORTH)

Mangapapa Lodge

466 Napier Rd, Havelock North, Hawkes
Bay, New Zealand
Tel: +64 6 878 3234
Fax: +64 6 878 1214

NORTH ISLAND (ROTORUA)

Treetops Lodge

Koaroha Road, Horohoro, Rotorua, New
Zealand
Tel: +64 9 579 1187
Fax: +64 9 579 7421

NORTH ISLAND (RUSSELL-BAY OF ISLANDS)

Kimberley lodge

Pitt Street , PO Box 166, Russell, Bay of
Island, New Zealand
Tel: +64 9 403 7090
Fax: +64 9 403 7239

NORTH ISLAND (KERIKERI - BAY OF ISLANDS)

Villa Maria Petit Hotel

Inlet Road, PO Box 230, Kerikeri, Bay of
Islands, New Zealand
Tel: +64 9 407 9311
Fax: +64 9 407 9311

NORTH ISLAND (PAUANUI BEACH)

Puka Park Resort

Private Bag, Pauanui Beach 2850, New
Zealand
Tel: +64 7 864 8088
Fax: +64 7 864 8112

NORTH ISLAND (ROTORUA)

Kawaha Point Lodge

171 Kawaha Point Road, Rotorua, New
Zealand
Tel: +64 7 346 3602
Fax: +64 7 346 3671

NORTH ISLAND (ROTORUA)

Solitaire Lodge

Lake Tarawera, Rotorua RD5, New Zealand
Tel: +64 7 362 8208
Fax: +64 7 362 8445

NORTH ISLAND (TAUPO)

Lake Taupo Lodge

41 Mapara Road, Acacia Road, Taupo, New
Zealand
Tel: +64 7 378 7386
Fax: +64 7 377 3226

NORTH ISLAND (TAUPO)

The Pillars

7 Deborah Rise, Bonshaw Park, Taupo, New
Zealand
Tel: +64 7 378 1512
Fax: +64 7 378 1511

NORTH ISLAND (TAURANGA)

Tinopai Lodge

20 Tinopai Drive, Tauranga, New Zealand
Tel: +64 7 548 1515
Fax: +64 7 548 1525

NORTH ISLAND (WAIKATO)

Brooklands Country Estate

RD1, Ngaruawahia, Waikato, New Zealand
Tel: +64 7 825 4756
Fax: +64 7 825 4873

NORTH ISLAND (WHANGAMATA)

Bushland Park

444 Wentworth Valley Road, Whangamata,
New Zealand
Tel: +64 7 865 7468
Fax: +64 7 865 7486

NORTH ISLAND (WHITIANGA)

Villa Toscana Lodge

Ohuka Park, Rimu Street, Whitianga, New
Zealand
Tel: +64 7 866 2293
Fax: +64 7 866 2269

SOUTH ISLAND (CASS)

Grasmere Lodge High Country Retreat

State Highway 73, Cass, Canterbury, New
Zealand
Tel: +64 3 318 8407
Fax: +64 3 318 8263

SOUTH ISLAND (CHRISTCHURCH)

The Charlotte Jane

110 Papanui Road, Merivale, Christchurch,
New Zealand
Tel: +64 3 355 1028
Fax: +64 3 355 8882

SOUTH ISLAND (DARFIELD)

Bangor Country Estate

Bangor Road, Darfield, New Zealand
Tel: +64 3 318 7588
Fax: +64 3 318 8485

SOUTH ISLAND (DUNEDIN)

Corstorphine House

23 Milburn Street, Dunedin, New Zealand
Tel: +64 3 487 6676
Fax: +64 3 487 6672

SOUTH ISLAND (MARLBOROUGH - BLENHEIM)

The Old St Mary's Convent

776 Rapaura Rd, Blenheim, Marlborough,
New Zealand
Tel: +64 3 570 5700
Fax: +64 3 570 5700

SOUTH ISLAND (NELSON)

The Lodge at Paratiho Farms

545 Waiwhero Rd, Rd 2 Upper Moutere,
Motueka, Nelson, New Zealand
Tel: +64 3 528 2100
Fax: +64 3 528 2101

SOUTH ISLAND (MURCHISON-LAKE ROTOROA)

Lake Rotoroa Lodge

RD3 Lake Rotoroa, Murchison, New
Zealand
Tel: +64 3 523 9121
Fax: +64 3 523 9028

SOUTH ISLAND (NELSON)

Cathedral Inn

369 Trafalgar Street South, Nelson, New
Zealand
Tel: +64 3 548 7369
Fax: +64 3 548 0369

SOUTH ISLAND (QUEENSTOWN)

Manata Lodge

111 Tucker Beach Road, Queenstown, New
Zealand
Tel: +64 3 442 3440
Fax: +64 3 442 3110

SOUTH ISLAND(QUEENSTOWN)

Matakauri Lodge

Glenorchy Rd, Queenstown, New Zealand
Tel: +64 3 441 1008
Fax: +64 3 441 2180

SOUTH ISLAND (QUEENSTOWN)

White Shadows Country Inn

58 Hunter Road, Queenstown, New Zealand
Tel: +64 3 442 0871
Fax: +64 3 442 0872

SOUTH ISLAND (RANGIORA)

Serenada Country Lodge

Food Hills Road, Rangiora, New Zealand
Tel: +64 3 313 2263
Fax: +64 3 313 2264

SOUTH ISLAND (WAIPANA)

Mountford Vineyard

431 Omihi Road, Waipara, North
Canterbury, New Zealand
Tel: +64 3 314 6819
Fax: +64 3 314 6820

ORDER FORM

order 3 titles get £5 off · order 4 titles get £10 off · order 5 titles get £20 off
or you can order the Chairman's collection and save £35

Simply indicate the quantity of each title you wish to order, total up the cost and then make your appropriate discount. Complete your order below and choose your preferred method of payment. Then send it to Johansens, FREEPOST (CB 264), 43 Millharbour, London E14 9BR (no stamp required). FREE gifts will automatically be dispatched with your order. Fax orders welcome on 0207 537 3594.

ALTERNATIVELY YOU CAN ORDER IMMEDIATELY ON FREEPHONE 0800 269 397 and quote ref   B14

Recommended Hotels - Great Britain & Ireland 2001
Publication date: October 2000

I wish to order
QUANTITY

copy/ies priced at £19.95 each.
Total cost
£

Recommended Country Houses - Great Britain & Ireland 2001
Publication date: October 2000

I wish to order
QUANTITY

copy/ies priced at £11.95 each.
Total cost
£

Recommended Traditional Inns, Hotels & Restaurants - Great Britain 2001
Publication date: October 2000

I wish to order
QUANTITY

copy/ies priced at £11.95 each.
Total cost
£

Historic Houses, Castles & Gardens 2001 (incorporating Museums & Galleries)
Publication date: December 2000

I wish to order
QUANTITY

copy/ies priced at £7.95 each.
Total cost
£

Recommended Hotels - Europe & The Mediterranean 2001
Publication date: October 2000

I wish to order
QUANTITY

copy/ies priced at £16.95 each.
Total cost
£

Recommended Hotels - North America, Bermuda & The Caribbean 2001
Publication date: October 2000

I wish to order
QUANTITY

copy/ies priced at £12.95 each.
Total cost
£

Recommended Hotels, Country Houses & Game Lodges – Southern Africa, Mauritius, The Seychelles 2001 Publ. date: October 2000

I wish to order
QUANTITY

copy/ies priced at £9.95 each.
Total cost
£

Recommended Hotels & Lodges Australia, New Zealand, The Pacific 2001
Publication date: October 2000

NEW

I wish to order
QUANTITY

copy/ies priced at £9.95 each.
Total cost
£

Recommended Business Meeting Venues 2001
Publication date: February 2001

I wish to order
QUANTITY

copy/ies priced at £25.00 each.
Total cost
£

Johansens Pocket Guide 2001
Publication date: January 2001

NEW

I wish to order
QUANTITY

copy/ies priced at £7.95 each.
Total cost
£

The Chairman's Collection
order the complete collection of Johansens Recommended Guides
for only £99.55 a saving of £35
PLUS FREE **P&P** worth £4.50
PLUS FREE **Luxury Luggage Tag** worth £15
PLUS FREE **Privilege Card** worth £20

The Chairman's Collection contains the following titles:
·Business Meetings Venues ·Traditional Inns, Hotels & Restaurants - GB ·Hotels - GB & Ireland ·Country Houses - GB & Ireland ·Historic Houses, Castles & Gardens ·Hotels, Country Houses & Game Lodges - Southern Africa ·Hotels - North America, Bermuda, The Caribbean ·Hotels - Europe & The Mediterranean ·Hotels & Lodges - Australia, New Zealand, The Pacific · Johansens Pocket Guide 2001

Now please complete your order and payment details

I have ordered 3 titles - £5 off   −£5.00

I have ordered 4 titles - £10 off   −£10.00

I have ordered 5 titles - £20 off   −£20.00

Total cost of books ordered minus discount
(not including the Chairman's Collection)   £

Privilege Card - FREE WITH ANY ORDER
Additional cards can be ordered for £20   £

Luxury Luggage Tag - Johansens branded polished steel tag at £15. Quantity and total cost: £

POSTAGE & PACKING
(UK) for a single item add £2.50
More than one item add £4.50
(Outside) UK for a single item add £4.00
More than one item add £6.00   £

I wish to order the Chairman's collection at £99.55
(no P&P required) **Enter quantity and total cost:**   £

Johansens Gold Blocked SLIP CASE at £5 for the Chairman's Collection. Quantity and total cost: £

GRAND TOTAL £

I have chosen my Johansens Guides and (please tick)

I enclose a cheque payable to Johansens ☐
I enclose my order on company letterheading, please invoice (UK only) ☐
Please note that books will be sent upon payment being received
Please debit my credit/charge card account (please tick) ☐

☐ **MasterCard**   ☐ **Amex**   ☐ **Visa**   ☐ **Switch** (Issue Number) ▭

Card Holders Name (Mr/Mrs/Miss)

Address

Postcode

Telephone

Card No.

Exp Date

Signature

NOW simply detach the order form and send it to Johansens, FREEPOST (CB264), 43 Millharbour, London E14 9BR (no stamp required)
FREE gifts will be dispatched with your order. Fax orders welcome on 0207 537 3594

GUEST SURVEY REPORT

Your own Johansens 'inspection' gives reliability to our guides
and assists in the selection of Award Nominations

Name of Hotel: _____

Location of Hotel: _____

Page No: _____

Date of visit: _____

Name of GUEST: _____

Address of GUEST: _____

_____Postcode _____

Please tick one box in each category below:	Excellent	Good	Disappointing	Poor
Bedrooms				
Public Rooms				
Restaurant/Cuisine				
Service				
Welcome/Friendliness				
Value For Money				

Occasionally we may allow other reputable organisations to write with offers which may be of interest.
If you prefer not to hear from them, tick this box ☐

To: Johansens, c/o Norwood Mailing CO Ltd, FREEPOST CB264, London SE27 0BR

ORDER FORM

order 3 titles get £5 off · order 4 titles get £10 off · order 5 titles get £20 off

or you can order the Chairman's collection and save £35

Simply indicate the quantity of each title you wish to order, total up the cost and then make your appropriate discount. Complete your order below and choose your preferred method of payment. Then send it to Johansens, FREEPOST (CB 264), 43 Millharbour, London E14 9BR (no stamp required). FREE gifts will automatically be dispatched with your order. Fax orders welcome on 0207 537 3594.

ALTERNATIVELY YOU CAN ORDER IMMEDIATELY ON FREEPHONE 0800 269 397 and quote ref B14

Recommended Hotels - Great Britain & Ireland 2001
Publication date: October 2000

I wish to order
QUANTITY
copy/ies priced at £19.95 each.
Total cost £

Recommended Country Houses - Great Britain & Ireland 2001
Publication date: October 2000

I wish to order
QUANTITY
copy/ies priced at £11.95 each.
Total cost £

Recommended Traditional Inns, Hotels & Restaurants - Great Britain 2001
Publication date: October 2000

I wish to order
QUANTITY
copy/ies priced at £11.95 each.
Total cost £

Historic Houses, Castles & Gardens 2001 (incorporating Museums & Galleries)
Publication date: December 2000

I wish to order
QUANTITY
copy/ies priced at £7.95 each.
Total cost £

Recommended Hotels - Europe & The Mediterranean 2001
Publication date: October 2000

I wish to order
QUANTITY
copy/ies priced at £16.95 each.
Total cost £

Recommended Hotels - North America, Bermuda & The Caribbean 2001
Publication date: October 2000

I wish to order
QUANTITY
copy/ies priced at £12.95 each.
Total cost £

Recommended Hotels, Country Houses & Game Lodges – Southern Africa, Mauritius, The Seychelles 2001 Publ. date: October 2000

I wish to order
QUANTITY
copy/ies priced at £9.95 each.
Total cost £

Recommended Hotels & Lodges Australia, New Zealand, The Pacific 2001
Publication date: October 2000

NEW

I wish to order
QUANTITY
copy/ies priced at £9.95 each.
Total cost £

Recommended Business Meeting Venues 2001
Publication date: February 2001

I wish to order
QUANTITY
copy/ies priced at £25.00 each.
Total cost £

Johansens Pocket Guide 2001
Publication date: January 2001

NEW

I wish to order
QUANTITY
copy/ies priced at £7.95 each.
Total cost £

The Chairman's Collection
order the complete collection of Johansens Recommended Guides
for only £99.55 a saving of **£35**
PLUS FREE P&P worth £4.50
PLUS FREE **Luxury Luggage Tag** worth £15
PLUS FREE **Privilege Card** worth £20

The Chairman's Collection contains the following titles:
•Business Meetings Venues •Traditional Inns, Hotels & Restaurants - GB •Hotels - GB & Ireland •Country Houses - GB & Ireland •Historic Houses, Castles & Gardens •Hotels, Country Houses & Game Lodges - Southern Africa •Hotels - North America, Bermuda, The Caribbean •Hotels - Europe & The Mediterranean •Hotels & Lodges - Australia, New Zealand, The Pacific • Johansens Pocket Guide 2001

Now please complete your order and payment details

I have ordered 3 titles - £5 off   −£5.00

I have ordered 4 titles - £10 off   −£10.00

I have ordered 5 titles - £20 off   −£20.00

Total cost of books ordered minus discount
(not including the Chairman's Collection) £

Privilege Card - FREE WITH ANY ORDER
Additional cards can be ordered for £20 £

Luxury Luggage Tag - Johansens branded polished steel tag at £15. Quantity and total cost: £

POSTAGE & PACKING
(UK) for a single item add £2.50
More than one item add £4.50
(Outside) UK for a single item add £4.00
More than one item add £6.00
£

I wish to order the Chairman's collection at £99.55
(no P&P required) Enter quantity and total cost: £

Johansens Gold Blocked SLIP CASE at £5 for the Chairman's Collection. Quantity and total cost: £

GRAND TOTAL £

I have chosen my Johansens Guides and (please tick)

I enclose a cheque payable to Johansens ☐
I enclose my order on company letterheading, please invoice (UK only) ☐
Please note that books will be sent upon payment being received
Please debit my credit/charge card account (please tick) ☐

☐ MasterCard   ☐ Amex   ☐ Visa   ☐ Switch (Issue Number)

Card Holders Name (Mr/Mrs/Miss)

Address

Postcode

Telephone

Card No.

Exp Date

Signature

NOW simply detach the order form and send it to Johansens, FREEPOST (CB264), 43 Millharbour, London E14 9BR (no stamp required)
FREE gifts will be dispatched with your order. Fax orders welcome on 0207 537 3594

GUEST SURVEY REPORT

Your own Johansens 'inspection' gives reliability to our guides
and assists in the selection of Award Nominations

Name of Hotel: _____

Location of Hotel: _____

Page No: _____

Date of visit: _____

Name of GUEST: _____

Address of GUEST: _____

_____ **Postcode** _____

Please tick one box in each category below:	Excellent	Good	Disappointing	Poor
Bedrooms				
Public Rooms				
Restaurant/Cuisine				
Service				
Welcome/Friendliness				
Value For Money				

Occasionally we may allow other reputable organisations to write with offers which may be of interest.
If you prefer not to hear from them, tick this box ☐

To: Johansens, c/o Norwood Mailing CO Ltd, FREEPOST CB264, London SE27 0BR

ORDER FORM

order 3 titles get £5 off • order 4 titles get £10 off • order 5 titles get £20 off

or you can order the Chairman's collection and save £35

Simply indicate the quantity of each title you wish to order, total up the cost and then make your appropriate discount. Complete your order below and choose your preferred method of payment. Then send it to Johansens, FREEPOST (CB 264), 43 Millharbour, London E14 9BR (no stamp required). FREE gifts will automatically be dispatched with your order. Fax orders welcome on 0207 537 3594.

ALTERNATIVELY YOU CAN ORDER IMMEDIATELY ON FREEPHONE 0800 269 397 and quote ref B14

Recommended Hotels - Great Britain & Ireland 2001
Publication date: October 2000

I wish to order
QUANTITY
copy/ies priced at £19.95 each.
Total cost £

Recommended Country Houses - Great Britain & Ireland 2001
Publication date: October 2000

I wish to order
QUANTITY
copy/ies priced at £11.95 each.
Total cost £

Recommended Traditional Inns, Hotels & Restaurants - Great Britain 2001
Publication date: October 2000

I wish to order
QUANTITY
copy/ies priced at £11.95 each.
Total cost £

Historic Houses, Castles & Gardens 2001 (incorporating Museums & Galleries)
Publication date: December 2000

I wish to order
QUANTITY
copy/ies priced at £7.95 each.
Total cost £

Recommended Hotels - Europe & The Mediterranean 2001
Publication date: October 2000

I wish to order
QUANTITY
copy/ies priced at £16.95 each.
Total cost £

Recommended Hotels - North America, Bermuda & The Caribbean 2001
Publication date: October 2000

I wish to order
QUANTITY
copy/ies priced at £12.95 each.
Total cost £

Recommended Hotels, Country Houses & Game Lodges – Southern Africa, Mauritius, The Seychelles 2001 Publ. date: October 2000

I wish to order
QUANTITY
copy/ies priced at £9.95 each.
Total cost £

Recommended Hotels & Lodges Australia, New Zealand, The Pacific 2001
Publication date: October 2000

NEW

I wish to order
QUANTITY
copy/ies priced at £9.95 each.
Total cost £

Recommended Business Meeting Venues 2001
Publication date: February 2001

I wish to order
QUANTITY
copy/ies priced at £25.00 each.
Total cost £

Johansens Pocket Guide 2001
Publication date: January 2001

NEW

I wish to order
QUANTITY
copy/ies priced at £7.95 each.
Total cost £

The Chairman's Collection

order the complete collection of Johansens Recommended Guides for only £99.55 a saving of £35
PLUS FREE P&P worth £4.50
PLUS FREE Luxury Luggage Tag worth £15
PLUS FREE Privilege Card worth £20

The Chairman's Collection contains the following titles:
•Business Meetings Venues •Traditional Inns, Hotels & Restaurants - GB •Hotels - GB & Ireland •Country Houses - GB & Ireland •Historic Houses, Castles & Gardens •Hotels, Country Houses & Game Lodges - Southern Africa •Hotels - North America, Bermuda, The Caribbean •Hotels - Europe & The Mediterranean •Hotels & Lodges - Australia, New Zealand, The Pacific • Johansens Pocket Guide 2001

Now please complete your order and payment details

I have ordered 3 titles - £5 off −£5.00

I have ordered 4 titles - £10 off −£10.00

I have ordered 5 titles - £20 off −£20.00

Total cost of books ordered minus discount
(not including the Chairman's Collection) £

Privilege Card - FREE WITH ANY ORDER
Additional cards can be ordered for £20 £

Luxury Luggage Tag - Johansens branded polished steel tag at £15. Quantity and total cost: £

POSTAGE & PACKING
(UK) for a single item add £2.50
More than one item add £4.50
(Outside) UK for a single item add £4.00
More than one item add £6.00
£

I wish to order the Chairman's collection at £99.55
(no P&P required) Enter quantity and total cost: £

Johansens Gold Blocked SLIP CASE at £5 for the Chairman's Collection. Quantity and total cost: £

GRAND TOTAL £

I have chosen my Johansens Guides and (please tick)

I enclose a cheque payable to Johansens ☐
I enclose my order on company letterheading, please invoice (UK only) ☐
Please note that books will be sent upon payment being received
Please debit my credit/charge card account (please tick) ☐

☐ MasterCard ☐ Amex ☐ Visa ☐ Switch (Issue Number)

Card Holders Name (Mr/Mrs/Miss)

Address

Postcode

Telephone

Card No.

Exp Date

Signature

NOW simply detach the order form and send it to Johansens, FREEPOST (CB264), 43 Millharbour, London E14 9BR (no stamp required)
FREE gifts will be dispatched with your order. Fax orders welcome on 0207 537 3594

GUEST SURVEY REPORT

Your own Johansens 'inspection' gives reliability to our guides,
and assists in the selection of Award Nominations

Name of Hotel: _____

Location of Hotel: _____

Page No: _____

Date of visit: _____

Name of GUEST: _____

Address of GUEST: _____

_____**Postcode** _____

Please tick one box in each category below:	*Excellent*	*Good*	*Disappointing*	*Poor*
Bedrooms				
Public Rooms				
Restaurant/Cuisine				
Service				
Welcome/Friendliness				
Value For Money				

Occasionally we may allow other reputable organisations to write with offers which may be of interest.
If you prefer not to hear from them, tick this box ☐

To: Johansens, c/o Norwood Mailing CO Ltd, FREEPOST CB264, London SE27 0BR